A THREE PEAKS

A THREE PEAKS UP AND UNDER

A Guide to Yorkshire's Limestone Wonderland

Stephen C. Oldfield

Scratching Shed Publishing Ltd

Words and photography
copyright © Stephen C. Oldfield 2015
All rights reserved
The moral right of the author has been asserted
First published by Scratching Shed Publishing Ltd in 2015
Registered in England & Wales No. 6588772.
Registered office:
47 Street Lane, Leeds, West Yorkshire. LS8 1AP
www.scratchingshedpublishing.co.uk
ISBN 978-0992991791

Cover: The Obelisk, a gigantic limestone boulder, dropped
by a retreating glacier, dominates the pavements of Scales
Moor. *Bottom*: The moor's Fluted Pothole, seen by many as
flock of petrified birds drinking from a sinister pool.

A catalogue record for this book is available from the
British Library.

Typeset in Warnock Pro Semi Bold and Palatino
Printed and bound in the United Kingdom by
Latimer Trend & Company Ltd,
Estover Road, Plymouth, PL6 7PY

For my family and Mr Ken Holgate - a great teacher.
I can't walk past a landscape feature without thinking:
'He would have loved this...'

Limestone Wonderland: Simplified structure of Ingleborough, with the alternating bands of the Yoredale Series sitting on a plinth of Great Scar Limestone.

Please be aware: All outdoor activities are potentially dangerous - and caving carries a higher risk than walking. Though clear instructions and tips are given, the author and publisher cannot accept responsibility for any accidents that may occur.

The author

Stephen C. Oldfield is a primary school headteacher with a lifelong passion for English landscapes, particularly those in Yorkshire. Along with exploring battlefields and burial chambers, and recording insects and amphibians, he has written and staged several historical plays for children. He lives with his wife and three children in Bacup, Lancashire, an hour's drive from his beloved Three Peaks.

Contents

Giggleswick Scar: The South Craven Fault. Limestone has been uplifted to form the cliffs on the left, and lies buried deep beneath the fields to the south of the fault on the right. *Top right:* Trow Gill, formed by meltwater towards the end of the last glaciation.

Preface

THERE have been only four years of my life when I have not known the Yorkshire Dales, and, thankfully, I can't remember those. Selecting an area to study has been largely governed by my enthusiasm for the Three Peaks region above all others, and by ease of access. During the course of my wanderings, it became apparent that volume upon volume could be written about the area: its geology, history, archaeology, wildlife and industry each deserving independent treatment. Though including elements of each, I have been necessarily selective; this work being, in simple terms, the celebration of a landscape. It is an attempt to re-assess the bare bones of an area so often overlooked by marathon walkers and peak baggers who achieve great feats, but otherwise may never return. It encourages observation rather than competition, and, while there is a place for both – there are few books available that promote the former. Most of these were written in the 'golden age' of the late 19th century, since when the phenomenon of the Three Peaks Walk has become so dominating that the need to examine these wonderful mountains with fresh eyes is well overdue.

It is with great reluctance that I have omitted Malham,

A Three Peaks Up and Under

Absent friend: Great Scar Limestone exposed at Malham Cove, to the east of the Three Peaks. Thinly-bedded Gordale limestone forms the lip, with the Cove limestone, devoid of bedding planes, forming the main face.

arguably the finest limestone scenery anywhere in Britain. Hundreds of hours in that unique area have convinced me that it deserves a book to itself, and, together with wanders into surrounding dales, it will form the basis of my next project. *A Three Peaks Up and Under* concentrates on an area from Ribblehead in the north to Settle and the Craven Fault scarps in the south. The eastern boundary is marked by Penyghent and the wild country of Ribblesdale, extending westwards through the Ingleborough massif as far as the Cumbria and Lancashire borders beyond Kingsdale. There has been an attempt to at least mention every noteworthy landscape feature, and many sleepless nights have resulted when one or two, for reasons of awkward location contrary to the routes, haven't managed to make it. I apologise in advance for these inadequacies, and for any errors in my geological or historical judgements, for which I am entirely responsible. Geologists and historians might, in reading this book, find much to criticize in the work of a layman who spends his working day teaching drama, dance and music as well as geography, and any amendments will be eagerly made to future editions!

This book could not have been written without the help and support of many. Firstly, I would like to thank my father, Brian Oldfield, who introduced me to limestone at the age of four, and who is an irreplaceable enthusiast on all things outdoors. He has encouraged every inch of the project from its inception. I owe much to John Cordingley, cave diver and dales enthusiast, who has probably forgotten more than I know about Ingleborough, and who has gladly supplied me with photographs of places I could never reach. He has also pointed me in the right direction when I was wandering way off course, and given me much information about access and conservation. Colin Newsome of English Nature has helped considerably with access to Colt Park Wood and Scar Close, and I thank him for his help and support. I have had much valuable correspondence with Richard Whinray: author, historian and grandson of legendary bone cave explorer, Tot Lord, repaying the help when I discovered the signature of his grandfather in Attermire Cave. This was enough to lure Richard and his son into the confines of the 'horse collar' in search of this family gem, so they can blame me for the bruises and bangs on the way! I have also valued the advice and support of Tony Waltham, whose superb books I have read and re-read more times than I can remember – and Mike Appleton, a fellow Dales explorer and writer. Finally, I thank the young Oldfields: Emily, Joseph and Lucy, who have been dragged from pillar to post around every square mile of the Three Peaks, and posed for far too many photographs in precarious places ….

To these people, and countless others I have met on my travels, I am sincerely grateful.

Stephen C. Oldfield
January 2015

xi

The Sleeping Crocodile: One of many impressions created by the vast expanse of pavement on Scales Moor - the finest in Britain. *Top right:* The author (*left*) with Richard Bargh of Springcote, Chapel-le-Dale, in August 1976 where it all began.

Introduction

I SUPPOSE it was inevitable from the start that there would be a devotion to wild hills and rocky things. If the surname, implying 'he who lives by the old field' wasn't enough, dad insisted on 'Craig' for starters – 'man of the crags'. His better half had the final say, however, and stuck the craggy bit in the middle: Thank-you, mum.

I have fuzzy memories of being on the hills as soon as I could toddle. Even after tea, dad would take me to the top of my 'mountain', Cowpe Lowe in Lancashire, and rhyme off the distant summits whose names fascinated me. To comfort himself after Leeds crashed to Sunderland in the 1973 cup final, dad borrowed an old tent and took me and his best mate to Malham. The great limestone cliff was, at that point, the magic flint which ignited a life-long devotion. I was just four years old.

'Jacko' also went with us, by the way. He was a toy monkey very much of his time: decidedly scary-looking, but a legend with hard plastic knuckles, blue and yellow arms and a red tank-top: as dreadfully garish as the decade that loved him. In the early hours we would unzip the tent and head onto the pavement above the cove. Making sure the coast was clear, dad would immortalise Jacko's reputation by hurling him the 260 feet after expertly turning him in a series of somersaults above our heads. The aim was to land him on the 'treasure island' in the beck below – but we never did. As he was released, dad would invariably shout like Eddie Waring, 'and it's an up and under!' The Cove, and that phrase, have stuck with me ever since.

The trip didn't do much for my daredevil monkey. The stuffing started coming out of his tummy, and before long the bin-men had him on the front of their cart as a mascot. I've hunted down a second-hand Jacko since, in memory of the great one, and of my first ever trip to the Yorkshire Dales. He smiles at me on the landing, but it's not the same.

During the boiling summer of '76 we camped at Springcote Farm in Chapel-le-Dale. The tent was pitched on a green carpet encased in gleaming white rock. All was charming in the vicinity, not least the spam butties dad had packed for us - and then … the mist suddenly lifted across the sheep-strewn valley. This was the supreme moment of my childhood. In front of me was a massive cone of dark grey, perched on its plinth: the very lord of the landscape that surrounded me. This was when I, for the very first time, set my eyes on Ingleborough. Here then, was my 'Mount Everest' – the undisputed master of my Yorkshire adventure that summer – and I was a mere servant from Lancashire.

Nearly forty years have passed – and I still am. Nothing has changed. Those two incidents: the Jacko sky-dive and the meeting with a marvellous mountain - have enslaved me for life to the wildest landscapes of the Yorkshire limestone. Opportunities for travel on a world scale have been scorned; company, pastimes – even friendships, neglected – for which I hope I can someday at least be partly forgiven. Over decades of climbing ladder stiles, ringing out soaking wet underpants and conversing with sheep, I've seen every major boulder, every pavement, every waterfall – each and every cave and pothole entrance – everything indeed worthy of making up 'everything' in this select little world of mine. And I've seen a lot of 'everybodies' walk past me sympathetically, casting worried glances with concern for my wellbeing – wondering 'what's that fella doing staring at a lump o'stone?'

    The occasional 'somebodies', however, would stop me and ask: and I'd tell them that this was here because this and that was here because that … and then I began to realise there were more 'somebodies' than I'd ever imagined: 'somebodies' who wanted to go, like myself, both 'up' and 'under'. Somebodies for whom the marathon walks and tried and tested routes were never quite enough: Somebodies who were, like me, in love with a limestone landscape. I began to share my adventures on the gossamer threads of the internet – and somebodies from not just this island of ours, but from all over the world, clearly thought Ingleborough was their 'Everest' too. It touched me that inhabitants of countries with 20, 000 feet giants were wowed by the cute little peaks and valleys of rainy Yorkshire.

    It is for all those somebodies, everywhere, that this book has been written.

Great ape: Jacko the monkey returns to Malham Cove, scene of his 1973 skydive. He loves it, really.

Glaciated valley: The impressive Chapel-le-Dale. The glacier would once have been as high as Ingleborough itself and moved from left to right across the picture.
Top right: The author's gear on a typical day out, with trusty OS map for company.

How To Use This Book

EXCITEMENT feeds on anticipation, of course, and each of the 'excursions' described in this book is intended to whet the appetite for **adventure**. Notice the emphasis on *adventure*, rather than walking? There are hundreds of walking books out there – some of them excellent; this book doesn't aim to reinforce their ranks. Rather, it is one person's passionate view of a Yorkshire landscape and its effect on his feelings and emotions. It is hoped that, through reading the text and combining it with reference to a good map, the reader will not only begin to empathize with these feelings, but will also be enticed to get out there and enjoy that ultimate experience of being 'immersed' in the Yorkshire limestone.

I admire those who hop, skip and jump the Yorkshire Three Peaks for good causes; those who run and conquer their 'previous best' There is a place for everyone's interests in the Three Peaks. But I do feel that the walk is in serious danger of causing irreparable damage that may prevent future generations even having access to these very special mountains. I also feel that, for many, the Yorkshire Dales are three localities: Malham, The Three Peaks Walk and the Waterfalls, with perhaps Bolton Abbey thrown in on a summer

A Three Peaks Up and Under

bank holiday for good measure. *A Three Peaks Up and Under* shows a new way of wandering on this limestone landscape, hopefully training others to slow down and savour.

The best advice for those wishing to go 'Up and Under' would be to firstly flick through the book, finding an adventure of interest, and then to build up the adventure like a classic painting, a stage at a time - as follows:

1)   **Read About Rock** (*prepare the canvas*)
Any marriage to limestone is necessarily a rocky one, so it helps to appreciate the landscape with some knowledge of how the rocks came to be there in the first place, and why the land looks as it does. Newcomers to the Dales may wish to skip this section at first, but inevitably, the more exposure to limestone, the more questions are likely to be asked. Therefore, **For Rock Fans Only** is intended as a concise introduction to limestones, caves, pavements, gorges, faults and all other things geological. It is a simplified picture, but the spice added to each adventure merits its inclusion in the menu.

2)   **Jump Into Bed** (*sketch the background…*)
This book is a bit bulky for the rucksack – and intentionally so. It is designed for relaxation 'under the duvet' like a good novel – not for being thrown about with a flask and butties! So settle down in bed, perhaps with a map by your side, and lose yourself in the adventure: cross the stiles, feel the force of the water and gaze at the pavements so that you can pop off the reading lamp with a vivid picture of the coming day's adventure. Don't rest until you know exactly what you are going to be seeing. If you can't sleep with sheer excitement, log in to Google Earth while the world is asleep and have a bird's eye view of where you'll be heading. I do this often.

3)   **Dig the Details** (*apply the finer pencil work*)
At the beginning of each adventure are the 'bold bits'. The first tells you where to park, giving a 6 figure grid reference, with the distance of the adventure usually given. The next section, **In a Nutshell**, explains what will be happening in just a few words, so you can decide for yourself if the adventure is for you.

The **Essentials** section then tells you all you need to know to keep safe. This is necessarily repeated for each adventure and it *is essential* that the Three Peaks are treated with the greatest respect at all times. Advice is given on what to take, whether there are local amenities or not, and other useful information.

Finally, prior to the **Adventure** itself, comes the **Access** information. This tells you how to get to the preferred parking spot and gives advice on keeping on the good side of farmers! At all times use common sense when parking and remember that the Yorkshire Dales is a busy working area. An irate farmer with his Massey Ferguson isn't going to care less when your precious sports car is blocking the way to his muck spreading.

4)   **Map Mark the Route** (*mix your palette*)
The Ordnance Survey (OL2) *Southern and Western Dales* is the only map needed for this book, and as many walking books require several, why not celebrate this fact by buying two copies: one for best, and one for marking? I always mark my routes with a **yellow highlighter** and use a **red felt pen** to 'dot' the big attractions. The red dots usually invariably indicate a food and drink stop, too. *With all cave adventures – read each chapter a few times so you become really familiar*

with what's coming. Draw yourself a little diagram of the highlights and slip it in a plastic wallet. All these little creature comforts can make a real difference to your enjoyment ... and they only take a few minutes of your time – but it's time well spent!

5)   **Feel the Adventure** (*apply the main wash*)
This is the bit you've been waiting for. Use a combination of your map and bed-time reading to tackle the adventure, but don't be limited by the scope of this book. Wander off the beaten track, explore the unknown ... and create your own routes. Take your camera for a visual record of your exploits, as limestone is wonderfully photogenic. Try the same adventures in different seasons and under different skies. Take a notebook: recording your thoughts and feelings ...

The appendices include information about limited access at certain times of year in the Dales. Take this advice seriously. Most of the land these days is open access, but there are notable exceptions. If in doubt, always ask permission at the nearest farm. A farmer can at worst say 'no' – but he will probably respect you for your courtesy and allow a peek on his property.

6)   **Head Back to Bed** (*frame the picture*)
If anticipating adventure is exciting, nothing can beat that feeling 'when you've done it' – so curl up again with the same chapter, re-living this boulder, that stile, this pavement, that pothole. In time you will develop a 'hit list' of your favourite adventures to enjoy and share with others. If you do that, then *A Three Peaks Up and Under* will have done its job.

For Rock Fans Only

MANY visitors to the Three Peaks, I suppose, are content to see that they look fantastic, and leave it at that, without considering why. Discomforting is the thought of moving into the world of the geologist; the threatening Thor with his fossil hammer and flaming beard. These rock gods are usually seen surrounded by huge numbers of students with clip boards, at such shrines as Malham Cove and Gaping Gill. When I was a spotty student myself, and a rebellious one at that, I used to hurry past them and think, 'Oh, to heck with all that garbage. Let's get the butties out.'

Magicians, however, do exist, and they can wave wands. They can even turn cynical sixteen-year-olds into thinkers. I had a marvellous geography teacher called Ken Holgate, who later became well known for his landscape photography. I can still see now his beautifully shiny bald head and his beaming face as he addressed us all each Friday morning. He had this great presence about him that few people have, and to inspire me at that age I'm quite sure he must have been bordering on a genius. Yet Ken wove his magic spells with little more than a box of coloured chalk. He didn't need computers and fancy technology. My spark was

A Three Peaks Up and Under

Sunken phenomenon: The 'Sugar Basin' on the flanks of Penyghent is one of the largest dolines in the UK. *Inset, previous page*: The splendid flowstone architecture in Skirwith Cave - an abandoned showcave near Ingleton.

ignited forever in one ten minute period when, in his exquisite handwriting, he chalked the title 'A Cross Section Through Ingleborough' on a well-worn blackboard, and proceeded to produce a drawing, from his head, that I can still see to every last detail. There, for the first time, was the blue brickwork representing the Great Scar limestone. What a name that was for a rock! It held me completely fascinated. Then came the Yoredale Beds, sounding like a setting from Tolkien, and what about the Ingletonian slates? While the rest of the lads carried on with the usual borrowing and sharpening of pencils, and the rumblings about who fancied who, I just sat there, stunned. This was the only mountain I had ever seen in my life. This was my Mount Everest, which, at the age of seven, had completely overpowered my humble little camping trip to Chapel-le-Dale. But now, here it was in a different dimension. I could see its skeleton, and its insides, like the layers of a gigantic sponge cake …

Nine years after a seed of interest had been sown in me, Ken germinated it with his knowledge and enthusiasm. Thanks to him, Ingleborough is still my Mount Everest and it always will be. After that lesson, landscapes and rocks took on a whole new meaning: Malham Cove became more than a pretty place to eat the butties. Things changed for me very quickly. No longer was I merely interested in the Yorkshire Dales. This was something quite different. I could feel the Yorkshire Dales: every stream, every boulder, every cave and every waterfall, in my blood … and in my bones.

Down in the Basement

Despite the change in me, I would never claim to be anywhere near a rock star myself, but I do feel that the adventures in this book will be better enjoyed by those who have at least some understanding of the hard stuff beneath their feet. Therefore I will try and pen the story of the Dales rocks in as Oldfieldish a way as possible, humbly requesting that any threatening Thors are not too harsh on me with their hammers if inaccuracies are present.

Imagine having a jigsaw of the earth and fitting Scotland onto the continent of North America. What a daft idea that is. Yet this was how the land lay some 500 million years ago, in the Ordovician Period, when the 'basement' rocks of the Yorkshire Dales were laid down. Scotland, North America and North West Ireland were all stuck together somewhere below the equator and formed a continent known as Laurentia. The narrow Iapetus ocean separated this land mass from Avalonia, containing what is now England, Wales and South West Ireland.

Rivers flowing into the ocean, across what is now

A Three Peaks Up and Under

Northern England, deposited sands and muds which were compressed, over a large time span, into the foundation rocks of the Dales, or what we sometimes call the 'Ingletonian' rocks, after the village in which they are most prominent. After some 10 million years, excitement levels were unbearable. High drama was everywhere. The plates below the bed of the ocean decided they didn't like each other and slowly clashed together, taking the continents with them. Their great strength buckled the beds of rock like sheets of corrugated iron. This 'buckling' can be witnessed today by anyone who walks the Ingleton waterfalls, where the slate beds below Thornton Force are almost vertical in contrast to the horizontal beds of limestone above.

The recipe for the basement rocks continued when, at around the same time, a mass of molten granite from deep within the earth's crust, simmered around the Ingletonian rocks and effectively 'cooked' them, turning much of the mudstone (sedimentary rocks) into the slates (metamorphic rocks) which are so evident around Ingleton. This granite formed an enormous rigid block under what is now the Dales, effectively lifting the land above the surrounding area. Later movements tilted this mass of rock gently toward the north – raising it further in the south. It is known as the Askrigg Block, as its central point is believed to lie far beneath that area of Wensleydale, and it is a source of fascination for rock fans.

This uplifting of the land may explain why, over the late Silurian and Devonian periods of the next 150 million years, the Yorkshire Dales was largely dry land. The ancient 'slates' had been joined in the Silurian by sandstones or 'greywackes' - laid down by sediments and shaped by the action of rivers and ocean currents. These could now enjoy a long period of sunbathing at the surface before the limestones came along to spoil their fun.

Going underground: Stalactites ('stals') in the ancient Old East Passage, Gaping Gill.

Body Building

Some 330 million years ago, during what geologists call the Carboniferous (coal forming) Period, the area that is now the Three Peaks still lay somewhere near the equator – which, after a freezing December day on Ingleborough, can seem a fantasy indeed. Sea levels rose, and the area took on shallow tropical marine conditions, ideal for little 'shelly' creatures and corals – composed largely of calcium carbonate – to flourish. After a massive period of time, and millions of generations of descendants, the remains of these creatures became compressed to form the thick layer of Great Scar Limestone for which the Yorkshire Dales is most famous: a rock made up mostly of calcite – a mineral form of the calcium carbonate. The 'basement' rocks were, therefore, hidden away after their long period at the surface.

A Three Peaks Up and Under

Fluctuating sea levels then saw rivers washing sands and gravels into the shallow water. In effect, a limestone-forming layer of shelly creatures was covered by a layer of smooth mud – to later form shales – and a layer of coarser material to form sandstones. These alternating 'sandwiches' of rock are known as the Yoredale Series: a name deriving from the old name for Wensleydale, where they are very prominent. The actual 'bodies' of the Three Peaks themselves – apart from the summits – are composed entirely of these Yoredale 'sandwiches.' Finally, as the waters subsided in the later Carboniferous, huge river deltas washed in coarser materials to eventually form the Millstone Grit (Grassington Grit) series – the highest and youngest of the Dales rocks which form the flat plateaus or 'caps' of the mountains, best seen on Ingleborough and Penyghent.

When describing the layers of rock to young children, I often compare them to the layers of sponge, jelly, custard and cream in a trifle. It works until you begin to look at the landscape and realise things are not quite as simple. The hidden basement layers are hardly ever fully horizontal, and great earth movements since they formed have folded the layers either upwards into convex shapes (anticlines) or downwards into a concave pattern (sinclines). This 'buckling' goes a great way to explaining the undulating and often unpredictable Dales landscape, but two other factors are mainly responsible for the dramatic scenes we enjoy today: the 'ice ages', the last of which ended some 12,000 years ago, and the dramatic local earth movements known as the Craven Faults.

Fault Finding

Standing on the Ingleton coalfield, south-west of the village, it is daunting to think that hundreds of feet beneath you (and below sea-level) lie beds of millstone grit that once 'connected' with those on the summit of Ingleborough, 2337 feet above sea level. During Carboniferous times, great fractures in the landscape, known as faults, resulted in massive sections of this layered rocky 'cake' moving, vertically, along the fracture or fault 'plane'. These were caused by plate movements deep inside the earth's crust. The result was upward movement to the north of the fault plane, bringing the lower layers closer to the surface, with a steep 'down-throw' to the south and west. The three famous 'Craven' faults are just the largest of a multitude of fractures spiralling all over the place in the Three Peaks area like the gossamers of a spider's web; 'Craven' originating from the Celtic Craig Ven or 'land of the crags.' Geologists have shown that the North and South Craven faults have displaced the rocky layers on Ingleborough by an incredible 4600 feet or 1400 metres! Clearly, when these faults were hard at work, the great San Francisco earthquake would have seemed miniscule in comparison. Experiencing them doesn't bear thinking about.

It is simple to mark out the line of the Mid Craven fault, between Settle and Grassington, on an Ordnance Survey map, by following the various features eastwards. From Settle, where the fault has formed the prominent cliff of Castleberg, we can move east to Warrendale Knots and the scars of Attermire, before descending to the fault's greatest handiworks: Malham Cove and Gordale Scar. The North Craven fault holds responsibility for the waterfalls of Stainforth and Catrigg Force, as well as for bringing slates to the surface to form Malham Tarn. Perhaps finest of all is the exposure of the South Craven fault at Giggleswick Scar. Driving towards Settle, underneath the scar, we have cliffs of Great Scar limestone on the left, while that same limestone,

Rising to the surface: Keld Head in Kingsdale, where the water from the cave systems to the west emerges into daylight.

on the opposite side of the road, lies hundreds of feet beneath the golfers on the surface. It is not often possible to see the actual fault lines, as these have been obscured by subsequent erosion, although one part of the Ingleton Waterfalls walk does allow us a brief glimpse. In many areas, the differences in vegetation and the colour of the landscape will be giveaways. Above Settle, the gleaming white limestone of Attermire Scar and the rich green lime-loving grasses contrast sharply with the sombre tones of the acidic grasslands south of the fault line – where gritstones and shales cover limestones buried far below.

The North and South Craven Faults have been active into recent times. The last movement of the South Fault was in 1944 when a local tremor shook the town of Settle. It was definitely not, as one local suggested – over indulgence with the dynamite at Giggleswick quarry!

Another Brick in the Wall

Before looking at the effects of glaciation, it is necessary to consider the structure of the Great Scar limestone in more detail. Nothing in geology is simple, and it will come as no surprise to know that this great layer of rock is itself divided into several distinct sub-layers, each representing changes in climate and marine conditions in the Carboniferous sea over great periods of time. The layers are named after the areas in which they are most prominent. The oldest limestones are found only in the extreme north and south west of the Dales, and the first 'bed' of limestone seen in the Three peaks area is the 'Kilnsey' limestone, named after the impressive crag which it forms in Wharfedale. This lower layer contains many fossils of corals and gastropods and can be seen clearly along Chapel-le-Dale.

Next up are the Horton and Cove limestones, the latter forming perhaps the Yorkshire Dales' single most famous feature – the great cliff of Malham Cove. Fossils are less prominent and horizontal layers – or bedding planes, caused by intervals in deposition of the 'shelly' creatures – are also weakly developed, suggesting a long period of continuous deposition when sea conditions were more or less consistent. The third layer, just beneath the Yoredale series, consists of the Kingsdale and Gordale limestones, 120 metres thick and forming both cliffs and, in the case of Twisleton and Raven Scars, a distinct 'stepped' landscape.

Limestone is shown on geological diagrams, and in countless school textbooks, as a 'brick wall' – and with good reason. The horizontal 'bedding planes', previously mentioned, vary in width – with some being barely discernible – while others are so prominent that they can be seen from some distance. Earth movements beginning in the

A Three Peaks Up and Under

Carboniferous, including the major faults, sent shock waves through the limestone and caused vertical cracks to appear at right angles to the bedding planes below. These are known as 'joints' and thus explain the popular representation of a limestone 'brick wall' familiar to so many geology students. These properties, combined with the fact that the rock is very strong, yet soluble in water over extremely long periods of time, are the key to understanding the magnificent landscape of caves, potholes and waterfalls seen in the Three Peaks area; a landscape that we shall investigate fully in the adventures that follow.

Frozen in Time

By about 300 million years ago, the rocks that we now see in the Yorkshire Dales had been formed, and were later concealed by younger rocks which have since eroded away. Rivers began to cut into the rocks and form the valleys such as Kingsdale, Chapel-le-Dale and Ribblesdale. These would originally have been a steep sided 'V' shape, and their present day width and flattened profile are a direct result of action by glaciers.

It is not known when glaciation first began, but during the past 500, 000 years there have been at least three of these 'ice ages' as they are popularly, but incorrectly, known. The last was the Devensian Glaciation which began some 110,000 years ago and ended about 12,000 years ago – or 10,000 years before Christ: nothing in geological terms! The most significant was the great Anglian Glaciation of between 460 and 380 000 years ago, when the ice sheets reached 4600 feet above sea level, covering the entire area, but flowing at a 'faster' rate down already established river valleys. The ice thus reshaped the valleys, widening and rounding them into the 'U' shapes we see today, and carrying huge amounts of

Insect kingdom: Moonmilk is an unusual soft, white formation often seen on cave walls. It forms an attractive backdrop to the colours of the Herald Moth.

boulder clay or till, scraped from the valley sides – and which was then plastered over wide areas, sometimes concealing the rocks below. Bare limestone pavements are a direct result of both glacial action, where the ice has swept the covering rock and material clear – and of erosion by water, enlarging the weaker joints to leave the classic clint and gryke moonscape. Many pavements actually originated beneath the soil cover.

Between each glaciation there were warmer periods where ice melted and rivers and streams continued to erode the valleys as well as form the classic caves and potholes later described. The very earliest caves have since been destroyed by subsequent 'ice ages', and the oldest remaining today date back to at least before the last glaciation. Of course, we are currently in an inter-glacial warm period where active cave formation is still taking place. About 120, 000 years ago, the interglacial was very warm: the Dales were near the equator – and the inhabitants might have evoked a trip to Chester zoo: rhinos, hippos, elephants and hyenas wandering freely over the Three Peaks area – as justified from the discoveries in Victoria Cave.

As each glaciation ended, thawing produced torrents of melt-water which themselves carved out impressive gorges and valleys. Those from the Anglian will have since been eroded away, but Trow Gill near Clapham is a perfect example of melt-water action from the most recent glaciation. The torrent couldn't find its way down the frozen Gaping Gill and so carved the famous gorge which has since, of course, been abandoned. Gaping Gill itself is an ancient system which may well have been blocked by ice over at least two successive glaciations!

Going Underground

Over perhaps the last million years, since weathering and erosion has exposed the Great Scar Limestone once more to the surface, an amazing and constantly changing underground landscape of caves and potholes has been forming. Water, rushing off impermeable slopes onto the soluble limestone, has naturally found its way through the rock's weaknesses to emerge at the basement layers beneath. In simple terms, all of the major caves and potholes of the Dales follow this principle.

Rainwater flowing through a soil and plant cover on the higher slopes of the fells has absorbed large quantities of carbon dioxide to become a weak, if effective, carbonic acid. On dropping down the first available joint into the limestone, not only has it found a way through a maze of further joints and bedding planes, but its chemical nature has gradually dissolved the limestone away to leave an impressive system of stream caves, canyons and passages. If, however, the water has encountered a major series of joints, often enlarged by faulting, it may have dropped through several layers, passing many bedding planes in the process and forming, over time, a great pothole shaft such as can be seen at Gaping Gill or Alum Pot.

Splashing through narrow, clean-washed stream passages is one of the delights of caving in Yorkshire. As the climate is cool, the plant cover – and hence the levels of carbon dioxide in the water, are relatively sparse. In a warmer climate with rich vegetation, solution rates would have been much higher and the Yorkshire cave passages would have been enormous indeed, though of course they are limited by the extent of the limestone layer. The water always follows the simplest route through the limestone: for example, down a joint and along a bedding plane or shale bed – and it is this pattern that has allowed the characteristic 'canyons' and underground shafts known as 'pitches' to develop. In the mostly 'walkable' stream cave passages, erosion is now taking place only at floor level, where the walls and ceiling are largely untouched unless in times of flooding. These are known as 'vadose' canyons or passages, and they can vary from crawling height to majestic proportions.

The vadose canyons typically end in what is known to cavers as a 'sump', best described as a totally flooded or 'phreatic' passage. As erosion is now consistent all around the walls, these phreatic 'tubes' are characteristically rounded like the profile of a railway tunnel. They are accessible only to cave divers, but there are many abandoned phreatic passages in the Three Peaks area that have been left permanently dry by a fall in the water table or lowering of valleys by glaciers. The tunnels of the Gaping Gill system are good examples, being formed fully underwater some 350, 000 years ago and now lying far above the present water table. The rounded form is still very obvious and the impression is

A Three Peaks Up and Under

Example of an anticline: This one is in Swilla Glen, on the Ingleton Waterfalls Trail. The Great Scar Limestone dips to the right - close to the South Craven Fault.

of being inside a giant rabbit burrow! It is believed that all caves in the Dales began life as phreatic passages before falling water tables and erosion altered their nature.

The underground streams in the great cave systems of the Three Peaks must eventually emerge into daylight when meeting the basement rocks at what are known as a 'resurgences'. The Kingsdale cave system described in the 'Pothole Promenade' chapter resurges at the murky pool of Keld Head, while all the caves on the west of Ingleborough see light at God's Bridge, close to the main road on the valley floor of Chapel-le-Dale. Most famously of all, the waters of Fell Beck plunge 340 feet down the great shaft of Gaping Gill, to emerge several days later close to the Ingleborough show cave at Clapham Beck Head.

The great 'give-away' to all this hidden activity lies in the dolines: casually known, at least to map-makers, as shakeholes. These are depressions in the surface varying in size from tiny hollows capable of holding no more than a sheep – to gigantic funnels that would swallow a church. Some of these holes have formed by solution where surface water has drained into a cave passage beneath, slowly enlarging the area around the drainage outlet. Others are a result of collapse, while still others are a result of a combination of the two. Strictly speaking, the true shakeholes have formed on a soil cover, often of glacial till, where the soil has been washed down into cavities in the limestone beneath, creating that familiar surface depression. So numerous are these that the Ordnance Survey have taken to using 'area of shakeholes' on their maps; but their appearance is important in giving a clue to that exciting underworld most of us will never see.

The Pretty Things
'Jetbomb' Phillips was my chemistry teacher – and a good one. Yet his scientific explanation to a group of impressionable twelve year-olds about to meet their first cave formations was a basic one: 'When the mites go up – the tights come down.' George Formby might have sung that line.

Stalactites and stalagmites – or 'stals' to the established caver, have the power to pull even the most reluctant into the underground world: most experiencing their beauty through 'showcaves', where artificial lights can show off their finer details better than any caver's lamp. These showcaves serve a double purpose in that they also protect the formations for future generations: the beautiful 'stals' of Ingleborough Cave look much the same today as they did to the first explorers in 1837.

The key to the beauty of caves is, believe it or not, carbon-dioxide. It 'chucks it down' quite often over Yorkshire limestone of course, and the rainwater picks up carbon-dioxide from the atmosphere. It grabs even more from the 'soil air', becoming a weak form of carbonic acid as it seeps through to the limestone beneath. Making its way along the fissures in the rock, the water dissolves the limestone – therefore carrying calcium carbonate in solution, or being 'saturated with lime' in simple terms. As the water drips through into a cave, it contains much more carbon dioxide than the 'cave air' so in order to balance out the two – some of the carbon dioxide in the water diffuses out into the cave. This causes a tiny film of calcium carbonate to be left behind or 'precipitated' on the cave ceiling in the form of the mineral calcite. In this way, stalactites, or the 'danglies' are formed over immense periods of time: each drip of water adding a miniscule amount of calcite to the process. Water falling onto the cave floor loses further carbon dioxide, causing calcite to be built upwards in the form of stalagmite. So 'Jetbomb' was quite accurate in his theory!

Stalactites and stalagmites are not dominant in active stream caves, as any early formation would soon be destroyed by the rushing water. They are more typical of abandoned or 'fossil passages' – such as Ingleborough Cave and the Gaping Gill system where calcite deposition has gone undisturbed for many centuries. How they look, and how fast they grow, depends on many factors: not least the amount of water and levels of carbon dioxide. Some take on the appearance of delicate straws while others resemble daggers and swords. Columns and pillars are formed where stalactites from the ceiling meet stalagmites on the cave floor. In the most ancient caves some stalagmites date back 350, 000 years, with most large examples originating from a warm inter-glacial period about 100,000 years ago. Obviously, the last 'ice age' stopped all calcite deposition, and the 'babies'

Two directions: Horizontal beds of Great Scar Limestone rest on vertically bedded slates at Thornton Force, with a thin layer of 'conglomerate' in between.

of the bunch – the most recently established 'stals' – can date back to the last ice retreat, about 13,000 years ago! Think of that, compared to the eighty-odd years we might manage on this planet, and make the most of every day.

Many of the caves described in this book contain 'curtain' formations, beautiful drapes of calcite formed when the water has seeped down sloping cave walls instead of dripping through the ceiling. Often these are stained red by mineral deposits, such as in Katnot Cave at Ribblehead, or they take on a golden 'honeycomb' colour, seen spectacularly in Great Douk Cave. Being less obtrusive than the 'stals', these curtains are often found in active stream passages and are amongst the most characteristic features of the Three Peaks caves. Another is 'moonmilk' – a soft, white mineral deposit associated with bacterial deposition, but with a very uncertain origin. It is usually to be seen along fracture lines in cave ceilings, providing contrasting colour and haunting beauty.

As with all aspects of the limestone Dales, the caves are extremely delicate and sensitive environments, and this is crucial to consider for all those who explore them. In the 19th century, masses of stalactites were mindlessly carried off as garden souvenirs by the early explorers and tourists. Even brushing against a flowstone curtain can cause damage, as can clumsy manoeuvres in cave passages. The golden rule with cave formations is the same as you give to your children when out shopping: look, but don't touch. Breakages can't be paid for in caves. No amount of money would make a difference. This book has been written with the assumption that its readers will love the Yorkshire limestone and want to preserve its beauties for future generations. I know you are one of them.

Enough of the formalities! Now we've enjoyed our starters, let's head off to the main course and really get our teeth into what these three great mountains have to offer.

Book One
UP

Surface opening: The massive doline of Braithwaite Wife Hole is one of the largest in Britain. *Top right:* The perimeter wall on Ingleborough's summit is thought to have enclosed an ancient cemetery - rather than the hill fort once suspected.

1. Ingleborough:
The Ridge Route

Grid Reference: SD745778 (starting point at Chapel-le-Dale). A 9.5 mile (15 km) adventure.

In a Nutshell: One of the most invigorating walks in the Pennines, this circuit takes in a wider sweep of the Three Peaks than any other in this book.

A straightforward but steep ascent of the mountain is followed by a traverse across the satellites of Southerscales Fell and Park Fell, before a descent into Ribblesdale. Easier ground then skirts around the base of Park Fell and passes the excellent Scar Close Nature reserve, returning via Great Douk Cave to the starting point. The views are awesome and varied throughout, as is the wildlife.

Essentials: Direction finding is helped by blue-arrowed markers provided by English Nature, but the Ordnance Survey OL2 map, the Southern and Western areas, is essential. A compass should also be taken. Mist and adverse weather could make things very tricky, so choose a day during a settled period with clear visibility. It will be worth the wait.

A Three Peaks Up and Under

Waterproofs and warm clothing should be carried, as well as ample amounts of food and drink. Footwear should be sturdy with good grips, as there are steep and rocky sections. My youngest child completed this walk at five, but she was well trained. Assess the fitness levels of all members of the party before undertaking this walk, and be realistic. Aim to start early as this is a full day's outing.

Access: Leave Ingleton on the B2655 Hawes road. Three miles later, after passing the hamlet of Chapel-le-Dale, the Hill Inn is reached on the right hand side. Parking spaces are available in two well-used lay-bys, a few yards up the road from the inn on the left. Aim to arrive early at weekends. Cars can also be tucked in on the opposite side close to the water treatment works.

Adventure: To traverse the ridge of Ingleborough is to make an intimate acquaintance with this most majestic of Pennine mountains. It is a chance to stand, not only on the crown of a true king, but to walk across the shoulders of his loyal if somewhat humbled courtiers: Southerscales Fell at the centre of the group going north, with Park Fell, the apex of the 'Ingleborough Triangle' watching resolutely over Ribblehead.

Leave the parking area, taking extreme care on the road with its fast moving traffic and blind summit. A short distance down on the left, beyond the water treatment works, a gate admits to Southerscales nature reserve, with an attractive old lime kiln flanking the path across lovely green turf, heading for the towering mass of Ingleborough ahead. Several ladder stiles are crossed, before the path swings through a delectable area of pavement. The surroundings here can drive wild flower enthusiasts, like my dad, completely bonkers. I recall taking him on the ridge route

4

when he was determined to show me it would be chicken-feed for a guy of three score years and ten. He launched himself from the car park, as if from starting blocks, evoking raised eyebrows from even clock-watching 'Three Peakers' nearby, but ground to a screeching halt on reaching the pavements. I presume folk thought he'd had a coronary, lying there on his stomach in the grass, but he was ecstatic. 'Scabious, Stephen!' was the passionate cry as he rummaged in his rucksack for the camera. Being an absolute novice on flowery things, I had taken 'scabious' to be a nasty disease you didn't speak of when the children were present. I learnt much that day. Others I was taught to recognize were tormentil and bird's foot trefoil. Early purple orchid and fragrant wild thyme are also to be seen, amongst many more, depending on the time of year.

Don't Mess With the Wife
The highlight of Southerscales for me, however, occurs on the left as the path swings south between limestone scars. The ground here suddenly plunges into a gigantic, funnel-shaped crater, of such astounding dimensions that with each anticipatory step towards the rim there still seems to be no sign of the bottom. This is Braithwaite Wife Hole, considered to be the largest 'shake hole' in the United Kingdom: presumably a stream sink of pre-glacial times and enlarged by subsidence due to collapsing of chambers beneath. There was once a way through to the cave system of Sunset Hole from the bottom, but this has now been choked by rubble. It is great fun, and perfectly safe, to descend the hole, the advantage being that it paints green stains on the rear end which have near luminous properties, and could be life-savers in mist! The disadvantage is that once down, you have to climb back up, which is easier said than done.

A Three Peaks Up and Under

Beyond the hole, a choice of stile or gate follows the procession of walkers through the Ingleborough Nature Reserve. Here ends the 650 feet thick band of Great Scar Limestone, forming the plinth on which the mountain stands, to be replaced by alternate bands of sandstones, shales, and thinner limestones, collectively known as the Yoredale Series. These are thought to be a result of fluctuating sea levels between the ice ages. The vegetation changes to coarser grassland, acid-loving plants such as Sphagnum Mosses, with peat bogs containing small pools. A path of sandstone slabs has been built across the reserve to prevent disturbance to the delicate habitat, and while for many this seems unacceptable on a 'wild' mountain, it does make what would be a nightmare of a walk considerably easier. Wooden bridges cleverly negotiate the deeper pools, and after several steep climbs the path arrives in the basin of Humphrey Bottom, ready to tackle the daunting prospect ahead. Here, a zig-zag path runs directly up an aggressively steep 300 foot (100 metre) slope, to emerge on a broad shoulder between Simon Fell and Ingleborough itself. It is up this same slope that exhausted 'Three Peakers' generally haul themselves in the early evenings of most weekends, having already climbed two grueling mountains. We are taught to 'save the best till last' and this is certainly true, but how they can really appreciate the Lord of the Limestone in some of the states I have witnessed them in is clearly beyond me.

Take extra care on the climb, as the rock steps are higher than your average stride, leading to easily grazed shins, and the going can be slippery. Pause often to look at the extensive views of the limestone plateau below, with Twistleton Scars directly opposite, topped by the impressive pavements of Scales Moor. A long ridge leads up to Whernside, looking tame in comparison to the colossus on which you now stand, with the Ribblehead Viaduct adding drama to a sombre landscape. To the south-west, the famous glaciated trough of Chapel-le-Dale ends as the gaping jaws of Twistleton Scar End and White Scars appear eager to devour a lighter meal of patchwork fields and villages; ending at the golden sweep of Morecambe Bay and the Irish Sea. The immediate surroundings are no less impressive. To the right, the less resistant rocks of the Yoredale Series have been worn away to leave the classic 'stepped' profile which is 'unmistakable Ingleborough', only here it can be seen in riveting detail. Just below the summit, horizontal limestones and sandstones can be traced across the full width of the mountain, bearing the splendid name of 'The Arks', and turning at a sharp angle to form the forbidding 'Black Shiver' ridge. Above the Arks, boulders of coarse gritstone can be seen cascading down the steep face. Immediately as the 'shoulder' is reached, Penyghent begins to appear to the east, and with it comes that delicious sense of being surrounded and dominated by this proud and majestic trio. To your left, the ridge path can be traced, hugging the perimeter of Simon Fell and promising great things for the walk ahead, but leave that for now. One of life's finest experiences is only minutes away.

Well on Top
The path picks its way through the gritstone to emerge at last on the flat summit plateau. With many mountains there is often anti-climax after the exertion of the climb up, but not here. After food, what to look at first is usually the main concern. Do you find a spot, get out the butties now, and risk that cloud coming along and spoiling everything? Or, like me, do you resist the temptation to eat for twenty minutes longer so you can spend an exhilarating half an hour circling the

entire summit? If so, leave the crowds by the wind shelter for a while, and starting at the cairn which marked your arrival at the plateau, turn left to a somewhat dilapidated wall, seemingly of no significance, but actually the shattered remains of what was once considered an ancient British 'fort' designed to repel the Romans. After years of speculation, modern archaeologists are now more in favour of it having enclosed a site of ritual or symbolic significance. That sounds like common sense to me. Are we to assume that the legions, known for their love of luxury, might have had anything to contest up here, apart, perhaps from the *view*? I often wonder what a Brigantian tribesman might have shouted as he clashed with his Roman counterpart in lashing rain, shield to shield, on the perimeter wall. *'There's no way you're coming in, pal – so you can keep your greedy Roman eyes off my dead sheep!'*

Many walkers, unaware of the importance of the wall, have removed stones to form their own cairns, so if you see anyone doing this, give them a history lesson and a severe telling off. From the wall, there are excellent views down across the pavements of Sulber Nick to Ribblesdale and Penyghent, and, a few yards further on, a cairn is met marking the path up from Clapham, the funnel-like depression of Gaping Gill being a highlight in this otherwise barren landscape. Walking slowly from this area towards the wind shelter, and scanning the ground carefully, a number of 'hut circles' can be made out, where the Brigantes were once thought to have been daft enough to set up home nearly two thousand years ago. Most of them are 'horse-shoe' shaped, further supporting the theory that they were never 'houses' at all. I mean, what would anyone living up here have eaten, you will ask yourself, aside from *Ingle-tucky Fried Crow*?

It can be quite tricky picking out the circles, especially when you're hungry, or if it's been snowing (pardon the joke).

We were once engaged in this activity when we saw a middle aged couple, with at least one half watching us with growing concern from the wind shelter. 'Go and ask them, Ron,' she was saying to her husband, nudging him in our direction while he seemed more concerned with finishing his coffee and refused to be budged. Eventually she left him to it and trotted up behind us. 'Can we help you?' she asked. 'Have you lost something, love?'

My Sweet Lord
Returning to your stroll round the summit plateau brings you to another cairn, perched above the 'tourist' path leading up from Ingleton. Shame that this is the one way many people climb Ingleborough, for it is a tedious ascent, with only the view of the mountain and the delightfully situated farmstead of Crina Bottom highlighting the journey. My preferred stopping point for sandwiches is on rocks just below the summit here, well away from the noise and commotion of the wind shelter and with what I consider to be the finest panorama from anywhere in the north of England spread beneath my feet. I am sure you will agree. Hundreds of feet below, a solitary and much photographed hawthorn can be made out on the pavements of White Scars, the only intruder in an otherwise treeless limestone landscape, forming the 'roof' of the famous White Scar Cave beneath. The surroundings are stark, aggressively angular and brutal in outline, yet people have been sitting here for generations just gaping at it all, no doubt pondering their own insignificance in the presence of the Limestone Lord. This, an established epithet for describing my favourite mountain, originated from a family once taking lunch behind us here, where the dominant male of the group was, according to my eldest daughter, 'even more obsessed with Ingleborough than you,

Dad.' She may have been right. 'This is the Mont Blanc of the Pennines,' he was enthusing to his son. 'Forget the other mountains, sunshine. Stop looking at Whernside, and listen to me. This is ..' (he had lost it completely) 'This is the king of the north! It's ...it's the absolute pinnacle! This is it, sunshine! This is the *Lord* of the Limestone!'

I could, at least, get into my bed that night, comforting myself with the fact that I was quite normal; that there were others prepared to step into my bracket. I was alone no longer. Oh, the joys of the Ingleborough gossip we had, and the friendly arguments over the view: of which was Great Gable and which was Scafell! No talk of the weather, the corned-beef butties - or if the plane had been booked for Lanzarote. This was heaven.

That day, there was a particularly stunning view of the Lakeland Fells, and, with binoculars, detail could be made out on Great Gable. Beyond was the Isle of Man, with the sweeping peninsulas of South Cumbria meeting the sands of Morecambe Bay: the ferry terminal of Heysham being the only man-made blot on the landscape. A sense of the immense power of nature is gained if one considers the village of Ingleton below. The land on which it lies once lay at the same level as that on which you are now sitting, 2337 feet (724 metres) above the sea, and it has slipped down along the Craven Faults over millions of years, one of the main reasons for the abrupt change from high to low ground as you look towards the coast. If one can imagine movement of such dimensions, then a collapse of the entire mountain into its cave-ridden plinth does not seem beyond possibility. In *Wainwright in the Limestone Dales*, the master fellwalker cannot resist teasing us with the subject: 'Someday its proud summit may collapse into its hollow base as erosion continues inexorably: but not yet awhile.' This sort of thing

On top of the world: Climbing the steep ridge from Humphrey Bottom, leading up to Ingleborough's summit plateau.

can startle young children, so make sure you tell them about it *after* the packed lunch is eaten, and not before. I'm speaking from experience here, and it wasn't a pleasant one.

Just before that heart-wrenching moment when you have to drag yourself away from the summit plateau, take a look at the ruins immediately behind you. At first, they appear to be an over-sized cairn, but careful inspection will show the remains of a more substantial structure. This was a battlemented 'hospice' tower, built with loving care in 1830, and destroyed with loving care during the alcoholic opening ceremony that ensued. I doubt whether even today's vandals could have matched the achievement. Perhaps the alcohol, yes, but the climb up Ingleborough is rather more than fifty yards from the car, and certainly from the nearest pub. Guys, you have been beaten.

11

A Three Peaks Up and Under

Mocking the Master

If you can't resist it, take yourself over to the wind shelter and its view indicator if you have time, then return to the last leg of the summit perimeter by passing over the stepped cliffs of the Black Shiver ridge, plunging down towards Chapel-le-Dale. The summit is left by returning to the cairn that welcomed your approach, before following the stony path carefully down to the grassy shoulder of Simon Fell. The prominent path to the right takes 'Three Peakers' back to Horton and should be ignored. Instead, locate a path seen earlier which hugs the very edge of Simon Fell, winding its way around a sweeping curve of peat-scarred moorland ahead. This is achieved by walking straight on at the junction, instead of taking the path back down the steep zig-zag. Every step of this high-level traverse is a delight, and each glance behind reveals a contrasting view of Ingleborough, as the Arks and the Black Shiver compete for prominence, passing alternately in and out of shadow. It is tempting to go back and climb the mountain all over again, but enjoy the peace and loneliness of this unfrequented path. It is easy to follow, the topography ahead being enough to indicate an obvious course. The route descends the slope of Black Rock on the shoulder of Souther Scales Fell, before following a wall onto Park Fell's wind-swept summit. At first, the Ordnance Survey column is seen on your right, behind the wall, and seems inaccessible, but the blue markers cleverly follow the wall to its terminus, the path doubling back on itself before crossing a stile to reach the column, 563 meters (1800 feet) above sea level. More attractive than any concrete column is the beautiful little tarn ahead, fringed with cotton grass and a haunt of frogs, diving beetles and dragonflies. Fortunately, Park Fell is within safe distance of Ingleborough to mock the master mountain and tell him, 'Now I've got something *you* haven't, pal', and he's quite justified in doing so.

From Park Fell's summit, head south, before the path swings away to the south-east, following the wall down South House Moor into Ribblesdale. Now, the view is dominated by the North Ribblesdale Drumlin Field, the drab moorland contorted into a classic 'basket of eggs' topography, where an ice age glacier has plastered clay and debris over boulders and projections to form a series of rounded hills. Trees are scarce, those in view indicating the nature reserve of Ling Gill, a gorge cut into the drumlins, with an obvious 'v' shape of woodland to the south sheltering the tiny hamlet of High Birkwith. Further south still, a rounded sheet of water, The Tarn, seems even more out of place in this barren yet beautiful landscape, dominated as it is by the brooding lion of Penyghent, who seems quite at ease with his surroundings. Not many make it this far along the ridge route, as can be seen by the sketchy nature of the path, but in contrast to the far reaches, the immediate surroundings are lush, with luxuriant vegetation and a wealth of flowers. All this is down to the work of English Nature, who, for the past few years, have helped turn South House Moor into the 'wild' habitat it once was, before our woolly friends came along to munch it into a memory. Now, small areas have been set aside for the planting of birch, oak, alder and hawthorn. The great grandchildren should see a lovely South House Moor.

If, like me, you are not a fan of walking downhill and your toes feel as though they are about to be amputated, the descent of the moor can seem like an eternity, though it is simple enough to follow the way-marked path. Eventually the surroundings change once more to limestone outcrops at Whit-a-Green Rocks (SD774761). Hurrah! From now on, all is level, and the surroundings are wonderful all the way to the car. The aim is to strike north through the rocks, but before doing so, a glance to the right at this point will reveal a clump of trees, barely a field away, but a conspicuous oddity in the surroundings. Those trees shelter Alum Pot, the single most spectacular pothole in the British Isles, while the nearby pavements contain the famous Long Churn Caves. All these are better left to a separate day of adventure, (*see book two*) but the view certainly whets the appetite for that day to arrive.

As you meet the rocks, the first feature to catch attention is a remarkable limestone boulder on the right, contorted into the shape of a mushroom or anvil. It is tempting to imagine that this stone had some significance with the ancient settlement nearby, marked on Ordnance Survey maps, as the outline always seems more the work of a hammer and chisel than water action to me. (I know I'm wrong here, but who cares when you're tired?) The 'mushroom' offers a superb pose for a photograph of the children, or perhaps even the better half, the exciting backdrop of Penyghent and Plover Hill being well worth the struggle of getting out the camera at this stage of the journey even if the better half isn't. Further on, a more obvious limestone outcrop to the left is worth a short detour as it contains the small cave of Washfold Sink, situated by an old sheepfold, and swallowing a small stream which sinks into a larger pothole just beyond. The cave can be entered with a torch. It is only 9 metres (30 feet) before the passage meets a 'sump' or totally flooded area. A short distance to the north east, and just off the path, a fenced enclosure will be noticed, with a stile tempting the unwary into it. And the unwary should be warned: severely. This is Washfold Pot, graded 5 in the caving guides (the most difficult of all), and containing nasty drops into the stream passage below. One part of the passage runs west to connect with Washfold Sink's sump, but the east route soon drops over a horrendous 40 metre (130 feet) pitch; as an invaluable caver once told me on the way past: 'So now you know.'

Amphibious Features
Filled with the joys of remaining alive, proceed along the limestone until the gnarled and ancient Colt Park Wood begins to decorate the route on the right hand side, conjuring up images of *The Chronicles of Narnia* and certainly, if the farmer isn't looking, worth a sneaky detour off the path to peep over the barbed wire fence surrounding it. The wood is a luxuriant garden of mosses and ferns, helped by the fact that sheep are, and always have been, banned, along with *homo sapiens*, unless permission is sought from the Nature Conservancy Council. All mammals, presumably, should proceed with caution, as Harry Ree and Caroline Forbes warn us in *The Three Peaks of Yorkshire*: 'it presents serious risks of a broken leg, for the grykes are often treacherously concealed by grass and foliage.' Cunningly grinning at this possibility, as though luring people to an untimely end in this deceiving little setting, is the 'Frog Prince', a bizarre boulder of gleaming white limestone guarding the edge of the wood; once a handsome dalesman, perhaps, and now seeking revenge for his amphibious features. Watch him staring at you between the ferns on the way past, and you can almost hear him cackling, '*Come closer into my kingdom, little fellow. Come closer …*'

Ignoring his demands, continue along the edge of hay meadows, passing an attractive old barn, until human habitation is at last glimpsed at Colt Park Farm .The one and only time that the ridge route encounters civilization, and pretty decent it is, too, being a handsome building with a welcoming porch. As you pass the farm, watch out for a date stone inscribed '1663 TH'. Harry Ree considers this to be much older than the present dwelling, indicating that an inhabited house may have stood here for much longer. I wonder where 'TH' did his shopping in those days?

The path leaves the farm, swinging westwards at New Close Rocks and entering Gauber High Pasture above attractive limestone pavements. Now we *do* have some history, for beyond the pavements to the north, hidden away near an old quarry, are the remains of a Viking farmstead: longhouse, kitchen, smithy – the lot! These were excavated in the 1970s and dated at the ninth century AD. There is probably no time for a detour now, but the remains can be explored in detail using English Nature's attractive 'Ribblehead Quarry Walk' leaflet, available free at most outdoor shops in the Dales. It's only a 1.5 mile (2.5km) walk, but what better way to spend an afternoon, or perhaps to combine with a trip to the Ribblehead caves? The next mile crosses a variety of stiles on an often squelchy path through a peat bog, skirting the south east edge of the gorgeous Scar Close Nature Reserve. Remember me telling you about my dad, earlier? Well, here he was clearly beside himself. He lost it completely – rummaging in his flower book as though a nearby orchid was going to uproot and run away at any second. 'Sorry, Dad: no time for that; got to move on.' His face for the rest of the walk was a picture. Here again, a permit is needed, so he couldn't have gone in, anyway. I keep telling him that. But the scene is spectacular, even from the path. Perched boulders, dropped by the retreating Chapel-le-Dale glacier, punctuate a rich tapestry of trees, ferns and flowers; yet another jewel in Ingleborough's glittering crown.

Having rounded the base of Park Fell, Whernside, to the right, has dominated the last mile of the journey, but now

Ingleborough once more thrusts himself to the front of the queue, and fittingly, too, for the Lord is determined not be outdone. He reminds us what we have all come to see and admire, yet his summit now seems a world away. If someone told you there was a fifty pound note waiting for you at the top now, would you go up and get it?

Scar Close is eventually exited through a gate (SD747770) and the route heads north- west, passing more impressive pavements on the right, and the massive crater of Great Douk Cave on the left, clothed in deciduous trees and encircled by a wall. The cave is an absolute gem, a stile at the western end revealing a steep path down to its daunting entrance, but the legs will be tired now, and Great Douk is far too good to be rushed when you can't enjoy it. Instead, come back on another day with your gear and give it a proper go.

Finally, the crossing of a ladder stile to the right picks up the morning's line of approach, with the car lying just a short distance away. Before reaching it, glance down the dale, perhaps at a gathering sunset, and say a final goodbye to the Lord of the Limestone. He can't yet settle for the night, poor fellow, for hordes of Three Peakers are still plodding onto his shoulders, even at this hour. Not long, now, and they will be back in Horton: finished. They will be elated, but no doubt exhausted. They will have achieved much, but will have missed out on your experience. For them, Ingleborough was 'one of the three', his profile admired, but his aggressive steepness something to complain about; his caves, potholes, 'fort' and circles, maybe even his view, largely ignored. For you, that early, intimate acquaintance has been accomplished. You are now on first name terms with the most famous mountain in the Pennines, and that, I feel, is where the real achievement lies.

Rocks off: Erratic couple on White Scars, deposited on the bench by the Chapel-le-Dale Glacier. *Top right:* The beautiful pavements of White Scars in closer detail - complete with the famous lonesome tree.

2. Ingleborough:
The Wild West

Grid Reference: SD745778 (starting point at Chapel-le-Dale). A 7 mile (11.9km) adventure.

In a Nutshell: An interesting and rewarding expedition, following the same path to the summit as the Ridge Route, before heading south west to cross some of the country's finest and best known limestone pavements. The walk visits the site of a former lead mine, passes some superb 'erratic' boulders, perched on the clints, and includes three of the most spectacular potholes in Britain. The views throughout are magnificent.

Essentials: As with all routes on Ingleborough, strong footwear, waterproofs and warm clothing are paramount, even in summer. The Ordnance Survey OL2 Explorer map covers the area, and a compass will be useful, especially if mist descends. Take plenty of food and drink, and choose a day with settled weather and clear visibility. Again, aim to start early, as days out on Ingleborough are usually full days. Children will enjoy the walk, but will need careful supervision near all pothole entrances, as well as on the pavements, where some of the grykes are often deep.

Access: Park in the lay-by at Chapel-le-Dale, as for the Ridge Route. If spaces are taken, cars may be tucked in at the opposite side. Take great care when leaving your vehicle, particularly with children, as the summit is blind and the traffic fast.

Adventure: Don't be too worried when beginning this one: for though the west is wild, and by that I do mean *wild* in every sense of the word, you won't be flattened by stampeding cattle or impaled on the spikes of a cactus on this adventure. Nor are you likely to be scalped by the Sioux Indians, though the excited whoops some walking parties make as they phone their loved ones from the summit do bear some resemblance to the cries of a thousand extras from a John Wayne film. *'I've done it, Mummy: woo, woo, woo, woo, woo!'* goes the oft-repeated cry, and who can blame them for being so excited on a mountain like this? It is not difficult to share their enthusiasm and scream along with them. In fact, it's quite easy.

It is also quite easy to, well … *fall into a hole* on this adventure; for holes there are everywhere here, and of every shape and size. The little ones could leave you with a sore ankle or a broken leg if you don't treat them kindly, while the 'biggies' have far more chance of finishing you off than a whole tribe of Apache. Take care to choose a dry day where the rocks are not so slippery, keep a steady eye on the kids, and our wild west might just be a little more accommodating than we imagined.

Climb Ingleborough by following the ridge-route path, and head south along the summit plateau to locate the cairned route down to Ingleton (SD741745). In any reasonable weather, the correct path can usually be confirmed by hordes of cowboys, Indians and squaws all panting their way laboriously towards the objective, many for the one and only time in their lives, and up the most boring way possible. Far better, I think, to go *down* that way, and then only for a short distance, even if it does mean missing the quaint little farmstead of Crina Bottom, tucked beneath the limestone scars to lessen the misery of the trudge. Desperate photographers and painters could, I suppose, leave their poor families tucking into the remains of the lunch box while they dash an extra half mile each way with the camera or sketch book, but for the majority of true explorers an early diversion to Quaking Pot will be much preferred, if only as a welcome retreat from the masses. This pothole is one of a series of 'craters' that keen eyes can easily pick out from the summit of Ingleborough by looking carefully to the right of the tourist path about a kilometre distant, in an area of dull moorland just beyond the main limestone bench. The trick is to head downhill until you are pretty sure you are in the vicinity of the hole, and then strike bravely 'northish' without falling into it!

The Crux of the Matter

Heading off the gritstone summit, the rocks of the Yoredale series soon become apparent, with the alternate limestones, sandstones and shales formed by fluctuations in sea levels well after the Great Scar Limestone was laid down. At the termination of these rocks, where the actual summit 'cone' of Ingleborough meets the massive limestone plinth on which it stands, scores of potholes have formed: water having flowed down the mainly impervious Yoredales of the cone to play havoc with the soluble Great Scar limestones beneath.

A Three Peaks Up and Under

Quaking Pot and its neighbours are fine examples. Turning right off the path, (SD731741) the trio of holes containing Quaking Pot are soon reached, just a few metres from the tourists who, for the most part, are oblivious to its existence. The first hole encountered is a shakehole with an unusual limestone bridge that children will love to play on. Just beyond is the diamond shaped hole of Quaking Pot itself, a small waterfall dropping into a choked shaft, overhung with heather and ferns and appearing decidedly inaccessible. Yet the determined (some might say 'mad') cowboys amongst us do occasionally find a way in, even though Quaking Pot is one of the nastiest caves in the Yorkshire Dales. Graded as super severe in the guidebooks, it consists of a narrow crawl leading to a series of underground pitches, and an arduous traverse over a streamway known as The Crux. 'Rescue from beyond it,' *Northern Caves* cheerily warns us, 'would be virtually impossible': enough to have Geronimo 'quaking' in his moccasins.

Big Chief White Scar

Two other holes admit to Quaking Pot. The first, next to the main pothole itself, has a concealed entrance beneath a large pointed boulder, while a few metres to the north is a massive shakehole that has been excavated to another way into the pot. From the drab surroundings of these holes, head north-west over Lead Mine Moss, aiming for a pair of conspicuous cairns, clearly marked on Ordnance Survey maps and appearing in my imagination as twin wigwams on a wild prairie. There are a number of erratic boulders perched on the limestone here, dumped by the retreating Chapel-le-Dale glacier at the end of the last ice age, and matching those on Scales Moor on the opposite side of the valley. All is now gleaming white rock and springy green turf, the clints and grykes of the Great Scar Limestone being as impressive as any in the country. The name 'White Scars' is appropriately simple, the chambers of the famous showcave lying far below. Once, when having a tour of the cave, our guide mischievously suggested that there may be points on the surface from which vocal connections could be made with tourists in the cave, and we have taken him up on that challenge ever since. Find a lovely deep gryke in the limestone, scream 'Hello – is there anybody down there?' and you will at least receive a disgusted stare from a nearby sheep. The deeper reaches of White Scar Cave are, in fact, far from touristy, features such as the Hall of Justice and The Sleepwalker Series being accessible to cavers only. Yet it is amazing to think that, until 1923, not an inch of this vast series of caverns had been explored. The discovery has become part of local folklore.

A young Cambridge undergraduate bearing the splendid name of Christopher Francis Drake Long, (1902 – 1924) perched himself on Scales Moor with a pair of binoculars and noticed water gushing from a small fissure close to the roadside. Wearing only shorts and a jersey, he crawled in with candles stuck into the brim of his hat and braved appalling conditions for hours, eventually discovering caverns of unbelievable beauty. Realising his ultimate ambition perhaps a shade too early, Long died from an overdose of chloral hydrate just a year later; a suspected suicide tragically ending a life dogged by depression. That's a far more powerful tale of triumph tinged by tragedy than any novel I can think of.

Plodding the Prairie
Before actually reaching the twin cairns on White Scars, swing to the right, locating a pleasant grassy terrace between

A Three Peaks Up and Under

Stack structure: The summit of Ingleborough, a flat, weather-beaten wilderness

the limestone pavements (SD725744). Soon the interesting walled ruins of an old lead mine are encountered, and fossils can sometimes be found by having a poke around in the spoils, evidence of the marine creatures that lived in tropical seas here some 300 million years ago. A short distance to the north, a ruined wall can be picked up, running up the scars from the valley below. The eastern termination of this wall marks the beginning of the fault scarp of Green Edge, one of the most interesting features on the west side of Ingleborough. A massive fracture in the Great Scar Limestone here has resulted in the rocks to the south, including those of White Scars, being lifted up in one huge slab, while those to the north have sunk down considerably along the fault plane. Green Edge marks the line of the fault itself and will be obvious once reached. It is particularly clear on Ordnance maps and very prominent on aerial photographs. The termination of the wall mentioned can be used as a convenient pointer to an exciting pothole, whose underground stream is guided splendidly by the nature of the fault plane. Walk about 300 metres east of the wall end, towards the Yoredale slopes of Ingleborough, and locate a large untidy shakehole, filled with boulders and rubble and appearing at first to be quite unspectacular. This is Tatham Wife Hole, one of a number of 'wives' present on the Wild West, the names presumably referring to the hideous places where the dalesmen of old would throw their 'nagging' spouses. Indians, be warned. Keep well out of spear-range of all squaws on this expedition if you dare to impart this delicate information.

Careful examination of Tatham Wife Hole will reveal its complexities. The fault has lifted the Great Scar Limestone level with the lowest layer of rock present in the Yoredale beds of Ingleborough, a thinner limestone known as Hardraw Scar Limestone. The effect is that water rushes out of that thin lower layer, sees daylight for a few seconds, and then vanishes into the Great Scar through a small hole in the rubble. To witness water moving from one type of limestone to another is quite unusual, even in the Yorkshire Dales. Caverns below were suspected, but only confirmed in 1967 when boulders were removed to reveal the entrance. A winding passage leads down to a chamber and a series of splendid underground pitches dropping to a total depth of 155 metres.

Tatham Wife Hole to the Totem Pole

Though this is exclusively the realm of experienced potholers, it is still possible for an adventurous adult who doesn't care about getting wet feet to have a tantalizing glimpse of Tatham's wife in the flesh, providing he or she (and a companion) are equipped with a helmet mounted lamp.

A Three Peaks Up and Under

Torches are no use here as both hands must be free to negotiate the passage inside. Taking care not to disturb the boulders and rubble near the entrance, carefully enter the hole feet first and it soon enlarges to a walking size passage, dropping down a smooth-washed cascade into Ogden Chamber, floored by shingle. Venture no further, but soak up the atmosphere of standing where relatively few have ever stood. Take great care throughout, as it is a privilege to enter the world of the experienced explorer even for just a few minutes. Beyond the chamber lies the first pitch of 9 metres, the passage itself soaring to a height of 24 metres (70 feet) just before it. Tatham Wife must be wonderful if you have all the gear, but perhaps not so wonderful when you consider the distance it would have to he hauled from the nearest car park to the entrance. The old cliché, 'bang in the middle of nowhere' could never be more appropriate.

Leave the pothole behind and head northwest over Tatham Wife Moss, a boggy depression caused by the downthrow of the fault, and containing a small tarn. The next objective is a quite majestic and intricately built cairn, standing on the edge of Raven Scars and peering down over the glaciated valley of Chapel-le-Dale, the unmistakable Totem Pole of our western adventure (SD732755). Wainwright, never one to champion any man-made object, was obsessed with cairns, and in *Walks in Limestone Country* (1970) shows the humble efforts of amateur cairn builders on White Scars balanced against an exquisite drawing of this noble specimen. 'The cairn of a professional' he calls it, and who is to disagree? Is there a finer man-made object anywhere on Ingleborough? Certainly the cairn, lit up by an afternoon sun with the mountain standing out as a stark backdrop, makes a superb photograph or sketch. My attention here is always shifted to Springcote Farm, far below, where I had my first taste of the Three Peaks country as an enthusiastic seven year-old in the 1970s. Behind and to either side lie the Twisleton Scars, one prominent buttress forming a natural climbing frame for us in that summer of '76 and still known to all Oldfields as 'Castle Rock.' The long ridge to Whernside rises along the skyline, the scars being crowned by the classic pavements of Scales Moor. If man had been around before the glaciers, it would of course have been possible for him to walk across on a continuous 'table' of limestone. As it happens, the greedy glaciers have eaten right down to the ancient 'Ingletonian' rocks forming the present valley floor, meaning that all water flowing from the caves must emerge into daylight when it reaches this impervious 'base'. The place of emergence for all the water is where Chapel Beck becomes the River Doe at 'God's Bridge', just to the east of Springcote Farm. Water has been proven to emerge here by dye-testing from a variety of caverns and potholes on the western flank. Strange what some people get up to in their spare time.

Another man-made feature of the Wild West can be found about 300 metres to the north east of our 'Big Cairn', or Totem Pole. Here, at the eastern flank of a prominent pavement stands Harry Hallam's Sheepfold, a circular walled enclosure that can be difficult at first to distinguish from the surrounding rocks. It is nothing to write home about, but serves as a useful marker to our next port of call. Harry Hallam, by educated guess, was a shepherd of long ago, who seems to have been a nicer bloke than Mr Tatham, as 'Hallam's Wife Hole' is nowhere about. Presumably, Mrs Hallam merited better than being thrown down a hole in the middle of nowhere. Dare I suggest she probably made a decent shepherd's pie?

Quiver at the Shiver

Using the sheepfold as a pointer, head directly east towards Ingleborough onto a notably raised grassy bench. A little patient searching hereabouts should reveal the shaft of Black Shiver Pot, located in a hole with a notable rock bridge. (SD737754) The shaft itself is only 4 metres deep, the sound of Big Chief Running Water indicating much activity below. As the name suggests, surprise, surprise, this is another severe pot. Tall explorers with good boots can, with care, climb down to the streambed, where water can be seen emerging from one passage into another. The caver's route is downstream, a long crawl and a 'pitch' being followed by the gruesome 'black rift', a double pitch of over 60 metres (200 feet) in total darkness with freezing cold water and awful draughts. Honestly, folks, there are people out there who relish the idea.

Most daunting of all, however, and easily the most spectacular of all potholes on this side of Ingleborough, lies some 300 metres to the northwest of Black Shiver Pot, where a massive fault known as the Rift has formed the astonishing Meregill Hole. There is no need for patient searching here, as Meregill cannot be missed, but it demands extreme care by all when approaching it, being an absolute 'no-go' area for children or nervous parents. A dry streambed at the southeastern end of the rift contains masses of cobbles and boulders, ideal for the kids to do a bit of building, well away from danger but still within sight and earshot while you inspect the hole. On first impressions there are two holes divided by a wide grassy 'saddle', but this saddle is in fact a massive bridge of rock, spanning a deep lake some 12 metres (40 feet) below, known to all cavers as 'The Mere'. In places, The Mere reaches depths of over 15 metres (50 feet), with

False pretences: One of the entrances to Sunset Hole. Sounds pleasant, but can be anything but in bad weather.

vertical limestone walls providing no handholds for those unlucky enough (or daft enough) to fall in. By all accounts, the water is icy cold and I doubt whether Butch Cassidy and the Sundance Kid would have even contemplated jumping in here. To describe the west as 'wild' at Meregill Hole would be an understatement indeed.

Merely Magnificent
Standing on the bridge and examining the upstream section of The Mere, water can be seen entering in a fine cascade from Meregill Cave, plunging down behind a remarkable detached limestone pinnacle, its surface richly clothed in mosses and ferns. Beyond, there is an ingenious diversion ditch, dug by cavers to send as much catchment water away from the entrance as possible. Careful observation of the Mere from the bridge will show why this is crucial. At the extreme south-

A Three Peaks Up and Under

eastern tip of the lake, in normal weather conditions, a low cave entrance can just be made out, especially in winter when there is less shade from the overhanging trees. Cavers usually abseil into the Mere above this point, then disappear into the darkness using this exit. Only then do the true horrors begin. The passage plunges down an awkward series of underground pitches, known as The Canyon, into the heart of Ingleborough, before twisting northwest to emerge at God's Bridge. There is no 'through trip' for an explorer. Anybody game enough to go down must be fit enough to climb back out the same way. Even a mild rain shower could have serious consequences, and a thunderstorm would be unthinkable. When the Mere is 'up' as cavers put it, the cave exit seen from the bridge completely floods, causing complications only confident cavers can tackle. There has been at least one fatality and many rescues at Meregill Hole. Stories of the 'sieges' the Yorkshire Rambler's Club set up in order to conquer its hazards in the early part of the last century have as much drama as anything from Clint Eastwood.

At the south east corner it is possible for intrepid scramblers, with great care, to wriggle beneath the overhanging branches onto a rocky parapet. This offers a superb view of the mere, the dark waters contrasting starkly with the creamy white limestone. The belay bolt that cavers use for their initial descent might also be noticed here, though great care should be taken both ways on the scramble. It is difficult to leave this fascinating place, but the way on is over a stile on the north side of the hole. Hidden away on the right once the stile is crossed are two more entrances into the Meregill system, used in wet weather when the mere is 'up.' These are the Aven Entrance, and Little Meregill. Despite friendly first impressions, they should not be entered as sheer drops into the main canyon are soon encountered.

Serene Sunset

With the main terrors of the Wild West experienced, the rest of our journey might well be seen as an anti-climax, but there is hardly an uninteresting square metre of the Ingleborough karst. From the Aven Entrance, head north-west (downhill) to an obvious junction of walls (SD739758). Now turn right, following the main wall running alongside on the left. Here, a thin layer of shale has formed over the Great Scar Limestone since glacial times, resulting in a boggy grassland of monotonous appearance. What a let-down, you will think, after the thrills of the potholes and pavements. But fear not. Within a couple of minutes an outcrop of weathered limestone is again encountered, and a short detour to the right will reveal the two entrances to Sunset Hole. This is one of Yorkshire's most popular novice caves, well worth a day out in its own right, and in *fine weather* can be explored with just torches and Wellingtons. Both the wet and dry entrances combine into a winding canyon of stooping height, perfectly safe for some 250 metres until a couple of awkward climbs are encountered, needing equipment and experience to be negotiated: Sunset's terminus for anyone with any sense. Beyond these is a final pitch into a chamber, popular with training cavers. Though friendlier than Meregill, Sunset similarly takes large volumes of water from Ingleborough in wet weather, and at an alarming speed. In rain, avoid under all circumstances.

From Sunset, it is a simple matter of picking up the path through Southerscales described fully on the Ridge Route Adventure. The Wild West of Ingleborough may well encompass *The Good, The Bad and The Ugly*, but there's enough 'good' there to make this seemingly featureless landscape become a firm favourite with the inquisitive limestone explorer.

31

The view below: The Main Limestone just below Ingleborough's summit ridge, with a sensational view over the Great Scar Limestone bench hundreds of feet below. *Top right:* Ingleborough is blessed with one of the finest showcaves in Britain.

3. Ingleborough:
The Classic From Clapham

Grid Reference: SD745692 (starting point at main car park in Clapham village). A 10 mile (16 km) adventure.

In a Nutshell: Generally considered to be 'the best way up', this walk is famous for its gradual and ever-contrasting approach to the summit, and offers everything to the adventurous. A beautiful village points the way to the woodlands of the Ingleborough Estate, through which a path meanders towards the famous Ingleborough Cave. Drama increases at the spectacular limestone gorge of Trow Gill, and intensifies at the entrance to perhaps the world's most famous pothole, Gaping Gill, where Fell Beck plunges 340 feet into the country's largest cavern. The route then climbs Little Ingleborough before visiting the summit itself, lying 4 miles (6.5 km) from the village. Return may use the same route, or divert to the wilderness of Newby Moss, visiting Pillar Holes and the awesome Long Kin West Pot. The word 'classic' is perhaps over-used in today's guidebooks, but here it applies with a capital 'C'.

A Three Peaks Up and Under

Essentials: Another full day out, this walk requires strong footwear, warm clothing and waterproofs, with plenty of food and drink. It also demands a good deal of fitness, so be realistic if taking children, and assess their ability carefully. The path is clear to the summit, though map (Ordnance Survey Explorer OL2) and compass should be taken as Newby Moss has obvious dangers in poor visibility. Extreme care should be taken near Gaping Gill and the Newby Moss potholes, particularly with children and dogs. It is worth taking extra money in case the weather changes, when a trip to Ingleborough cave would be a fine idea.

Access: Clapham village is signposted off the A65, 5 miles (8km) south east of Ingleton, or 6 miles (10km) north-west of Settle. There is a large National Park Car Park in the village, for use of which a charge is made. A small charge is also made to enter the land of the Ingleborough Estate at the start of the walk, where tickets are issued from a machine just inside the grounds.

Adventure: Clapham used to make me giggle when I was a kid. On my first ever visit to the Dales, at the age of four – not only did the gleaming white cliff of Malham Cove have pulling power, but what were these brown crusty 'pies' dotting the grass around our tent? My dad gave them their Lancashire name: 'cow claps' and this alliterative description stuck in my mind for months afterwards. So much so that when 'Clapham' was mentioned as the destination for our next port of call, I couldn't say the word without a hint of mischief – expecting a cow-inhabited town with an abnormal proportion of pies adorning the landscape.

Of course, forty years later – there is some guilt when I look around the place. Clapham is unique amongst Dales villages in being clothed in trees and vegetation – largely thanks to the Farrer family, who, for generations, occupied the impressive Ingleborough Hall – hidden in woodland to the east of the church. Reginald Farrer (1881-1920) had a short life but a massive impact on his native village. Not only did he cram painting and writing into those limited years, but he travelled extensively around Asia studying botany in mountainous areas, pioneering as he did the alpine gardens of today. His first 'garden' was Clapham itself, where he painstakingly introduced a range of foreign species – transforming the Farrer estate into the delightful walkway we see now.

To experience it, turn right on leaving the car park and, on passing the gates of the hall itself on the right, swing left in front of the church of St James. This dates back to Norman times, though the tower is 14th century and was built after the village was sacked by the Scots following the Battle of Bannockburn. The rest dates from Victorian times. It would seem the Scots did us a favour as the 'new' tower is attractive indeed, blending as well with the surrounding woodlands as would any limestone outcrop. No time to pop in now, so bear right and, passing the Clapham Falls, the entrance to the Ingleborough estate nature trail presents itself with a small 'honesty' charge being made to enter. It would be worth a hundred pounds to see what lies ahead, so no grumbling allowed. The falls, by the way, were artificially constructed by the Farrers in 1837 to give a touch of drama to the village. In flood they are a torrent of white foam every bit as impressive as the Ingleton waterfalls. The Farrers, by all accounts, knew what they were doing.

The trail climbs through the woodland and soon reaches the artificial lake created when James and Oliver Farrer decided to dam the beck in the 19th century. Eminent visitors to the estate would doubtless have strolled along its western promenade having admired the falls – or continued up the elegant carriageway to the wonders of Ingleborough Cave and the great ravine of Trow Gill. Often referred to as 'Clapham Tarn', the lake is undeniably beautiful, its surface a mirror reflection of the sylvan surroundings expertly created by Reginald Farrer. He had some ingenious ways of operating, one of which involved replacing gunpowder in his shot-gun cartridges with seeds of exotic plants, before rowing out on the lake and firing them into the cliffs on the far side. The bamboo he introduced can still be seen at the head of the lake, where a Yorkshire panda would be a perfect accompaniment to pheasant and partridge. If only!

Leaving the lake, the path crosses a sometimes dry resurgence channel coming in from the right, and close examination of the stream bed shows almost vertical ribs of dark grey rock. This is Cat Hole Syke, where the movement of the North Craven Fault, crossed at this point, has lifted these ancient basement slates to the surface, their covering limestone having long since been eroded away by successive glaciations. The result is a more acidic soil cover in the woodlands beyond, and Reginald Farrer exploited this, planting some of the finest shows of rhododendrons in the country in conditions so perfect that they still flourish to this day. Equally resilient is the 'Grotto', an elaborately constructed shelter by the woodland path, with arched windows and projecting lumps of limestone adorning the walls in gargoyle-like fashion. No doubt the Farrers and their eminent guests sheltered in here, but the muddy floor would nowadays play havoc with a lady's skirt. It's bad enough with hiking boots. The vaulted limestone ceiling gives the impression of a church, and I wonder if the Farrers prayed as often in here as the Oldfields have since done for deliverance from a drenching – and for a clear view from Ingleborough?

The path steepens and, on the right, slopes of ever-increasing height plunge down to the beck below, where the melt-water has eroded the steep-sided valley through the Great Scar Limestone. Between the Grotto and Cathole Syke, well protected by the difficult terrain, the important springs of Moses Well make their way into the beck, bringing all the water from the deep potholes of Newby Moss to the north-west. The basement slates onto which these emerge must be massively buckled like a piece of corrugated iron, as they lie an incredible 23 metres (70 feet) *below* the Cat Hole Syke resurgence we met earlier – yet still on the same bed of rock! Like many of the resurgences, Moses Well leads to a progressively narrow passage choked with boulders. Unlocking the secrets of the Clapham landscape has already taken several lifetimes … and will continue to do so.

Just before the woodlands end, a small ravine is passed on the left, caused by the Clapdale Fault – and not long after the path emerges into 'daylight', a curious thumping sound can be heard emanating from a small building close to the beck on the right. This is a 'ram pump', powerfully forcing water from the beck to Clapdale Farm, hidden well up on the left. The ingenious contraption is well described in Harry Ree's excellent *The Three Peaks of Yorkshire*, along with a diagram of the mechanics – well beyond the grasp of an Oldfield. A short distance beyond, at the base of an impressive limestone scar clothed in mature trees, lies the area's main attraction …

Breaking the Barrier

Once known as Clapdale Great Cave, Ingleborough Cave was inaccessible beyond the first few yards until 1837 - the passage terminating in a barrier of stalagmite holding back a lake, close to ceiling level. In that year, James Farrer's

A Three Peaks Up and Under

Shadows cast on water: The artificial lake at Clapham blends superbly into the limestone surroundings.

curiosity got the better of him, and he and a workman removed the barrier, allowing access to a wonderfully decorated cavern. I have always had visions of them, hacking away with pick axes before being swept away by the ensuing torrent in true 'Laurel and Hardy' fashion. Presumably it was a more gentle affair, and what they discovered is now advertised as 'the best show-cave in England' and with some justification. Remoteness from a main road means it lacks the 'commercialism' of those in the Peak District or Somerset – and even the little shop fits perfectly into the surroundings; only a hand rail interrupting what would have been the same view in the 19th century.

We have, quite literally, a mountain to climb – so it is far better to explore Ingleborough Cave on a rainy day when the fell tops won't be so appealing. That way, legendary features such as The Sword of Damocles, The Elephant's Legs,

The Beehive – and, believe it or not, Queen Victoria's Bloomers, can be fully appreciated without having to tell the guide to get a move on. It's always fascinating, when in the cave, to trace the line of the old water level on the walls, and get an idea of the incredibly slow growth of stalactites by seeing how far they have pushed themselves beyond this threshold in nearly 180 years. The distance is miniscule, indicating the immense age of some of the monsters dangling from the ceiling. Much work on stalactite growth has been carried out in this cave, and there is still much to be discovered.

You Put Your Left Leg In …

An elegant bridge crosses the beck just beyond the entrance, where the water can be seen, on the left, resurging from the low cave mouth of Clapham Beck Head. Always suspected as carrying the waters from Gaping Gill to the north, the Yorkshire Geological Society proved the matter once and for all in 1900 when placing a ton of ammonium salt in Gaping Gill and detecting it here an incredible five days later! Frustratingly, the cave became narrow and impassable to early explorers who, instead, found ways into the flooded reaches well beyond the show-cave limits of Ingleborough Cave. A combination of incredible bravery, determination and ingenious links between surface and underground mapping meant that the link was finally made in January, 1983. That was when cave diver Geoff Crossley forced himself feet-first into a tiny flooded rift, allowing Gerald Benn, who was diving in the Far Waters of Gaping Gill, to stretch forward and grab at his boot; the intricacies meaning not even a hand shake was possible! The under-water gap was widened to allow a full 'exchange' trip a month later, with two sets of cavers historically passing each other under water: one pair having descended Gaping Gill while the other entered the Ingleborough Cave end. Howard Beck's classic work *Gaping Gill: 150 Years of Exploration* (1984) provides a fascinating, step by step account of the adventure.

An attractive melt-water valley, hemmed in between limestone scars, continues towards Trow Gill and two more interesting caves are passed. The first, Beck Head Stream Cave, might not be noticed at all as it is shyly hidden under the base of the scar on the left side, just a few metres beyond Ingleborough Cave. Stand next to the small hole and the distant rumbling of underground waters can be heard. Cavers enter feet first and this is, in fact, a 'window' into the main drain – leading through really active and constricted passages to the Broadbent Falls before once again meeting constrictions beyond. The second cave, again on the same side, is reached by entering a small dry valley a short distance ahead. This is Foxholes, an ancient cave that was, until 1913, completely blocked by glacial debris before excavations by Dr Charles Hill. There is debate as to whether it was a pre-glacial sink or resurgence, but it has certainly been used by animals and men throughout history. Excavations revealed portions of human skulls, as well as wild boar, horse and deer skeletons. The remains of a fireplace were also discovered and it is probable that the cave was used for temporary shelter and ritual rather than for permanent habitation. Foxholes has been gated inside no doubt to protect the public from being too curious for their own good – as I often am.

The path swings to the left beyond Foxholes and, at a stile, a track veers off towards Clapham Bottoms on the right. Ignore this for now, as it is worth exploring when time permits. It leads to an undulating and somewhat confusing area of shakeholes, sinkholes and small pots, all lying over the area where that famous connection between Gaping Gill and Ingleborough Cave was made. Lying amongst them is

Body Pot, where the 'Trow Gill Skeleton' was discovered in August 1947 – a supposed German spy who was found walled into a small chamber with a scarf tied around his face and a bottle of cyanide for company. It is a mystery that will never be solved.

Take a Bow to the Trow

Trow Gill itself, reached by keeping straight ahead at the junction, has held mysteries of its own, not least in the way it was formed. For many years the great gorge was believed to be a collapsed cavern, though this has now been largely discarded. Towering cliffs of Great Scar limestone enclose a spectacular 'dry' waterfall of slippery boulders, above which a narrow ravine can be followed onto the moor above. The present theory is that this dramatic slice through the landscape was created by melt-water towards the end of the last glaciation, when the great shaft of Gaping Gill was blocked by ice and glacial debris. This seems straightforward enough; the gorge, in many ways, being a smaller and obviously redundant version of Gordale Scar. Standing at the foot of the dry waterfall, it's hard to believe things haven't been fiercely active just a few hours before – as though the supply has been temporarily switched off to the main feature of some affluent giant's water garden. It's certainly a place to remember.

Indications of the meltwater's power are seen not only in the height of the gorge, but in the various caves which never had chance to get past the earliest stages of formation. The swirling water has hollowed out crescent-shaped recesses on both sides of the dry fall, easily seen on the scramble up – but the best developed cave is on the left side just before the climb: the 'Devil's Kitchen.' Here the water has hungrily devoured a major bedding plane to leave a perfect shelter, made somehow domestic by a 'table' of limestone that has fallen from the ceiling especially for his satanic majesty. I once led a party of schoolchildren in here for lunch after a visit to Ingleborough Cave, when fascination quickly turned to fear thanks to the kindness of their teacher. Not one would place their lunch box anywhere near the dreaded table, while several complained of the presence of another character of my imagination: the Trow Gill Troll. Happy days indeed!

A treeless landscape lies above Trow Gill, where the melt-water valley continues for half a mile or so before emerging onto a boggy plateau – and at last the objective is seen ahead. The great rounded 'bump' of Little Ingleborough, succeeded by the master himself, is, more often than not, hidden in mist or swathed in low cloud, and many first-timers can be forgiven for assuming Little Ingleborough to be the main summit. My friend Colin and I certainly thought we'd 'done it' as teenagers when patting each other's soaking backs at Little Ingleborough's cairn, in true Hillary and Tenzing fashion: only for a gap in the scudding clouds to uncover for just a few seconds the head and shoulders of a giant. And so, more than a few swear words later - the expedition continued …

Crossing a wall stile onto the plateau (SD752723), the drab cover of glacial till is relieved by the attractive entrance to Bar Pot, seen on the left. Cleared of debris in 1949 by the British Speleological Association, this collapse doline now contains the most popular entrance into the Gaping Gill system for the ordinary caver, who doesn't need half the tackle that the main shaft itself demands, even though ropes, ladders and a lot of know-how are essential. If you do wander down into the hole, a sanctuary for bat colonies as well as for many lime-loving plants, never be tempted to enter the dark cavity at the north side, even though it is worn smooth by caver's bottoms. There are nasty drops just inside which would invariably be your last.

Swallowing St Paul's

Gaping Gill itself – or 'GG' to the caving masses, is reached in a few minutes by turning right where the paths fork: a welcome diversion from the continuous climb. Easily Britain's most famous pothole, it lies at the bottom of a steep-sided funnel, fenced only on the south side, and collects the waters of Fell Beck as they make their way off the Yoredale slopes meeting a fault guided joint in the Great Scar Limestone … in the most dramatic way imaginable. Those who wish to examine the surface hole should avoid the winch meets of the Bradford and Craven Pothole Clubs in June and August, when for safety reasons the hole is fenced off and the waterfall diverted to allow the winch chair easy access. Away from the winch meets, it is a different story altogether, with the full force of Fell Beck snarling into the black void in Britain's highest unbroken waterfall. Intrepid adventurers won't be able to resist a hands and knees traverse around the well-worn lip at the south east side, where a wriggle on the tummy allows, without any exaggeration, a quite terrifying view of the disappearing water, and no sign of what lies hidden beneath. The full secrets of the shaft, plunging 340 feet into a chamber big enough to hold the nave of St Paul's Cathedral, were unknown until the late 19th century. French explorer Edouard Martel was the first to unravel these, when he made the first descent in August, 1895, and those who wish to follow in his 'rung-steps' – all be it in the comfort of a 'bosuns chair' – are referred to the 'Dangling Down the Plughole' chapter – fully dedicated to the cause.

Horrific tales of the unthinkable surrounding Gaping

A Three Peaks Up and Under

Gill abound in the social gatherings of the caving clubs. A reliable source from the Craven once related to me the story of a farmer who, in a harsh winter, went up onto the snow-covered fell on his quad bike to look for isolated sheep. A week later, the tracks of his bike were seen to end abruptly on the east side of the hole before reappearing on the opposite side. Since his visit, a massive cornice of snow, covering the shaft, had thawed and plummeted down into the chamber. The farmer had, unbeknown to himself, crossed the 340 foot void on just a few feet of hardened snow. The gods were watching him that day.

Returning to the junction, the opening to Flood Entrance Pot may be noticed on the left, another way-in for experienced cavers when Fell Beck is a torrent, while Disappointment Pot lies in a shake-hole to the right. The latter originally 'disappointed' its discoverers, Eli Simpson and Blackburn Holden in 1908, who hoped for a quick way into the system below, only to be barred by a very low passage in water. These days, brave souls simply duck through the freezing stream to reach passages and drops into the 'Far Country' lying beneath Clapham Bottoms. It's more enthralling than disappointing, but the name has stuck.

The Lord's Little Boy
The toughest part of the climb now begins, up the slopes of Little Ingleborough, although the views cross to Simon Fell and the great catchment of Fell Beck more than compensate for the hard labour. The National Park Authority have admirably solved the erosion problem by a combination of gravel pathways and slabs of stone, creating steps that always seem to play havoc with the knee joints. Once the cairn on Little Ingleborough is reached, the rest of the climb is pure joy: a gently sloping ridge connecting the servant with his

Bubbling up: Clapham Beck Head sees the Gaping Gill water finally emerging after a journey underground of several days, in normal conditions.

master in sensational fashion. There are few more exhilarating places in Yorkshire, with views on all sides being outstanding, and the massive saddle of the Black Shiver ridge, that famous 'spur' on Ingleborough, sweeping up to the summit plateau of a great mountain. Two obvious shelves of rock encircle the highest reaches, and the trick now is to leave the beaten track and turn north-eastwards onto the second of these (SD743740) where a line of shake-holes indicates the highest limestone layer on Ingleborough, nearly 700 metres, (2200 feet) above the sea.

Not many will follow your journey here, though you are likely to meet a procession of walkers momentarily as the shelf crosses the 'tourist' route up from Ingleton. Just beyond, an obvious semi-circular breach in the sandstone shelf below marks the position of the Falls Foot Landslip – a fault-guided slump visible on Ingleborough from miles away, and appearing as though a hungry giant has taken a bite from a tasty-looking Yoredale sandwich cake (SD737745). If time permits it is worth scrambling down to view the impressive gorge left by the collapse, with a chaotic jumble of boulders cascading down the rift: the 'Lord's Rake' of Ingleborough. On another day it is a taste of real mountaineering to climb up the ravine itself, feeling the wind whistling down the narrow confines from the summit – and, no doubt, feeling very much alone.

'Shiver me Timbers'

Continuing along the terrace, a smaller 'notch' is perhaps the finest situation of all, where massive boulders of grit, some precariously balanced, stand watch over the tremendous plunge down the 'Black Shiver'. (SD739748) Here another landslip is encountered, insignificant from this great height and made more so by the beautiful swathes of white limestone decorating the benches beyond. This is Ingleborough for the true mountaineer: a place of unrelenting winds and enveloping wildness befitting its bleak, even horrifying, name. Those with a steady head and good grips can scramble down a grassy chute to stand on an exposed outcrop of sandstone – the ultimate experience on Yorkshire's finest peak; the miniscule signs of human existence lying on the floor of Chapel-le-Dale a thousand feet below.

The terrace eventually peters out as the huge sweep of the Humphrey Bottom amphitheatre dominates the view to the north, the flanks of Park Fell and Southerscales Fell joined smoothly to the mountain in a graceful curve, adding welcome beauty to the savage surroundings of 'The Arks'. Possibly originating from the Old English *aerc* or 'chest' of the mountain, these are shattered rocky slopes of unremitting steepness which give an awe-struck observer the impression of being sat in the upper tiers of the Coliseum. There is no surrounding audience, but tiny moving spots of colour give away the procession of 'Three Peaks' walkers, zig-zagging their way up the final stages of what is, more often than not, their third mountain.

Circle Time

The north-west corner of the summit plateau can now be conveniently reached by a short scramble up to the right. If this is your first visit you will want to head immediately for the trig point and cairn (*see the Ridge Route for details*), but those who have been before can from this point have a fascinating stroll around the perimeter of the entire summit mass.

Having survived being blown away at the plateau edge, keep the Arks on your left and head for the opposite corner – the north-east, where two paths can be seen at 'Swine Tail': one heading down to Chapel-Dale and the other following the flanks of Simon Fell down to Horton-in-Ribblesdale (SD745746). Ignore both and swing southwards (right), following the remains of the ancient wall and ditch which define the Ingleborough 'Hill Fort.' I was taught many years ago that this was the highest defended place in England, visions of Iron Age natives hurling stones down on the Roman invaders firmly implanted in my mind. More recently, studies noting a lack of flints, hearths and spoil heaps around the many 'hut circles' have speculated ruling out that this was ever a fort at all. Following the 'fort wall' southwards along the summit, diversions to the right will quickly pick up the remarkable 'hut circles' and it is striking how many are actually semi-circular in outline rather than being complete. Are these circles burial cairns, rather than dwellings? Was the summit of this mountain a cemetery of symbolic and ritual significance? The proposal, as landscape archaeologist David Johnson (2008) notes, is certainly an attractive one. Whatever the story: walking alongside stonework that has stood at such a height for centuries, and in all weathers, is a wonderful experience.

The perimeter route soon reaches the well-trodden route down to Little Ingleborough that we diverted off on the approaching journey. In describing the 'classic' from Clapham, Wainwright (1970) concluded that 'no way back is better than the way here described; there may even be *eagerness* to revisit the many wonderful places already seen on the ascent.' I can second that feeling as I have succumbed to the same eagerness on many occasions. However, if time permits – and there is no cloud or mist approaching – I can recommend a lonely alternative that will double the amount of features and leave you wondering just how much more Ingleborough can offer - but the good weather, I will repeat, is crucial and half-decent map reading skills are welcome, too.

Newby for Newbies

Once the summit of Little Ingleborough has been revisited, instead of heading down the 'steps' to Gaping Gill, take the path heading SSW onto the till covered wasteland of Newby Moss. The trick is to find the only obvious stream channel at this height, reached after a kilometre or so, on the 450 metre contour (SD737723) Here, Grey Wife Sike sinks into an obscure-sounding pothole with the name of P2a. This is a recent sink as in the past, and in times of flood, the Sike used to sink much further down the hillside. If anything, the shakehole of P2 can be remembered as offering two routes – with the 'a' route, that of excellence, leading to the right. All seems drab, even boring, after previous excitements, but a wander along the contour line soon reveals another shakehole with a beautifully sculptured shaft at the bottom, and tired limbs are rejuvenated by the sight of the 'Fairy's Throne' – better known to potholers as the Fluted Hole. At 457 metres, this is the highest shakehole on Ingleborough's Great Scar Limestone. It doesn't lead down very far, but this 'botanical gem', as Wainwright calls it, is one of the more secretive highlights of the mountain: pinnacles of weathered white limestone emerging from a pinkish, water-worn shaft, gleaming like polished marble. Encrusted with mosses, ferns and other lime-loving plants, it is certainly a fitting place for Pan – the god of the woods and fields, to sit and contemplate his kingdom. The north-west corner sees a stream running into the shaft, with a wickedly poised boulder bridging a very narrow drop into the hole – where many a poor sheep has taken its final steps over the years.

Equally regal in structure are the magnificent Pillar Holes, unmissable just a few metres to the west (SD733724). Several shafts lie in a line, richly decorated in late summer with rowan berries. The name is a good one: standing above the largest shaft is like peering down from the balcony of a great cathedral to the head of the nave below – massive columns of limestone, stained pink with impurities - towering up out of the depths. The Newby Moss potholes are unique in that they are merely shafts, with no horizontal passages below, and it is thought that they were formed by glacial melt-water exploiting an area of minor faulting, though there is still much to learn about their origin. Certainly I wouldn't fancy falling down one, and they are to be avoided at all costs in mist, as our next objective makes appallingly obvious.

As many of the world's deadliest spiders are misleadingly small – so the deadliest potholes can seem nothing from the surface, and Long Kin West (SD731724) or the 'L' Hole from its capital letter shape, is a fine example. 'Hell' indeed, would be a more fitting description and Wainwright pulls no punches in his summary (1991): 'If life is considered precious,' he writes, 'keep well away.' There are no fences or warning signs just beyond Pillar Holes, where an old track up from Cold Cotes crosses a natural bridge with two 'small' openings, each often partly obscured by grass, on either side. 'Small' at the surface, that is; the northern shaft being no more than six feet wide and an incredible 92 metres (292 feet) deep! For anything with four or two legs, this has to be one of the most dangerous places in the UK. The golden rule with potholes is never to throw stones down, but on Newby Moss, no ropes dangling down must mean no cavers below – as there is no horizontal way in from beneath. Taking great care, drop a stone down the hole, keeping it as central as possible … and count. How many seconds is it before you here that final 'ping'? This place makes even the most seasoned explorer shudder at his own vulnerability.

Finally, normal service is resumed with falling water very much in evidence at the Boggart's Roaring Holes, so-named by the Balderstons in their 1888 classic *Ingleton, Bygone and Present*. (SD728738) These lie a few minutes' walk to the north west of the 'L Hole' and the 19th century husband and wife team, finding them nameless, became aware of strange 'roaring' noises emanating from the depths when pebbles were dropped down – hence their romantic 'christening'. Take great care not to go waist deep in the surrounding peat bogs, as I once did in my rush to beat the fading light. There are three main holes, the deepest being 34 metres, with the northern end having a fine cascade down the customary walls of polished, pinkish limestone. 'Boggart's' marks an exciting end to our exploration of Newby Moss – and from it fine views of Whernside and the Falls Foot landslip on Ingleborough beckon for the camera.

All that remains is to retrace your footsteps back to Grey Wife Sike, taking care not to fall down Long Kin West as you do so. The views down over the Craven Lowlands to the Bowland Fells beyond, and over the Irish Sea to the west – are a glorious accompaniment to the journey's end – and well deserved. From the Sike, a diversion to the east will soon pick up the unusual entrance to Newby Moss Pot – one of the few pots in the vicinity to have any horizontal development – but most minds now will be trained on Clapham. This is reached by turning down the normally dry channel of Grey Wife, passing the curious Harryhorse Stone with its 'foal' of limestone over to the left, its mossy countenance worth a diversion for the day's final photograph. An easy descent down the moor meets a wall corner just behind Newby Cote, where a left turn follows the old road back to Clapham village.

Whether or not you simply retrace the direct route from the summit, or choose to navigate the adventurous option of Newby Moss – Ingleborough from Clapham, in good weather, is a major life experience and one of the great day-long adventures that England has to offer. There are many contenders for 'greatest', 'finest' and 'most famous' here: the finest village and show cave; the most famous pothole and highest waterfall; the most fascinating history. What this adventure proves, once and for good is that, while Ingleborough may be far from the highest mountain in the country, in terms of sheer fascination, it is head and shoulders above them all.

Stunning approach: Many believe Penyghent to be the most beautiful of the three, and they may well be right. *Top right:* The notorious Penyghent Pot, leading to energy-sapping crawls in water. All cavers must exit the same way.

4. Penyghent:
Climbing on the Lion's Back

Grid Reference: SD844715 (starting point close to Dale Head Farm on the minor road between Stainforth and Halton Gill). A 4 mile (6.4 km) adventure.

In a Nutshell: The first half of this wild adventure traverses the limestone plateau surrounding Penyghent's imposing summit mass, keeping well off the trodden footpaths and revealing little-visited highlights of the karst landscape. After examining the gigantic doline of the 'Sugar Basin' and the contrasting potholes of Larch tree Hole and Penyghent Pot, we finally rejoin the Pennine Way close to the mountain's best known limestone features: Hunt Pot, with its cunning 'slit' engulfing a stream, and the massive 'crater' of the unforgettable Hull Pot. To finish the day, an easy walk onto the summit plateau of this fine mountain is rewarded by some of the finest views in the north of England.

Essentials: Clear, settled weather is essential, as no mountain is fun without a view! Map and compass should be at hand throughout, though for much of the way the 'pathless' route involves following a wall with little chance of going astray. The entire route is on the Ordnance Survey OL2 (Yorkshire Dales Southern and Western) map. Penyghent can feel even wilder than Ingleborough on the summit, so several layers should at least be carried, even in summer – along with a good waterproof. Good boots with strong grips are a must, as the descent of the 'nose' of the mountain calls for a steady head for heights and sure-footing. There are no facilities of any kind on the route: this is a raw adventure, so take plenty of food and drink, and be prepared.

Access: The village of Stainforth is just off the B6479, between Settle and Horton-in-Ribblesdale. Once in the village, follow the route for Halton Gill, along one of the most lonely and dramatic roads in the country. After 3 miles, with Penyghent becoming ever more dominant to the north – the farmstead of Dale Head is passed on the left. Beyond it, close to a cattle grid, is parking for several cars with an honesty box on the wall. Take care to leave the road clear for farm vehicles and ensure that you hide any valuables in this isolated spot.

Adventure: Undeterred by the elements – the feline presence of Penyghent has stretched its lithe body along Ribblesdale since man has walked the earth. In some ways it is the 'cute' little one of the three – when it contrasts against a spring or summer sky and the gorgeous purple saxifrage delicately adorns its upper reaches. In others – when the storm clouds gather, and biting gales eat into the faces of its most die-hard fanatics, it is as nasty a *felis silvestris* as there ever was. A *Panthera leo*, maybe – though this is no snoozing male lion with luxurious mane, but a female in every sense; the lioness: alert, proud, bare-headed and demanding we treat her with the utmost respect.

This celebrated 'hill of the winds' as the Celtic name suggests – is in no way daunted by the presence of Ingleborough to the west. Indeed, the lioness may even put the lord to shame across Ribblesdale, her presence from all sides being majestic – while that of her larger neighbour is more subdued – tamed by its gentler eastern slopes. She is many things to many people: a sphinx, a cruising liner, a sacred place; a means of escape. A mountain which, as one man explained to me as we crossed paths on the summit one freezing February day: 'makes it feel good to be alive.'

Delivering the Milk
We begin our journey on the 'front legs' of the lioness – on the swathe of wild, drift-covered moorland stretching between the 'nose' of the peak and the prehistoric uplands of Settle. The gaunt wilderness of Fountains Fell lies to our left as we head towards Dale Head farm, turning right onto an enticing stretch of the Pennine Way. The farm is one of the most photographed and painted dwellings in the Three Peaks – and deservedly so: its arched porchway and wisping smoke often presenting a homely contrast to the savage winds testing its endurance. Round the bend beyond, where a wall comes down on the right, a pathway veers away to the daunting Dale Head Pot, (SD840718) located a hundred yards or so away in a deep shakehole. Classed as 'super severe' in the caving guides, it is best imagined than experienced in the flesh, dropping in a series of vertical pitches to a total depth of 165 metres. Far more accommodating is the impressive doline of Churn Milk Hole, reached in a few minutes on the left of the Pennine Way. Caused by collapse of the underlying rock due to solution underneath, it is one of the better known dolines in the Dales, passed by every Pennine Way buff and those who take the quick route up Penyghent. Huge blocks

of Great Scar limestone litter its floor, which contains an oil drum entrance into a small chamber below. Many attempts have been made to link this 'cat's saucer' to the other holes in the vicinity, but without much success – the distinctive name probably referring to its proximity to the path offering a cool storage for milk in the days before refrigeration.

Impressive it may be – but Churn Milk is a mere mouse in comparison to what lies just to the west. Beyond the hole, a finger post is reached pointing in three directions – with the way on lying immediately behind it to the left, striking across unpromising and pathless heathery moorland (SD835718). Over the brow of the hill a wall corner is met, and a glance to the right (north) reveals an open gateway into the adjacent field (SD833719). Pass through this, turn immediately left, and an astonishing sight suddenly numbs the senses. The monotonous grassland ends abruptly on the brink of a truly massive crater – completely unexpected – and playing the usual doline trick of revealing itself just as you are about to fall into it!

Do You Take Sugar?

Many sources give Braithwaite Wife Hole, in Chapel-le-Dale, as the biggest doline in the Dales, but I'd love to turn up here one day with tape measure and patience, just to have a go at changing the record. Certainly, it can take a good five minutes to encircle the perimeter of this one, and those new to dolines could be forgiven for suspecting this to be the work of the Luftwaffe. The broken rocks in the bottom have been likened to 'ants in a sugar bowl' and since finding that description, I have opted for the more elegant name of 'Sugar Basin.' Clearly, something melodramatic has gone on here below the surface to cause this colossal slump, and the hole deserves to be named and labeled by the map-makers. Those with an insatiable appetite for exploration might want to slither down the slopes for a belittling experience; rather like standing alone on the stage of a vast theatre with no sign of an audience. Returning to the surface, the view from the south across the hole seems to humble Penyghent herself, the lion seemingly tottering on the edge of a poacher's trap.

Walking this perimeter route of Penyghent is like tackling a golf course. There is no flag at the 'third hole', but instead two sycamores mark our next objective, reached after a five minute walk to the west over the moor. (SD830720) The brow of the hill at first hides them, but, keeping Ingleborough in the line of sight, two conspicuous trees will be seen ahead as the land slopes down towards Horton. Make the most of them, as they are the last you will see on this wild and exposed journey. Thankfully, they lie alongside a wall that will be the guiding hand for the next stage of our adventure, preventing all possibilities of getting lost.

The trees are just inside the enclosing walls of Larch Tree Hole, an attractive, mossy rift formed on the same east-west fault as the Sugar Basin and Churn Milk Hole, and lined up with Sulber Nick on the opposite side of Ribblesdale. A stream evidently once cascaded into the eastern side, and if the perimeter wall is crossed with care, the route of the water may be followed down into the rift. Carcasses of animals and birds usually litter the bottom in profusion, almost as if the Lion of Ribblesdale has been casting her victims away from prying eyes.

Having failed, like me, to find a larch tree – our route now swings at a right angle to the north, following the wall under the flanks of the sleeping lion. We are now crossing Gavel Rigg, an area of glacial drift covering the division between the Yordedale slopes of the mountain and the Great Scar limestone to the west. Gavel Rigg Pot can be hunted for just off the path to the right, about 200 metres from Larch Tree Hole. It is covered by a sheet of rusty iron and is flanked by a neat limestone wall covering the spoil that 'cave diggers' have thrown out. Don't be tempted to uncover the iron as it doesn't lead very far and the metal is sharp and rusty.

Size Doesn't Matter

Continuing along the wall, dolines are seemingly everywhere and the Lion of Ribblesdale looks more impressive with every step. It is from this position that some liken her to an ocean liner – the limestone buttresses of her upper flanks catching the late afternoon sun and appearing like the lights of a great ship. Ignore the route coming up from Brackenbottom, where, if you are lucky, you may encounter *homo sapiens*, and continue across it alongside the guiding wall (SD830727). The wall swings slightly north-west, and all is seemingly monotonous for a while, a glance behind revealing those two sycamores to be insignificant dots in an uncompromising landscape. The key now is to watch for walls running up from the Horton side to meet our guiding wall, and, where the second of these is encountered (SD828734) this is the signal to divert off the path to the right, towards the mountain, for the notorious Penyghent Pot.

Ingleborough may have some daunting underground challenges, but the Lion fittingly provides what, for many, is the hardest of the lot. First-time visitors, equipped with an Ordnance Survey map, may wander round in frustration seeking a great shaft worthy of the alliterative name – but in vain. Instead, hidden away in a tiny dry valley off the path is the most insignificant looking excuse for a pothole there ever was: a tiny hole – no more than a drain it would seem, and supported by rusty scaffolding. Even the lid is a mess: three pieces of old fence only just covering the aperture, but no doubt serving a purpose in saving another ewe or two from you know who!

Uncovered in 1949 by the Northern Pennine Club, this infamous hole drops to a stream that can easily be seen by removing the planks. Until the scaffolding was erected, the surrounding boulders were, according to *Northern Caves*, of 'dubious stability.' Now they have made at least the first twelve feet of the journey comparatively pleasant. The rest, for even an average caver, must seem like a trip into hell. For a start, there is no way out at the bottom: a large sump feeding to the resurgence at Brant's Gill Head (SD813730), so 'what goes in – must come out', so to speak – including all ropes, ladders and, hopefully, humans! The problem is that the passages are low, very long and almost always in water … and it can take so long to negotiate the crawls and pitches that many have become exhausted on the way out, needing rescue. The stream you can see, for example, leads after a short drop to a hands-and-knees crawl in water for over 300 feet, with just two standing places along its length. Beyond this, a series of drops requiring ropes or ladders leads down to the 'Friday the Thirteenth Series' and the 'Living Dead Extensions.' Lovely: I'd rather remain living on the surface, thank you very much.

The Meeting of the Hunt
Leave Penyghent Pot to the imagination, ensuring you have replaced the planks, and return to the friendly wall, continuing north until an area of boggy ground threatens to swallow you up. At this point, skirt the bog by heading briefly north-east, crossing a small stream and a few pillows of couchy heather to meet the Pennine Way (SD828741). Turning right here will take us up onto the Lion's back, but we will first take a short detour downhill to the two great showpieces of lion country.

Impressive panorama: The Old Man of Penyghent points the way off the summit.

The first is hidden in a valley a few metres away on the left. Here, a surface stream bubbles merrily over the last few metres of the Yoredale rocks before meeting the Great Scar Limestone – in the most dramatic way possible, at Hunt Pot. Don't let children or dogs run ahead, as this place is lethal indeed. There are many cunningly hidden holes beside the main shaft, where an evil-looking slit, only four metres wide at the centre, and three times as long, swallows the stream in one glorious gulp. Before its climax at the shaft, there are a series of attractive cascades at the northern end, and it is possible, with great care, to cross the stream and traverse to the eastern end of the hole for an unforgettable view in. Access is easiest at the western side, where a series of boulders seemingly provides a parapet and barrier to the abyss, but a word of warning: almost hidden between these is a small hole behind a wedged boulder into which a body would drop easily and not come to rest until hitting the floor 200 feet below. Make sure you spot it and take note for future visits. It gives me the heebie-jeebies!

The water falling into 'Thund Pot', as it is called by the locals, moves through flooded passages into Penyghent Pot and eventually resurges at Brants Gill Head. It is cited by many authors as the archetypal Yorkshire pothole: a classic example of an active stream crossing from impermeable rock onto limestone, and dropping down a major, fault-guided-joint. In winter, the falling water turns memorably into swathes of ice crystals, and at all times beauty manages to mask the savagery. For this reason, Hunt Pot is much photographed, yet it is still surprising how many people don't know of its existence. By all means enjoy it, but it has undoubted dangers, and should be treated with respect. For some it's a wonderful picnic spot. For others: a place to shudder and retreat.

Lion Meets Hippo

Not too far away lurks another monster, but this time of a very different character. To reach it, return to the Pennine way and continue downhill for a short distance, where a crossroads sees a bridle path going right across springy green turf. There is little sign of anything untoward in the landscape at first, and a horizontal ridge ahead appears to be a path coming up from the west. Then, in just a few seconds, all is chaos. The ground suddenly plunges with shocking effect into an immense crater; the 'ridge' now revealing itself as the lip of the hole at the northern end. This is Hull or 'Thirl' Pot, and, though not quite big enough to capture the Lion herself, is certainly a useful trap for her victims! Its long, symmetrical profile does resemble the hull of a ship – but without the elegance. There is no gently inclining Sugar Basin here; this is limestone at its starkest – with vertical fractured walls of grey rock plunging to a floor of cobbles and boulders. The yawning chasm is 90 metres (270 feet) long and about 18 metres (60 feet) deep and wide. At its western end is a massive detached boulder that from certain angles looks like an overweight grazing animal and which I have always called the 'Hull Pot Hippo'. Brave climbers step across, with ropes, onto the Hippo's back before descending, while others brave the gully at the eastern side, far too difficult for ordinary mortals.

There is still debate as to how Hull Pot was formed, but it is believed to be a major collapse doline formed on a series of parallel faults. Ribs of limestone left by the faulting have gradually been eroded away by solution and have slowly 'peeled' off the sides of the hole, enlarging it to its current proportions. No doubt the hippo will go the same way one day, poor chap. Water can be heard entering the hole in the depths of the eastern end, but the dominating feature is a dry river bed on the north side, cut into the lowest limestone of the Yoredale series which overlies the Great Scar Limestone of the main hole. Only in the highest floods does the river bed become active, when a foaming white cascade of terrific proportions roars into the pot. It's worth walking up from Horton in gale force winds and a downpour to witness this Hull Pot spectacular. Once conditions subside, the water once again finds its way underground – emerging, like so much of the Lion's water, at Brant's Gill Head.

Retracing your route to the Pennine Way involves experiencing the 'Hull Pot Illusion' where there is no sign of the hole after just a few steps south of the brink. One second it's there – the next, it's gone. One can only imagine the amount of sheep and other four legged beasts that have hit the bottom over the centuries. The lioness has a lot to answer for.

Reach for the Pinnacle

We won't tell her that, though, as the last part of our adventure involves a climb onto her back. Risky stuff, indeed, you might assume – and we must proceed with caution. After the thrills of the pots, it can be a monotonous slog up the Pennine Way onto the summit ridge of Penyghent. Tempting it is to follow Albert of Marriott Edgar's famous monologue, and give the lion a poke with your walking stick. It's all her fault for putting this slope here. For a short while, animosity is unavoidable: your relationship with the big cat hanging in the balance …

All is forgiven, however, when the gleaming limestone scars of the ridge are reached at last (SD838742). A small cave will be noticed in the cliff, nothing to write home about, but shyly hiding itself beyond is the precarious Penyghent Pinnacle. He is not easily seen from the Pennine Way, but a detour over the scree gradually reveals him, detached from the shattered cliffs of Main Limestone, the upper reaches of the Yoredale series. He appears to have had an argument with the lion, as in recent years he has lost both his facial features and the fine mop of tussocky hair that he once sported. Perhaps it's just a matter of time before her relentless weather destroys him altogether. Certainly, he appears to be leaning further backwards each time I visit. The Main Limestone, just below the summit cap, has a considerably thicker layer than on Ingleborough, allowing such features to develop. Get up there, quick, and see him while he's still alive!

The Pinnacle provides welcome respite to the steepest

section, but after that all is delightful, as a 'Penyghent Promenade' is reached, running south towards the summit. This gradually sloping terrace soars hundreds of feet above the limestone benches below, and from here Hull pot looks no more than a hole on a putting green. The whole of the area between the pot and the mountain east of 'Tarn Bar', was once a lake, the remnants of which can be seen in the pool clearly visible from the promenade. The views across to the Ingleborough massif and north to Whernside are superb, and distance thankfully masks the eyesore of the Horton limestone quarry.

The exhilaration increases as the Pennine Way swings eastwards up a stony saddle to the summit, 2237 feet above sea-level, and feeling, especially on bleak winter days, more like 20, 000! Crowned with the customary large cairn, shelter and ordnance survey column, all neatly arranged at a wall junction – the feeling of exposure can be even more severe than on Ingleborough. Is this really the cute little one? Climbing on any lion's back would be flirting with danger, and the Lioness herself, except on the rare occasions when she's snoozing under a warm sun, certainly lets you pay for the experience. Her flanks can be a perfect shelter on the way up, but once you traverse her spine on that summit ridge, aggressive gales usually kick in, making the Celtic 'Hill of the Winds' more than live up to her name.

Through Feline Eyes

The view is extensive: the east taking in the upper reaches of Wharfedale and Great Whernside, with the massive bulk of Fountains Fell squaring up to the Lion nose-to-nose along the southern aspect. The 'Dolomites' of Warrendale Knots lie beyond, while the Ingleborough massif, as ever, dominates the view west. There is a temptation to avoid 'take off' by clinging to the wind shelter, but the highlight of the whole adventure has yet to come.

Head south along the Lion's back, following the wall and feeling relentless westerlies biting into your right cheek. The feline spine suddenly gives way to an aggressive head, with the south ridge of Penyghent plunging sensationally down to the moorland across which we traversed to begin our adventure. As befits the riskiest of all places to mess with a lion, this famous 'nose' is mountaineering at its very best, and demands much care in descent. Pointing the way, in the grit stone cliffs of the summit cap, is the unmistakable 'Old Man', a precarious collection of unsteady rocks which seemingly won't be around much longer. The untidy jumble of grey weathered boulders lying below indicates that many other old men and women have taken a tumble over the years on this exposed face. Those with a good head for heights will descend the rocky staircase in the grit stone confidently, but remember to keep eyes on the ground at all times and stop if you want to take in the view. To be put out of action on the lion's nose doesn't bear thinking about!

And so her outstretched paws once more lie in front of you, as, with sore toes and wind-beaten countenance, you return to the relative sanctuary of the Pennine Way. A short stroll past Dalc Head returns you to the parking spot, but, now you're a seasoned lion hunter, you'll no doubt be wary of that feline presence, watching your every step. Though proud and alert, Penyghent is, like all the big cats, content to sit in a prominent position and survey her kingdom. Treat her unique landscape with respect and she'll not only remain so, but will become your friend for life.

Watersplash: The splendid lower fall of Force Gill thunders into a natural amphitheatre. *Top right*: Sheep on the Whernside summit ridge.

5. Whernside:
Whernie by the Water

Grid Reference: SD767795 (starting point at the Ribblehead layby). An 8 mile (12.8 km) adventure.

In a Nutshell: A gradual but exciting ascent of Yorkshire's highest mountain, diverting from the main 'tourist' routes along the secretive and dramatic ravine of Force Gill. After admiring man's attempts at taming a wild landscape, two superb waterfalls are enjoyed, as well as constantly changing rock scenery. Emergence onto a limestone plateau meets the unusual Greensett Tarn – and the route then takes in stunning views from the summit before returning via the ancient farmstead of Ivescar, which hides its own historical secrets. There's a bit of everything on this one: upland wildlife, ancient and modern history, geological wonders and magnificent views throughout.

Essentials: As this is a lengthy walk on demanding terrain, good boots and waterproofs are essential – even in summer. Some of the walking is on pathless moorland and in case of mist a compass is essential. The Station Inn lies at Ribblehead and there is usually a refreshment van, but beyond the start and finish there are no facilities of any kind. Take plenty of food and drink – and choose a clear, settled day if possible. In winter an early start is a must on this adventure. Unlike Ingleborough, Whernside's summit offers the safety of a wall making it virtually impossible to get lost on the highest and most exposed parts of the journey.

Access: Ribblehead lies between Ingleton and Hawes on the B6255. Immediately north of the Station Inn and beyond the T junction with the B6479 there is a large parking area. This can get very busy so try to get there bright and early!

Adventure: 'Avoid at all costs,' they will tell you. After all, it is only 'woeful Whernie' – the beached whale; the great useless lump; the boring wedge of monotony to be ticked off, with a sigh of relief, and then ignored for life. In short, why on earth would anyone want to drag himself up there? True – if the three were queens in a beauty contest, Whernie would struggle to get a whistle. Penny's feminine outline and majestic stance would have the judges drooling, no doubt. Ingle's sophisticated class would win the crown hands down – but what of poor old Whernie? Would it be worth her while even turning up?

You can judge for yourself after this adventure. Whernie is a modest giant and is content to be so, not once proposing to live up to the thrills of her more celebrated sisters, and yet quietly displaying a series of unique features that in many ways leave both Penny and Ingle gasping with envy.

As if aware of her natural inferiority, lacking the immediate impact provided by the gleaming pavements and spectacular shafts of her neighbours, Whernie has relied on man to smarten up her monotonous lower slopes, and he has responded in spectacular fashion. Nothing on the other two can match the sudden impression of the Ribblehead viaduct. The great twenty-four arch masterpiece is a magnet to the eyes, drawing seemingly endless crowds of visitors and giving Whernie the fame she richly deserves. If only some of the masses would turn off the regular routes, and seek out the treasures that lie buried by the shyness of this great mountain?

She Will Drive You Batty

The first highlight lies just by the main road. Close to the Station Inn, with its famous 'loo with a view' is the site of the Batty Green 'shanty town' and hospital – set up when the viaduct was being constructed between 1870 and 1875. An obvious small hole by the roadside is Batty Wife Cave, its legend described by Harry Speight (1892) in *The Craven and North-West Yorkshire Highlands.* Here a Mr Batty agreed to meet his wife and talk over their failing relationship. At the time, before the railway was built, this was a deep pothole that has since been filled in. Anyway – for some reason or other, Mrs Batty ended up in the bottom of the hole; presumably the row re-kindled, and she was either thrown into the shaft or jumped in herself. It's a sad story, but Speight does say the husband, in his old age, was often heard by the hole shouting, 'Betty, Betty, where art thou, lass?' Maybe he missed her altogether and she escaped in the dark, realizing her mistake in marrying him? 'Betty Batty', after all, was a bit of a mouthful!

Having examined this legendary spot, take the route across Batty Green to the viaduct. Much has been written about the shocking conditions in which the navvies of the Midland Railway toiled to produce this scheduled ancient monument in the 1870s. The twenty-four arches of dark limestone loom menacingly; spectacular but never quite pleasant: admirable, but seldom viewed without suspicion. Was it really necessary, you will ask yourself, for so many families to suffer in building a link between such obscure and remote localities? It's hardly London to Bristol up here. On the right of the path, a few humps in the landscape indicate the former 'town' of 'Sebastopol', where, amongst other things, the bricks were produced for the lining of the arches. The two largest heaps are the remains of the brickworks chimney – and the raised plateau of 'Belgravia' just above contains the rough outlines of huts and offices. Clearly, the bosses had the comforts of higher and drier ground and could keep a close eye on the work force, though this was often in vain. Fights were frequent, drunkenness rife – and work carried out in unthinkable gloom amongst seas of mud and disease. Shocking it is to think that, after so much labour and sacrifice, the arches were under threat of demolition in the 1980s. Ribblehead without the viaduct would be London without the tower: unthinkable.

Instead of going under the arches, continue northwards alongside them – admiring the way they frame Ingleborough in a dramatic picture. The route then passes to the east of the railway along Blue Clay Ridge into Little Dale, passing the Blea Moor Signal Box and one remaining railway cottage. Little Dale is famous as the spot from which the 'dark blue limestone' of the viaduct was quarried – and the water will be a welcome friend from this point almost to the summit of the mountain. At one point there is ford over the beck formed from large boulders of gritstone, but those who don't like to wet their tootsies might prefer a pleasant wooden bridge. Whernie caters for all types, bless her.

She Will Surprise You

Not least with her variety. Two more man-made wonders are next on the menu at the head of the dale. The first is a

70

beautifully constructed aqueduct, where the navvies painstakingly carried the waters of Force Gill across the railway. Again you will ask yourself – wouldn't it have been easier to tunnel underneath? The cobbled construction is a perfect little Victorian street, stepped in a series of elaborate waterfalls. Neither Penny nor Ingle has anything in comparison and this deserves to be more famous. It makes a great photograph and lies in perfect harmony in the landscape. The next is the massive Blea Moor tunnel, its inky black mouth sucking in the line to the right of the aqueduct and invoking a shudder even on a summer's day. Built at the same time as the viaduct to a length of 2.4 km (2629 yards), it has, perhaps, a seemingly futile mission in linking with Dent Station, one of the most remote railway outposts in England. Conditions for the tunnel navvies were arguably even worse than at Ribblehead, as a series of shafts 200 feet in depth were sunk into the moor for the men to be lowered to their work. They laboured only in candlelight with picks, shovels and gunpowder for as much as 12 hours a day, seeing no daylight in winter, with many drowning when relentless rain turned the moor into a quagmire, and the shafts into underground lakes.

She Will Force You

Whernie has so far laid bare her works of man, and, as impressive as they are, they come a close second in my book to what lies hidden in Force Gill, just beyond the aqueduct. This is one of the great unsung valleys of the Yorkshire Dales: known to few but no doubt adored by those who do. Not only does it contain two stunning waterfalls, but it is probably the best place in the Three Peaks to see the contrasting 'sandwich' rock scenery of the Yordedale Series, for which these mountains are well-known.

A Three Peaks Up and Under

Ignore the masses following the obvious route to the summit, and stay with the water, following it upstream into the lower confines of the gill. Keep to the right banking of the beck, noting how a large mass of glacial till has slumped over the lower slopes here, clearly visible just above water surface on the opposite bank. Round a corner, a diamond-shaped island is met in the stream bed, beyond which roars the spectacular white plume of Force Gill's 'Lower Fall.' Nothing on the Ingleton Waterfalls Walk can compete with this; not in beauty – but in splendid isolation. You can sit here for hours in a wild landscape, surrounded by ferns, mosses, ruby red rowan berries and catching the refreshing cold spray of the tumbling water: and there will be no crowds, no patient waits for a photographs, no litter. This is geological heaven, but so few desire it. Often I have watched scores march past on the treadmill to the summit – a minute's walk away, but on not one occasion has anyone made the diversion to join me – even when they have seen me, endlessly snapping away with my camera. Over many years, the fall has cut back the shale beneath its lip of sandstone to leave a splendid 'U'-shaped amphitheatre, and 'Force Gill Lower Fall' is a grave insult. I call this wonder 'Horseshoe Spout' – and it deserves it. Besides, 'force' is a little over-used in the Ingleton area.

The lowest of the Yoredale limestones have been covered by glacial till, and here we see a succession of shales topped with a thin band of sandstone and formed in late Carboniferous times when falling sea levels allowed rivers to wash sand and mud into a swampy, tropical lagoon. The wall of the 'horseshoe' on the right shows a clear division between the two rocks, and boulders of both sandstone and limestone litter the base of the fall. To scramble up the right bank to the brink of the 'Horseshoe' is a wonderful experience, and to watch a sheet of slow moving water suddenly erupt into

On the right tracks: Blea Moor Tunnel swallows the Settle and Carlisle Railway line, below Force Gill.

white turmoil is unforgettable. The views down the ravine to Little Dale are equally stunning, and as the stream splits either side of the resistant island we encountered earlier, the water takes on the shape of a silver wine bottle, its wide body tapering downstream to a graceful neck.

Continuing upstream, a band of limestone is encountered just above the next small cascade, indicating a time when rising sea levels will have allowed tiny marine creatures to flourish. Though stained by impurities to often resemble the sandstone in colour – it is less angular in structure with a soluble nature given away by the many runnels where water has seeped down its surface. Further on (SD757821) the stream cuts through cushions of limestone which often gleam salmon pink in the sunlight, creating a series of beautiful cascades. The alternating 'sandwiches' of sandstone and shale above these are very thin, indicating that extended periods of shallow, muddy water followed the limestone formation. Once a small rocky island is reached in the stream, a slither of sandstone can be seen jutting from the right bank with shale beds above and below. Here the gorge is so narrow that it is necessary to traverse the steep right bank before returning to the water a few yards upstream, where the walls close around another series of cascades, formed in the rocky Yoredale succession. As height is gained, the view across Blea Moor appears almost alien: conical mounds being topped by what appear to be little round chimneys, with not a wall or tree in sight. These are the shafts used by the workers when building the tunnel, later modified into a ventilation system which always reminds me of my childhood ... and *The Clangers*.

She Will Uncover Her Secrets

The sense of wildness intensifies before reaching its climax at the upper force, the majestic plume of the 'Mare's Tail.' This gorgeous ribbon of white water plunges some 50 feet (16 metres) from a lip of limestone into a rocky arena of unstable shales and sandstones; living up to its name in normal weather, but doubling up spectacularly in flood. This is Whernie's majestic steed: her secret showpiece. No surface cascade on Penny or Ingle can live with this – but modestly she just lies back and lets a few determined wanderers in on the secret. Scrambling to the brink of the fall is one of the great thrills of the Three Peaks – yet the only signs of life will invariably consist of the odd nosey sheep and calling curlew.

Above the waterfall the stream divides into three courses at Grain Ings (SD753824) and navigation is made easy by following each and every left hand branch or diversion. At last, the head of Force Gill is reached at the relatively thick bed of Main Limestone, the uppermost limestone in the 'Yoredale sandwich' and the water is seen emerging from the lower entrance to the Greensett Caves (SD747824). Whernie can't live with her sisters cave-wise, and it's no good pretending that she can. As with most caves in the Main Limestone, these are shallow, unstable and lack decoration, but it's refreshing to emerge from the confines of the gill and follow their erratic course over the plateau. The stream has, over thousands of years, played havoc with the edges of a much weathered limestone pavement in finding its way to the shale beds below. One detached pinnacle appears to grin slyly and exude so much personality that I have christened it the 'Greensett Gremlin.' It watches over a chaotic landscape where cavern collapse has left 'windows' into the cave system: the stream playing hide and seek with the explorer by emerging from one bed of limestone before plunging into another.

There is a way in for the determined, of course – the most accommodating entrance lying close to a notable peat hag and easily identified by a 'beard' of ferns dangling over the darkness (SD747822). A helmet mounted lamp is essential, but the problems of carting the gear up to this altitude, coupled with the constricted and unstable nature of the passages, no doubt deter all but the most fanatical.

This high altitude plateau was believed to have been scoured clean by a 'niche glacier' – a relatively small ice sheet formed during a 'stadial' or cold period which interrupted the otherwise gradual thawing of the main glaciers about 11, 000 years ago. Evidence is seen not only in the pavements, but in a barrier of glacial moraine holding back the waters of the remote Greensett Tarn, originally formed, no doubt, from the melting ice. This unexpected sheet of water is reached by heading westwards along the moraine barrier, its peaty waters indicating warmer times when trees and other vegetation flourished at these heights. There is a 'Lake

The nature of industry: Whernside boasts several man-made wonders. This fine aqueduct taking the beck over the railway line is a perfect example.

District' feel here, the boggy ground and cotton grass giving way to an irregular shoreline with steep slopes plunging into the far side. The black-headed gulls may have reduced in recent years, but the dark waters are breeding grounds for dragonflies and even an upland water beetle with the splendid name of *Agabus arcticus*. Yes, Whernie wins hands-down when it comes to standing water.

Avoiding a wet bottom when resting by the tarn is difficult, but, once accomplished, the route to the summit ridge beckons irresistibly ahead; the steepest pull on the adventure so far. There is no path here – and as you ascend the grassy ridge, the sight of other humans heading onto it from the main route on the right can be welcoming after so much time alone. Greensett Tarn looks wonderful as height is gained; a glittering silver island amidst a green-brown sea, far below on the plateau: Whernie's hidden jewel.

Once the ridge is gained, it is a simple case of following the wall to the summit. This is Whernside's life-line, helping weary walkers stay on course, but on the other hand it detracts from the sense of wild grandeur seen on the other two, particularly Ingleborough. Whernie therefore has the 'least scary' summit – but arguably the best view. Being further west than Ingleborough, the emerald greens of Dentdale and the Howgills beyond are much more in evidence, with Gragareth and Kingsdale stark in their solitude. And for once, and from this spot only, Ingleborough might just seem defeated, or at least tamed. You are never quite looking downhill onto her summit, but Whernie has had a good go of it. She is 82 feet higher, she'll have you know!

She Will Punish You

Leaving the wall shelter and column behind, the route now heads south-west along the ridge towards High Pike, with ever-impressive views of Chapel-le-Dale and the gleaming white swathes of the Scales Moor pavements in the distance. The skylarks are singing: the wall gives a sense of security, the climbing has been done and it's a cause for celebration … surely?

Not quite – as the path leaves the ridge and swings south-east towards Bruntscar (SD734803) where the 'toe curling' begins. This steep downward slope is a horrendous mixture of steps, slabs and loose rock designed to play havoc with the lower appendages and you will not thank Whernie for it one ha'porth. As each brave step is like being hit on the toe nails with a sledge hammer, you may consider why she is now treating you with such cruelty. You admired her views, marveled at her water features – even placed her above her sisters on certain terms, and what kind of gratitude is this? Cursing turns to prayers of thanks-giving as level ground is at last reached (SD739790), with another of Whernie's treasures hidden on the right – though with no time for seeking out today. In 1865, behind the farmhouse at Bruntscar, the curious owner broke into the cliff to reveal a richly decorated cave (see book two), still accessible today on payment of a small donation to St Leonard's church – and one of Yorkshire's truly unique experiences. Maybe the toe-curling can be forgiven after all.

Turn left through a succession of ancient farmsteads whose origins date back to the Viking occupations of the 10th century. The first of these, Broadrake, is currently moving towards accommodating visitors and even has its own blog and website. Homeshaw Cave lies beyond it, hidden away in a steep, rubbish-filled shakehole up to the left, and currently awaiting a much needed makeover. This will be welcomed, as two beautiful stream caves have for years been made inaccessible and dangerous: one of man's more shameful practices on Whernside. Cars, bicycles, bedsteads – you name it – everything seems to have been thrown at poor Homeshaw over the last century, even within the boundaries of a National Park. It still happens.

She Will Tantalise You

Behind the next farm, at Ivescar, (SD748798) a clump of trees hide the entrances to the 'Boggart Holes', where far more startling human deposits were discovered in the early 19th century. After heavy floods, silver coins from the reign of Edward I (1239-1307), were washed out of these little caves – and Speight (1892) mentions a tradition that 'loads of gold' lie concealed within them. Perhaps the coins were part of a 'treasure hoard' hidden by the English from the rampaging Scots after Bannockburn? Whatever the story, it is unlikely that an active stream cave would have been chosen for a hiding place – and maybe the coins were washed in from somewhere higher up the hillside. With permission and a good torch, both entrances can be explored: the left cave quickly closing to rubble while that on the right, with an emerging stream, was more likely the 'treasure cave.' Over a century ago, Speight wrote that since the original spate of findings, 'many a search has been made, and never a coin has been found.' I always find cave spiders, flood debris and various remains of dead sheep!

From Ivescar, turn right and follow the path down to a junction near Winterscales Beck (SD748792). Here, a path leads north-eastwards though pastures to Gunnerfleet, where an obvious route to the right heads once more to the looming presence of the Ribblehead viaduct and our starting point. In the recently 'refurbished' Gunnerfleet Caves, up on the left (SD757797) I once encountered Yorkshire humour at its most bizarre. Crawling through into the Stalactite Chamber with my son – we were greeted by a crude stone table surrounded by the grinning faces of a dozen sheep's skulls. Harmless fun, I suppose, but I nearly wet myself with the shock.

And Whernie's shocked you, hasn't she? Admit it. No longer woeful by any means, she will now become a source of endless fascination: where man and nature combine as effectively as anywhere in England to draw back those who truly appreciate wild, historical landscapes.

Ticked off with relief and ignored for life? They don't know what they're missing.

Serenity: Robin Proctor's Scar - where the poor fellow's horse proved much more formidable than he was while, *above,* Moughton's superb dry waterfall is the final highlight of our tour. *Top right*: You are likely to have the summit of Moughton all to yourself - along with the eternal presence of Penyghent.

6. Crummackdale:
A Stadium Tour

Grid Reference: SD769683. Limited roadside parking opp hotel in Austwick village. An 8 mile (12.8 km) adventure.

In a Nutshell: The dramatic, natural limestone 'stadium' of Crummackdale makes for a challenging yet uniquely rewarding adventure. This clock-wise circuit, beginning in the village of Austwick, contains some text-book geology for the limestone explorer. After taking in the nationally famous 'Norber Boulders' and the geological wonder of Nappa Scar – the route avoids crowds and paths in some of Britain's wildest scenery, traversing the western flank of the dale until reaching the limestone 'moonscape' of Thieves Moss. An exciting cliff-top traverse of Moughton Scars then follows, before the gentle climb onto Moughton itself, through one of the country's few remaining Juniper 'forests'. The 'Stadium of Echoes' and the abandoned waterfall of Studrigg Scar ensure that excitement is retained until the last steps of the journey.

Essentials: Clear weather and a settled forecast are a must for this adventure – as are map and compass. There are no paths

A Three Peaks Up and Under

for much of the walking and the route requires visibility of cairns ahead – often difficult to distinguish from the surrounding rock. The entire route is clear on the Ordnance Survey (OL2) 1:25000 Yorkshire Dales South and West map. As the weather on Ingleborough is so unpredictable, warm clothes and waterproofs should be in the rucksack – along with plenty of food and drink. There are no facilities of any kind, and there are few walks where the sight of a 'watering hole' at the end can be such a blessing. The Game Cock pulls a fine pint of Wainwright, and after this walk you can consider yourself up there with the master fellwalker.

Access: Austwick is just north of the A65 between Clapham and Settle. The Traddock hotel is just outside the village centre, on the minor road linking the A65. The section of road in front is usually easy to park on without obstructing other vehicles, but please be considerate of the locals.

Adventure: Many football stadiums today offer tours to enhance the match experience – the rows of coloured seats spelling out the club's name or that of its most famous personality. Crummackdale offers no such commercialism although its 'stadium' dwarfs anything achieved by man. It has always been empty and always will be, save for a few farmers and discerning walkers dotting the wilderness here and there. Yet despite the desolation, the dale is as spectacular an amphitheatre as can be found in Britain. No season ticket is required; no admission price. A clockwise tour of the terraces, with the 'Norber Stand' on one side and the 'Moughton' on the other, is as interesting and exciting a journey as anywhere in the Three Peaks area.

Austwick is the sort of place that stimulates the first-time traveler to buy his first-time *Craven Herald* and rush to the 'property for sale' section. As you nod at the first car-washer or gardener you encounter, it's usually with a grumble of 'you lucky old so and so' – and no wonder. The place is beautiful indeed, showing little evidence of disturbance and almost nonchalance at being the gateway to such astounding scenery. It is not adverse to humour, either. One stone built trough at the road side bearing a 'Hot Dogs' sign – and no doubt your pooch will be glad of it at the journey's end.

From the parking spot, head for the village centre and turn right past the Game Cock inn and the school. The knowledge that the former will still be there at the end of the walk is like being promised a mortgage pay off at the summit of Everest. Leave it for now and turn left beyond the school into Townhead Lane.

The path climbs steeply past attractive cottages and gardens, with dominating pines, until a crossroads is reached where Thwaite Lane, part of an old route from Clapham to Settle, crosses the path. Turn immediately left onto the track towards Clapham, and then right over a ladder stile into the adjacent field. Ahead now is the fine cliff of Robin Proctor's Scar – dominating a landscape of drystone walls and punctuated by barns and boulders.

Flying Horseman

The Robin Proctor connection has many variations. Traditionally Robin was a Crummackdale farmer keener than any walker on a pint, and more likely to down several after a hard day. His horse was used to guiding him home in a drunken state and dropping him off into the stable straw so he could sleep away his hangover before Mrs Proctor got her hands on him. One night he emerged from the watering hole in a thick mist and grabbed any old horse instead. Both Robin and horse plunged tragically over the cliff face and legend has it that the horse survived. The thump of horse's hooves are said to be heard often around the cliffs – and one of the climber's routes up the limestone is known as the 'Flying Horseman' – linked to the Farrer family of Clapham but still very fitting for Robin. It seems today's climbers must like all types of 'rock' as Bob Dylan's classics have also found their way onto Robin Proctor's Scar in the climbing guides: 'Knocking on Heavens Door' (hopefully Robin did!) and 'Subterranean Homesick Blues' being just two examples.

The attention is divided between admiring the scar and gasping at the various Silurian 'erratics' – some ingeniously incorporated into the walls by the farmers of yester-year - but more about those later. There is a feeling of great things ahead, and watch should be kept, following the wall on the left, for an obvious gate beneath the scars. To its right, a wall stile requires care but admits to a virtual wonderland of curiosities – so varied that one is tempted to spend the rest of the day in this vicinity alone. Four precariously poised boulders lie above, and climbing upwards, as the gap between wall and scar narrows to an obvious 'nick' – trees will appear on the right beckoning a short detour to Nappa Scars. Cross the wall stile and follow the sketchy path to the quaint little cliffs, enveloped in mature trees.

Refusing to Conform

Nappa Scars is one of the best places to see what have been, in the remote past, strange occurrences in the 'rocky trifle'. As it lies on the line of the North Craven fault, the upthrust has lifted the ancient basement rocks up to the point that they make up the path on which you are walking – hundreds of feet above the 'basement' buried beneath the fields far below. 'One lot went up, while the other lot went down', is how

Lancastrians might describe it. As the sponge, jelly and cream layers make up the trifle – here we see the oldest Ordovician rocks separated from the overhanging Great Scar limestone by a thin layer of 'conglomerate' – pebbles and boulders 'cemented together' in an earlier limestone mixture. Clearly absent are the expected Silurian rocks of the 'second layer' – though there are remnants of these amongst the conglomerate. The Silurian rocks must have been eroded away over an immense space of time, before the sea levels rose and the Great Scar limestone was laid down on top. As you touch it, consider that this 'creamy' conglomerate was once the pebbly surface of an exposed beach that existed in the Devonian period between 420 and 360 million years ago! This 'unconformity' on Nappa Scars is one of the best known in the kingdom – and as it lies on a distinct path, it is easy to show to the children and ignite a spark for geology.

Leaving 'unconformities' behind, time now bids us to conform to the planned journey and return to the wall stile. Climbing this, and ascending the slope straight ahead beyond the 270 meter contour – the finest of the famous Norber boulders will excite even the most discerning adventurer. If you have children with you, the challenge will be tempting them away from these geological showpieces. Hours can be spent exploring and admiring these freaks of nature, and even the most unobservant walker, with his mind set on the lures of the Gamecock inn, can't fail to notice the obvious 'oddity' of these dark rocks perched on the bare limestone as if dropped by some immense prehistoric bird in an attempt to smash the ice smothering its kingdom. The main Crummackdale glacier, during the last ice age, plucked these Silurian giants from the valley sides, less than a kilometer away. Eventually the western flank of this 'tributary' glacier rode slowly upwards over Norber brow to meet the main ice flow. As it began to melt, it deposited the boulders on this shoulder of limestone where they have remained ever since.

Magic Mushrooms

The finest of them all – the much photographed 'Norber Mushroom' lies just beyond the summit of this initial plateau (SD765699). Three pedestals of limestone precariously support a boulder variously autographed with hammer and chisel over the centuries. The effect is startling to the point that one wonders how some well-fed sheep hasn't dislodged it, or at least the Ingleborough wind. The limestone benches, swept clean by the Crummackdale glacier, have been eroded away to leave small fragment 'pedestals', protected from the elements by the 'erratics' themselves. Indeed, the lush grassland of the Norber boulder field hides much eroded limestone underfoot, almost like walking along a field of fossilized tree stumps, so take care when introducing yourself to each and every boulder, as it is tempting to do. One particular grouping, close to the Mushroom, resembles a set of six toppling dominoes or, perhaps, the pages of a petrified book. No doubt you will leave the area with your own interpretations, and this is a place to return to again and again.

From the 'Mushroom', head towards the summit of Norber itself, following the wall on your right to where it meets a ladder stile in the corner of the field. In doing so, you pass another of the finer erratics, sitting on a plinth of limestone and incorporated into the wall by a long gone farmer who no doubt saved himself a lot of work in the process. Crossing the ladder stile gives two options. There are no paths here and it's very much 'proceed at your own risk' territory. If there is the least sign of mist or cloud approaching it makes sense to turn sharp right over the stile and to follow the wall towards Thieves Moss. That way, you cannot get lost even with a blindfold. If it's clear, however, head upwards onto the summit ridge ahead, passing more scattered erratics. There are fine views now across the 'stadium' to Moughton, Studrigg Scar and the abandoned waterfall visited later in the journey. Penyghent and Fountains Fell rear up behind: dark and sinister vessels on an ocean of white limestone that Moughton appears to be from this distance.

It is rare to see another human from this point. Most are still admiring the boulders and posing for photographs. Here, when the wind is absent, it is mute indeed: a seemingly sterile, lifeless landscape where the grinding of jaws eating a sandwich from the rucksack has the effect of a four-by-four crossing the desert. Even swallowing seems to echo on Norber.

Trilby and Scarf

The cairns along the ridge to the north are the only signs that some kind of life has hitherto passed this way at some stage or other. The terrain is unfriendly and once the limestone has been left, the eye and heart yearn for its return. Patience is rewarded when the third prominent cairn is reached (SD764718), and a fine view of Clapham Bottoms, with the wooded slice of Trow Gill, opens up to the North West. Shakeholes immediately east of the Gill punctuate the glacial till, one huge specimen taking on the appearance of a bomb crater even from this distance. Above it, towards the top right of the 'Shakehole Field' lies a hole with a gory story. Jim Leach and Harold Burgess – 'Jim and Budge' – of the Northern Pennine club, were exploring here in August 1947 when they saw a human leg poking out from beneath boulders at the bottom of a shakehole, now christened 'Body Pot.' Horrified, they pulled the rocks aside to reveal the corpse of a man dressed in a tweed herringbone coat and grey

A Three Peaks Up and Under

Read all about it: The Giant's Book on the slopes of Norber - where huge Silurian rocks are arranged like toppling dominoes.

trilby, with a plum coloured scarf tied around his face. Besides the shaving gear, toothbrush and coins found with him, there was a bottle of cyanide. Had he taken his own life or had someone taken his? Had he been a German spy? Detailed investigations for months afterwards proved inconclusive – and 'Body Pot' remains one of Ingleborough's great human mysteries.

Soon after the cairn, the appropriately named Long Lane is met, rising up from Clapham Bottoms – and threading through increasingly breathtaking limestone scars to Sulber Gate: a fitting half way point at the Northern end of the Crummackdale stadium. Straight ahead, through the gate itself, is the route to Selside which joins Sulber Nick above Horton. Ignore this for now and take the smaller gate in the wall to the right. (SD775732) Stepping through this is like walking up the last few steps inside the Coliseum before meeting the encircling vastness of the arena – only this is on a scale of its own in both time and space: for as great rulers and dynasties have been and gone – Penyghent has stood resolute, watching over a scene that hasn't changed for 12 000 years. The cliffs to the north, with their aprons of scree cascading down to the plateau, haven't changed. The fragments of limestone littering the pavements – the grotesque figurines and fangs of bare rock jammed vertically into the grykes – haven't changed. Only the skies and shadows above have constantly done so – brushing varying shades and tones onto a canvas of bleak, but nevertheless unforgettable beauty. Such is the first impression of Thieves Moss on the senses.

The name, it is thought, derives from bandits who once roamed these parts when travellers passing this way were obviously sitting ducks. The moss itself is the raised marshy plateau beneath the cliffs in front – an obvious oddity in the otherwise bone-white landscape.

Beggars Can't be Choosers

The way on is to take the sketchy path down into the ampitheatre and to head south across the clints towards Beggar's Stile, clearly marked on all OS maps but a notoriously tricky object to locate in mist. Take great care on the clints, as many are wobbly and unsteady, and this is not a place to rush. These great benches were swept clean by the same glacier that transported the Norber erratics, illustrating the variety of landforms once created by these ancient rivers of ice. Keeping the edges of the scars in view, Beggar's Stile is soon reached, crossing the wall to the right of a major prominence in the scar, and offering a stunning view of the fertile green landscapes in the floor of the stadium. Immediately to the right, just over the stile, the remains of a

Romano-British settlement can be clearly made out. Yes –
someone was mad enough to live up here. Presumably the
view was worth it.

The stile offers an escape route back to Austwick if the
weather is turning. If it is not, the route now climbs the knoll
to its left and begins a thrilling traverse of the edge of
Moughton Scars – the 'northern end' of the stadium, and a
place of high drama. The views, encompassing the morning's
route over Norber to the west and taking in the entire sweep
of the dale, are sensational. Far below, a large stream can be
seen emerging suddenly into the landscape – a trail of silver
when it catches the rays of a mid-afternoon sun. This famous
emergence, at Austwick Beck head, marks the point at which
all the water from Juniper Gulf and the allotment potholes
finally reaches daylight, and the impermeable basement
rocks beneath the limestone. It does the same job as Clapham
Beck head, in the adjacent valley – but as there are no trees
hiding it, it is somehow more spectacular.

It is always a hair-raising experience walking along
the edge of Moughton Scars, and great care should be taken
with children. I can think of no better place in Yorkshire to
eat the sandwiches and soak in the atmosphere of a karst
landscape, and the traverse deserves leisurely exploration.
The scars eventually terminate at a prominent cairn,
(SD788720) and another potential escape route opens up in
the valley on the right. If limbs are tired or mist is forming,
thio will bo very welcome as it connects with Hunterstye Lane
for an easy descent along the valley floor. In any event, it is
worth a short detour for a few yards to see the famous
'Whetstone Hole of Moughton' (SD784719) where fragments
of a beautifully banded mudstone can be found in the stream
bed. This stone, originally green in colour but now banded
with red and purple – was formed in pre-Carboniferous

times. Metal ions in the sediments forming it reacted chemically when exposed to the atmosphere at times of lower sea levels by effectively decomposing the rock in a similar way to rusting. Fluctuating sea levels therefore correspond with the alternate coloured bands – and children will love finding the ultimate example of this 'rainbow rock'. The whetstones were used extensively in Sheffield for sharpening knives and blades – though no quarrying is evident here on Moughton itself.

Mother's Ruin

If the weather is clear – return to the path beyond the cairn and the way up onto Moughton is now a wild 'free for all' across the limestone pavements intersected at right angles by former stream channels cut during the last stages of the melting glacier. Many of these channels are hidden by wind-sculpted Juniper bushes – remnants from a time when this attractive evergreen covered a much wider part of the Craven highlands. The flaking reddish bark, prickly foliage and blue-black berries characterize this upland survivor, which here serves to soften a harsh but beautiful landscape devoid of any other landmarks. Juniper berries, of course, are the main components of 'mother's ruin' – but I have often thought how well a stiff gin and tonic would go down at this stage of the journey. The shrub, by the way – is extremely prickly. Trip up and fall into it at your peril!

Heading for the highest part of the fell, keep a prominent cluster of Juniper bushes on the horizon in your line of sight. Arriving at these, the cairn at the summit of Moughton – the 'east stand' of the stadium, will soon be reached. It feels almost Himalayan here, despite being a mere 427 metres (1402 feet) above the sea. The only guaranteed company – in clear weather at least, is Penyghent – and the only sound that of a curlew or wheatear. Facing south, to your left – beyond the pavements and thankfully out of sight, are the massive limestone quarries of Horton, while to your right the hidden cliffs of Studrigg scar plunge down into Crummackdale. Civilisation of any kind can seem days away.

A Mexican Wave

A few minutes' walk across the pavements to the south of the summit, and bearing right towards the valley, a magnificent spectacle presents itself. I call this the 'Stadium of Echoes'. The limestone suddenly ends in a wide sweeping scar, where terraces of glacial drift and aprons of scree encircle a massive expanse of flat grassland, free entirely of rock but softened by bracken. (SD786708) It is yet another 'stadium within a stadium', but here we have a 'pitch' big enough to accommodate an Olympic opening ceremony, backed by limestone galleries that could hold thousands; yet all is without life: motionless: mute. It has remained so for 12 000 years, while stadiums world-wide have reverberated - from the thundering of chariots and mock naval battles to the massed ranks of storm-troopers. This stadium can, however, seem very much alive. Walk into the centre of the arena, facing towards the limestone terracing and break the silence with a shout – maybe one word. I usually go for 'hello' - and as though a full house at the Coliseum are greeting you – the sound will ring around the walls of the arena from left to right like a Mexican wave. Other classics here include 'Are we back yet?' and 'What's for tea dad?' This place will lodge in the memory forever.

Such is the level of fun that exiting the stadium can be tricky – especially with children. Continue along the north side of the feature until the ground once more lowers onto further rough grassland, when watch should be kept for an obvious 'notch' or depression in the cliffs ahead. Here, a ladder stile admits to the last great wonder of the day, Moughton's abandoned waterfall. The way on appears suicidal at first, but head for the fall itself by keeping left and a sketchy path can be seen making its way down the slope on the right hand side. Take great care here and pause if you wish to take in the view. Meltwater during the last ice age couldn't make its way down into the frozen ground beneath, so presumably carved out a major joint and tumbled its way over the scar, in a similar way to Trow Gill in the adjacent valley. A stream now bubbles its way out of the ground below and this can be followed down to a footpath, parallel with the lane, where the way on is to the left. Glancing back now, there is a fine view of the abandoned fall and Studrigg Scar, where basement rocks are exposed in vertical layers beneath the limestone, a result of the Craven fault uplifting and glacial erosion. Beds of Silurian rocks at Whitestones can be seen tilted at an angle of 45 degrees, and large boulders are dotted everywhere amongst the scree, corresponding with the Norber erratics on the opposite side of the valley.

The path now crosses over a ruined wall in a narrow field before a stone stile admits to the lane itself. Once the village of Wharfe is reached, bear sharp right and a twisting path has Austwick Beck for company until the road is reached. It is then a short walk on tarmac back to Austwick and – as I promised – the Gamecock inn. Most great stadiums are left in a sea of people – Crummackdale is an exception. You may have been its sole spectator – but smiling faces at the Gamecock will no doubt share with you the memories of their own stadium adventures. Don't forget to tell them about yours.

Deceptively deep: The garden's greatest hole - the magnificent Juniper Gulf.
Top right: The Yoredale slopes of the Ingleborough massif, with Simon Fell on the right, tower over the pavements at Sulber.

94

7. The Allotment: Garden of the Underworld

Grid Reference: SD783757 (starting point at Selside). A 7 mile (11 km) adventure.

In a Nutshell: An absorbing day out, exploring some of Ingleborough's less frequented slopes, with classic karst scenery on display throughout. The walk leaves the hamlet of Selside, eventually linking up with Sulber Nick, a path along a natural fault in the limestone above Horton-in-Ribblesdale. Three secretive but spectacular potholes are visited, before a wild area of grouse moorland becomes the focus of attention. Here, shyly hidden in the hollows and shake holes of the moor, are some of the finest caves and potholes in Britain, dominated by the splendid Juniper Gulf. There is also a fine cave to explore in safety, exciting rock scrambling and plenty of wildlife to enjoy. If you want perfect peace and quiet after a hard week at work, this is the one for you.

Essentials: This is a fairly strenuous walk onto challenging terrain, with little shelter from wind, rain or sun. Choose a settled day with clear visibility. Waterproofs should be taken in case the weather changes, and footwear should be strong with good grips. Take plenty of food and drink. The Ordnance Survey OL2 (Southern and Western Dales) map covers this walk, and a compass should also be taken to help in locating the caves and potholes. The Allotment is closed March to October so save this adventure for the late autumn and winter months. Long Kin East can be explored with a cycle helmet and a good torch, though Wellingtons are a must here, so consider the distance that these items must be carried before attempting it. The Allotment is part of the Ingleborough Estate and strictly speaking permission should be sought before entering any caves. For peace of mind, write to the estate office (*see appendices*) before visiting. Children will enjoy this walk, but extreme care and common sense should be observed at all pothole entrances.

Access: Selside is a hamlet on the B6479, about 3 miles (5km) north of Horton-in-Ribblesdale, the hamlet's name being indicated by a former railway sign on a building to the right. Immediately beyond the hamlet, turn left onto the unsurfaced Alum Pot Lane (the police warning about vehicle theft being a sign of the times). Park close to the wall on the left, leaving ample room for farming and caving vehicles. Take care with your car on the bumpy surface. At weekends, aim to arrive early or you might find cavers have claimed all the spaces before you.

Adventure: Explorers here are generally faced with two choices: the wonders of the North Ribblesdale Drumlin Field on one side, or the horrors of the North Ribblesdale Bull Field on the other. Since this adventure begins with the latter, visitors from the city are strongly advised to leave Liverpool and Manchester United shirts at home. They would look out of place in the Dales anyway, without stirring up the bellowing of the bovine beasties. Leeds United are, of course, permitted.

Walk up the uneven Alum Pot Lane until a junction is reached, with a notice giving information about the famous sights ahead; but our route lies along a green lane striking off to the south, where a ruined barn can be seen down to the left. A ladder stile is then crossed into the next field, where the route bisects Gillgarth Beck, with Penyghent now beginning to provide a stunning backdrop to the attractive Gillgarth Farm: the day's first photograph. The path at this point runs parallel with a wall on the right, and as this terminates, veer left down a gentle slope to a gateway above the farm that will set the adrenalin pumping wildly. Here beginneth the bull field.

Speak Ye Not

Walking through a bull field with just a solitary occupant can be daunting in itself, but tackling a field with at least *twenty* bullocks is the stuff of nightmares. Try combining the latter with three boisterous offspring, two of which are wearing bright red fleeces, and the mission appears to be bordering on masochism. The trick, as I have discovered, is to avoid the provocative stares of any bulls, keep close together and remain mute until the next stile is reached. This is my tried and tested formula and it has worked (up to now) every time. I have often thought what it would be best to do in different circumstances, and after contemplating every logical alternative and its drawbacks, my advice would have to be quite simple: *Leg it.*

Reach the next ladder stile with a triumphant sigh of relief, and enter a friendlier field, dominated by Borrins Farm down on the left. Ahead you will see yet another ladder stile at a wall corner, close to a ford on the Ordnance Survey Map

A Three Peaks Up and Under

(SD783746). Once over this, a track now heads right and the walking is on fine green turf where explorers are instructed to 'follow the waymarked path.' This is a gentle climb with impressive views across Ribblesdale to Penyghent and Plover Hill. Keep straight ahead through Over Pasture, and the landscape now becomes more typical moorland as altitude increases. At the crossing of the next stile, the natural fault of Sulber Nick can be seen coming up from Horton on the left, and here it is usual to see spots of colour as hikers head for the summit of Ingle borough. Probably up this same 'nick' in the limestone, many moons ago, marched the Brigantian tribesmen on their way to the Ingleborough summit complex – whatever it was. The scenery will have barely changed since, though cloaks and swords have now been replaced by fluorescent anoraks and ski poles.

To the Hangman's Gallows

Heading to meet the fault, the path traverses a grassy terrace, usually with a few more bulls down to the left – and a wonderfully preserved Iron Age Settlement up on the plateau to the right: much the safer option! The Nick is met where an attractive finger post indicates 'Ingleborough 2.75 miles' at an abrupt turn to the north-west. Take this route and cross another ladder stile, where beautiful limestone clints just beg to be explored to the right of the stony path. Perched on the pavements here is an unmissable limestone boulder, dumped by the retreating Ribblesdale glacier at the end of the last ice age, and well worth a visit. It is of an unusually rounded outline, its beauty enhanced by a clothing of moss which contrasts superbly with the gleaming white limestone. Penyghent, as always, provides the perfect backdrop to a painting or photograph from this position.

Before returning to the main path, three secretive

The Allotment: Garden of the Underworld

Fixed in time: A fine example of an Iron Age settlement, near Sulber Nick.

potholes should be visited in order to whet the appetite for
the Allotment to follow. These lie in an area of rough
moorland just west of the pavements, and only a few metres
from the main path up Ingleborough, though they are seldom
even suspected by walkers in the area. The first of the trio,
Sulber Pot, is easily identified by the broken wall at the
western end, and is an open shaft 8 metres long, potentially
more dangerous than any bull. At the southern end, a vertical
iron ladder, precariously roped, descends to the boulder-
strewn floor about 15 metres (45 feet) below. It would, of
course, be madness to attempt the climb without a lifeline
attached to a firm anchor point, and anyway the pot doesn't
advance very far at horizontal level. Far more spectacular in
this sense, though clearly out of bounds to all but the bravest
cavers, is Hangman's hole, an innocent looking shaft lying in
a small shakehole about 100 metres west, containing masses
of loose boulders and stated, in the caving guides, as being

'not for the faint hearted.' The names of the underground pitches in this pot are daunting in themselves: cavers being able to tackle the 'Gallows' Chamber, 'The Mangle' and even 'The Executioner', all of which must live in the imagination of those on the surface.

Secrets of Old Nick

Just beyond, its main entrance obscured by a tree, is the fascinating Nick Pot, not to be outdone by its neighbours as it sports the second deepest underground pitch in the country, though the entrance itself is pleasant enough. A scramble down below the tree reveals the stream flowing out of a low cave and into a larger passage. This seems very inviting, but a series of nasty drops soon lead to the infamous 76 metre 'Big Pitch', the thought of which makes the Ribblesdale Bullfield seem like a holiday resort. It is best left well alone. The smaller entrance, from which the water flows, is Nick Cave, and if you have waterproofs and a torch it provides a great hands and knees crawl to a small chamber, beyond which a crawl under a rock curtain leads to one of several exits, just over 100 metres to the west. Because the ceiling is low, this cave should only be tackled in settled weather, and then only by those prepared to walk the rest of the journey with squelchy socks.

The main Ingleborough path can be regained by one of two ways: either scramble under the barbed wire where the wall is broken in sections, or, more sensibly, return past Sulber Pot to the wall corner east of the pavements, where a stile admits to the route ahead. Continue up the gentle slope with the pots now hidden on the right, until a double ladder stile is soon reached. This is the 'door' to the Allotment, and what a bleak and unpromising wilderness it appears to be: a never-ending plain of pathless moorland with no pavements in sight, no boulders, no trees. You may ask yourself, why has he sent me here of all places, when there is so much lovely limestone not too far away? It is difficult to imagine a worm making himself at home in the Allotment soil, and those who stare in disbelief as you turn left at the ladder stile can be forgiven. They know not of the wonders that await you. Wonders that you are ninety-nine-per-cent certain to have all to yourself, for there is as much chance of being eaten by a bull as there is of seeing a person wandering here. Even cavers are put off by the long journey from the nearest habitation. A nudist camp set up on the Allotment would probably go unnoticed for years.

A Step Inside the Garden

By keeping the wall at the eastern edge of the Allotment close at hand, you are less likely to become lost if the mist descends, and more likely to locate the caves and potholes that so few have ever seen. The wall swings south and after about 200 metres a broken ladder stile is the pointer to the first of these, though it is not much to write home about. This is Stile Cave, a steep sided shakehole to the left of the path. Just beyond, on the right, is the rusty oil drum entrance of Vein Pot, a 7 metre climb into an excavated passage. How on earth, you will wonder, did they ever get an oil-drum up here? After passing Drabble and Dribble pots, further on the right, exposed limestone is then reached close to the wall, and from here a watch should be kept for an obvious area of circular fencing, hiding a larger pothole about 100 metres to the west. This one is Little Juniper, a foretaste of things to come, having an attractive fluted shaft down which it is possible to scramble with care. The gleaming benches of white limestone contrast superbly with the deeper tones of a solitary Juniper and a wealth of mosses and ferns, the picture

A Three Peaks Up and Under

Big drop: The massive doline of Marble Pot is one of the largest in the UK. The limestone at the entrance has been polished to a marble-like effect by water action.

being framed perfectly by Simon Fell rising behind. Children should be supervised on the scramble down, where the cool moisture is as near as the Allotment gets to providing any kind of refreshment for a sweating explorer. No ice cream vans up here, sorry.

Gob-smacking Gulf
From Little Juniper head west, the lack of natural landmarks being compensated for by keeping the col between Simon Fell and Ingleborough in the line of sight. An obvious small valley ahead beckons the way to a spectacular and unexpected feature, a maze of crevasses in the Great Scar Limestone forming the notable 's' shape of Juniper Gulf, the best known and most spectacular of the Allotment potholes, and an absolute classic in caving circles. The name itself is beautiful,

and though Juniper trees are largely absent, there is still a magnetic charm about the place making even a surface inspection linger in the memory.

The pothole has been formed along a fault, a large fracture in the limestone, and the stream enters at the north western end, crashing noisily onto the boulder floor 18 metres (55 feet) below, eventually dropping down a series of underground pitches to a total depth of 128 metres. All this, of course, is unsuspected from the surface, but the dangers of the entrance pitch are obvious. At several points it is literally possible to stride over the full 18 metre drop, and to do so, where the crevasses are at their narrowest, without realizing it. Juniper Gulf is, in effect, the most dangerous 'limestone pavement' in the Dales, and should be treated with great respect. The best view down the shaft is provided by a protruding slab of limestone at the southern side, the lip of which can be reached by a cautious hands-and-knees crawl, revealing the sight of a boulder-strewn floor far below, usually littered with sheep carcasses and flood debris. Children, should, however, be kept well away. Juniper Gulf does not merely merit parental guidance: it is for adults only.

Gardeners' World

The less daunting Juniper Cave can be located, usually with some difficulty, by walking about 200 metres south and slightly east from Juniper Gulf. It consists of a drop down into a stream passage and a further descent into a small chamber, and can be explored with care. A far more exciting cave, Long Kin East, is the next port of call: best located by returning to the Allotment wall and continuing along it until a symmetrical hillock is seen rising gently to the right, an obvious change in the monotonous landscape. Leave the wall once exposed limestone is reached, and head over the centre point of this hillock, effectively 'slicing it in two.' Descent is then made to an area of clints, penetrated by the small but impressive shaft of Long Kin East Pot.

This entrance is one of four into the system, but a scramble down the slippery five- metre chimney would be risking a helicopter ride to hospital: something that would, no doubt, give a superb aerial view of Ingleborough, but has little else to recommend it. Instead, walk a few paces north west to Long Kin East's botanical showpiece. This is another pothole shaft, almost a perfect circle in outline, and ringed with an ancient and crumbling wall of limestone, framing masses of ferns and rowan trees: the 'hanging basket' of the Allotment. There are no lawns, borders or flowerbeds, but at least the creator has provided a touch of paradise to the place, if admittedly miniscule. The effect is like that of a single tub of nasturtiums placed in the tiny back yard of an urban terrace. It calms the mind and the body for a few minutes, reminding us that nature, though so often harsh and hostile, still provides that simple beauty which man can only stand back and admire.

A Way In – to Long Kin

The least hazardous way into the Long Kin East system is through either of two cave entrances, located in a gully about 100 metres north east of the two pots. A walk across a particularly boggy area of the Allotment reveals a small dry entrance, while just beyond the Long Kin East stream sinks into a smooth canyon, leading down a series of small cascades into the wet entrance. With a torch or helmet-mounted lamp, this is one of the finest caves in the Dales for a novice to explore, though a thorough soaking should be expected. At one point the cave passes beneath a 'window' out to the surface and there is a real sense of remoteness being both underground and miles from anywhere. Perfect weather is essential as the caves floods nastily, as well as dropping down a series of huge pitches before which, of course, a full retreat is necessary. In fairness, not many have been bothered to cart the gear up to this altitude, and those who do invariably go for the 'biggies.'

Cave fans who are addicted enough not to allow a drenching to dampen their enthusiasm for holes, should, from Long Kin East, head 200 metres south west, where faulting has opened up two impressive crevasses on the moor; 'fit subjects for nightmares' according to Wainwright. The first of these, the curiously named Jockey Hole, lies in the bottom of a funnel-shaped shakehole, making an approach dodgy from just about any angle. Interest is increased by a massive detached block of limestone standing precariously to one side of the main shaft. With care, and despite the horror of first impressions, it is actually quite easy to play the role of jockey and mount the 'horse's back' yourself, stepping gingerly across onto this boulder from the eastern side of the hole. This allows a view down the full 67 metre shaft, disappointing only in that it doesn't lead much further than the bottom, a visit to which (it should be added) would be life's final journey. Keep children well clear, 'mounting the horse' only on the understanding that the last details of your will have been sorted.

A few metres along the fault to the south, Rift Pot penetrates the moor as a narrow crevasse, dropping initially 34 metres, before further pitches eventually link it with Long Kin East Pot. The beautifully fluted sides of the shaft are more richly vegetated than those of Jockey Hole, but this is merely sheep's clothing, hiding a wolf certainly as nasty as anything else on the Allotment. A slip into his jaws would be unthinkable.

A Three Peaks Up and Under

Intriguing debris: Delicately poised limestone boulders are a legacy of the great Ribblesdale Glacier at Sulber.

Marvel at the Marble

For those who still have the energy, The Allotment should not be left without a final, weary trudge about 200 metres to the west of Jockey Hole. Here, the massive natural funnel of Marble Pot – one of the largest in the Dales, is an equally forbidding sight. In 1980 a great slice of glacial till slumped into the hole at the south side, obscuring the polished 'marble' bridges below, and only now, over 30 years later, is it being gradually washed away by the stream. The interiors of both this and Marble Sink, just to the south, are best left to the imagination. Both are quite horrendous.

With the day's excitements finally over, a return journey can simply be made by following the Allotment wall back to the stile just above Nick Pot, and the morning's steps retraced to Selside. A more interesting alternative, however, and my personal favourite, is to strike north at Nick Pot, following the base of the slope to its left across initially boggy ground before picking up the attractive limestone pavements of Fell Close. Children will love clambering over the clints, though care should be taken. There are a confusing number of cave entrances into the Great Scar Limestone, but no distinct path. The trick is to follow the pavements north until the wall to the right converges with that running down Borrins Moor ahead at a sheepfold (SD772752). There seems no way on, but on entering the sheepfold, careful inspection reveals that the left hand wall is actually built on a huge outcrop of limestone, giving good footing for an easy climb over (take special care with youngsters here). This gives access to a gate, tricky to open, the way ahead now turning sharply east down a track clearly shown on the Ordnance Survey map. Head downhill and after climbing a rather awkward gate (SD777752), the outward journey's route is reached above Gillgarth farm, the starting point on Alum Pot Lane lying just a short distance to the left.

With Penyghent, the Lion of Ribblesdale, slumbering peacefully in a late afternoon sun, the horrors of the Allotment potholes, and even the North Ribblesdale Bullfield, can momentarily be forgotten; but the chances are they will resurface again in your mind before the day is out – perhaps on the drive home; reminding you once again of your privilege in sharing, with Ingleborough, the elusive dangers of his own secret garden. The Garden of the Underworld …

Astonishing: Passing beneath the bridge at Weathercote, with flood debris rammed into the crack on the right. Both sight and sound are overwhelming. *Top right:* The tiny church of St Leonard, Chapel-le-Dale, behind which lie the three pots.

8. Chapel-le-Dale:
Three Pots of Gold and a Rainbow

Grid Reference: SD 739775. A simple but rewarding one-mile stroll in a magical place.

In a Nutshell: A trio of potholes lie hidden behind the quaint little church of St Leonard's at Chapel-le-Dale, and make for a memorable half day's adventure, especially when the mist is down on the higher ground. Hurtle Pot is shrouded in trees – and in legends, while its shy cousin, Jingle Pot, is another window into the underground Chapel Beck, making its way through constricted passages to God's Bridge. Reigning supreme, however, is the famous and unforgettable Weathercote Cave – the darling of early tourists to the Dales and arguably the finest individual sight in the Three Peaks area.

Essentials: Visitors will no doubt want to view the tiny church of St Leonard, from which access to Hurtle and Jingle Pots is a simple stroll. Weathercote, however, is on private land, and the temptation to jump over the low wall surrounding it should be resisted. Instead, write to the owner of Weathercote House for special permission, stating your interest in limestone. As there is some loose rock, entry is at your own risk and a disclaimer must be signed. Children, cavers and large parties are not permitted. The steep slope down to The Bridge is suitable only for fit, agile and confident scramblers.

Access: From Ingleton, take the B6255 road, signposted for Hawes. This climbs out of the village and passes the famous show caves of White Scar, before heading in a straight line towards Chapel-le-Dale, about three miles distant. The road rises past the famous Hill Inn, and fifty yards higher up there is a parking space on the left, well used by cavers and walkers, so get there early. (Grid reference: 745777). Alternative spaces are on the church car park, hidden in the trees at Chapel-le-Dale (738773), or in a lay by opposite the church, if one car doesn't already occupy the large space. Passing places are essential for the farm traffic, so please respect those who live here.

Adventure: If ever there was a truly enchanted place – a location in which visions of *The Hobbit* or *The Secret Garden* become suddenly real and touchable, then this is it. It is a pity that, since its closure as a show-cave in 1971, Weathercote has scarcely been mentioned in guide books to the region; as if privacy has somehow relegated its importance in the landscape. Surely this secrecy has promoted it? Many are those who drive and walk through the area, completely unaware that they have just passed this 'hiatus in the rock' – described by Harry Speight (1892) as 'certainly without rival in England.' In Georgian and Victorian times, eminent gentlemen would escort their ladies, in full skirts, down the steps beneath the rock arch to view this great waterfall: scenes that were captured for posterity by the noted engraver, William Westall. Nowadays, for every thousand walkers who have admired the waterfalls of the Ingleton glens, perhaps a single lucky soul will have visited Weathercote Cave. This then, is a place for the limestone connoisseur.

Weathercote is the finest of a trio of potholes in the floor of Chapel-le-Dale. If you have time to spare, and permission to visit this 'pot of gold', it makes sense to visit the other two first, so that there is a gradual build up to the stunning climax. Children will enjoy the first two, but should be fully supervised at all times. All three holes are linked underground, by passages which are completely flooded. They are, therefore, windows into a lost world. Each is clothed in luxuriant vegetation, hidden by mature trees. Each gives the appearance of being untouched; one can sense guilt at even treading on the fleecy moss and fragrant ferns surrounding the yawning entrances.

Go back down the road from the car park at the Hill Inn, passing the old school house on the right hand side, and being wary of fast moving traffic, especially if children are around. Ingleborough looms up on the left, like a monster pondering its latest tiny victim. Further down on the right, the gate to Weathercote House is reached, and, a few yards further on the same side, a minor road turns off into Chapel-le-Dale itself; a cluster of farmsteads and cottages spread loosely around the exquisite little church of St Leonard. When I first came past here as a child of seven, this church delighted me, and still does. Writing in *The Doctor* in 1847, Robert Southey concluded that, 'a hermit who might wish his grave to be as quiet as his cell, could imagine no fitter resting place.' This still holds true today.

Inside is a plaque in memory of those who died in appalling conditions when working on the Ribblehead viaduct. Many are buried in the churchyard. Curiosities, both man-made and natural, are the trademark of Chapel-le-Dale, and a track leading across a cattle grid behind the church points the way to the first: Hurtle Pot.

A Boggart in the Basement

Above the cattle grid, a gate on the right gives access to this eerie place. The hole has steep cliffs on one side, with smooth mud sloping down on the other to a dark and sinister pool. When water levels fluctuate underneath after heavy rain, strange noises arise from the depths. The people of past centuries attributed these to a 'boggart', blessed with the habit of drowning folk in this perilous pond. You *have* to tell your children about that!

One rainy Saturday, we had been forced off Ingleborough, so I decided to pay a visit to the potholes in the valley – telling Emily, Joe and Lucy about the boggart and his ghastly deeds as we munched our butties by the church. Arriving at Hurtle Pot, strange noises were indeed issuing from the depths, and I must admit I'd frightened myself by this point. Noises became screams, but any sound of a flute would have well and truly finished us. In the mid 19th century, Walter White wrote about a local courting couple, fleeing the place after similar sounds were heard. 'Soon afterwards,' he relates: 'a man clambered from the pot and made his way to Weathercote House, where he had been staying. He was carrying a flute, and, like Orpheus, he had been playing in the underworld.' Scary!

Relief was met with a twinge of disappointment when a toddler of no more than eighteen months appeared on reins, quickly followed by an embarrassed mum, brother, auntie, uncle and grandma. They were all there, bar grandad. *How odd*, I thought. Here we were on a rainy Saturday afternoon next to a boggart-ridden pothole in the middle of nowhere, and there were these people fresh from our world, grinning as if they half felt the same way about us. Mum, in fact, looked startled. I proudly suspect that for an instant she thought I was the boggart – until Emily, Joe and Lucy all appeared behind me. The sinister presence of Hurtle Pot was in a few seconds humbled by fluorescent rucksacks, waterproofs and digital cameras. To cap it all, a glance down the shaft itself revealed a smiling grandad with another little explorer of about Joe's age. They were pulling themselves up on a length of dirty rope.

'Did you escape from the boggart, then?' Joe asked him. 'Watch out for the boggart!'

Grandad, clearly, was well aware. Hauling his young companion out, he shook my hand and ruffled Joe's hair.

'Oh, a' wun't worry about that, son,' he said, in lovely Yorkshire twang. 'Av' finished 'im off long since.'

That man, to this day, remains a hero to the Oldfield family.

Hurtle Pot was first described by the Reverend John Hutton in his *Tour to the Caves in the Environs of Ingleton and Settle* (1781). 'The trees,' he wrote, 'almost meet in the centre, and spread a gloom over a chasm dreadful enough of itself without being heightened with any additional appendages.' He considered the pot to be 'one of the most dismal prospects I had yet been presented with,' while the depth of the pool could not be guessed at, as 'from the length of time the sinking stones we threw in continued to send up bubbles from this black abyss, we concluded it to be very profound.' Hutton could only shudder at the thought of a 'subterranean embarkation'. Today, Hurtle Pot is one of the most popular cave dives in the Dales, having first been explored by the Cave Diving Group in the mid-1970s. The flooded passages connect upstream with Jingle Pot and Weathercote, and downstream with Midge Hole. Pause for a few seconds as you stare at Hutton's 'Horrid Place', and consider the bravery of the guys who dare drop themselves into the boggart's bedroom.

Of Swords and Shields

One of the most memorable dives of recent years saw the rescue of a grotesque metal statue which, in 1983, had been mindlessly thrown into Hurtle Pot by unknown vandals. The figure, sculpted by Charles l'Anson, is difficult to interpret accurately, but appears to have some kind of military significance with its sword and shield. It is certainly not out of place in the mysterious atmosphere of Chapel-le-Dale, and is now back in its original position, further up the lane on the left. Wonder at two things here, then: the sheer strength of the statue snatchers, and the sheer determination of the divers who hauled this rusting treasure piece back to the surface.

Cave diving may not be for you – but the divers have at least left a way down for the humble Oldfield who wishes to see the 'Avernian Lake' of Hutton's writing. That's the same grimy rope that 'Grandad-the-Boggart-Killer' was using. The first trick is to go down backwards. You must cling onto the rope for dear life, feeling around for 'steps' in the mud that the divers have kindly provided to help them with their weighty tackle. The second trick is to go at just the right speed. Too slow and your feet sink in the mud, grinding you to a curving halt. Too fast and it's a backward somersault into the Avernian Lake! Joe and I managed both tricks to the bottom. Don't worry too much – there's a flattish area by the pool so it's not *so* easy to drown. On the return we quickly realised that one to the rope at a time was essential to survival. I sensed the chance for a great photo of Joe climbing out so I whizzed up the rope, wishing Grandad was still

Go with the flow: Weathercote Cave is divided by a spectacular bridge of limestone. Normally conditions are dry, but it soon becomes a torrent after heavy rain.

about to see how fast I could do it – before setting up the digital camera. "Hold it right there, Joe, while Dad gets a picture.' The result: An overexposed blonde-haired blob looking bored stiff in a black hole. Not quite the romantic prose of a Hutton description, but never mind.

Close to Hurtle Pot there's a rusty gate, which won't open, leaning against a wire fence. Climb over this gate, and you can follow the dry river bed up to Jingle Pot. This is reached on the left after five minutes of slippery scrambling, and is well worth a look. Hutton, in his *Tour to the Caves* suggested that an enterprising person with a head for heights might leap over it. Considering that people in the 18th century were smaller than today, then leaping over a six foot gap with a drop of twenty-three metres seems as mad as diving Hurtle Pot without oxygen. The hole itself is attractive enough, with mosses, liverworts and ferns everywhere.

A Three Peaks Up and Under

There's a small gully at the eastern end (the end you arrive at first) where you can pose for a photo while someone else dashes round the other side to take it.

Two down: one to go. And, providing permission is granted – one that will stay in your memory forever.

Retrace your steps to the main road, passing the church again, and head back up towards the Hill Inn. A few yards up on the left is the gate admitting to Weathercote. Through it, on the left, is an attractive farm, but the house at this point is shyly hidden by a grassy mound, increasing the excitement further. A first view of it never fails to impress. It is raised up above the valley floor, its emerald lawns decorated with mature trees of darker shades, and the paths and flowerbeds trimmed with jewels of white limestone: the perfect children's book setting. An iron gate allows an enticing walk up to the front door, and at this stage your dream begins, for this is surely not the 21st century. We expect to meet a servant at the door, and hear the clatter of hooves as a carriage draws up outside. We expect the elegant skirts of fashionable ladies - the watches and waistcoats of the Victorian gentry.

Key to the Underworld

Your dream is intensified as the door creaks open and a tiny key is passed into your hand. The iron ring holding this key seems itself to be from another age. It is twisted and contorted. You place it carefully in your pocket, wondering how many other pockets have warmed it up through the centuries. There is no tossing and turning in this dream. You are fixed. You suddenly feel enlightened. Something is pulling you away from the house, towards a strange little white door, set in a limestone wall in a corner of the grounds beyond. So intently are your eyes fixed on this door that all else around you fades into oblivion. 'CLOSED' is the message in stark black letters – but not for you. Your dream is perfected, and the door swings slowly open.

The light fades, and the darkness catches hold of you. The moisture swathes your skin, and the roaring of a hidden monster fills the senses. Ahead, a flight of tiny steps drop into the abyss, up which a bearded gentleman is striving to help his lady, struggling a little on the slippery rocks. They nod to you as they pass, but human voices would be sinful here. You peer through the open door and watch them – heading back towards a waiting carriage; slowly fading ...

Time has healed the wounds made by the tourists of long ago, and nature has taken over. The shaft occasionally fills to the brim with water, and overflows down past the house. Little wonder it is raised up. The perimeter wall itself contains holes for the water to escape. The steps now are scarcely discernible, clothed as they are with mosses, ferns and lichens. Down them, a curious bridge of limestone is the gateway to the monster's lair – delaying your encounter for a few minutes more. Hutton (1781) described this bridge as 'a grotesque arch', and there are some loose rocks dangling here, so take care not to pull at them as you pass underneath. Just before the bridge, a bedding plane passage opens on the right, and below it is Hutton's 'petrifying well.' This contains a deposit of *tufa* which is in fact calcium carbonate precipitated from water saturated in limestone. Unlike stalagmites in caves, it forms in daylight where algae and mosses cause the precipitation by altering the chemical make-up of the water. The passage is a crawl into a rocky chamber, but is only possible if you are wearing a helmet mounted lamp, and much better things lie ahead, so don't be disappointed. While Hutton mentioned 'a natural seat and table in the corner of this grotesque room, well suited for a poet or philosopher,' Enys, only two years later, wrote, 'these I looked for in vain.' So did I. It is probable that Hutton actually

referred to a different part of the cave, more likely to be under
the bridge itself, or that flooding in the years between the two
eccentrics removed the furniture completely.

The Coffin Bearer

The rocks beneath the bridge are quite often bone dry, and
refreshingly free from mosses and algae. They make a great
place to leave the rucksacks, and prepare for the *pièce de
résistance*. The noise is deafening. The pulse quickens, and not
a little fear grips even the bravest limestone explorer. My dad
once hung back here and let me go on. There is something
about Weathercote Cave that affects you like this. It is what
made JMW Turner excited when he painted the cave on two
occasions in the early 19th century. It is what John Hutton
meant when his 'ears and eyes were equally astonished with
the sublime and the terrible.' It is what you will remember.

Slippery boulders, blanketed in moss, slope down to
the very foot of the shaft. Don't try to clamber down and look
ahead at the same time or you will almost certainly hit the
floor. When you can first feel the cold spray on your face,
compose yourself. Take a deep breath. Stand still and lift your
eyes. Over 20 metres up, an opening in the cliff is hidden by
a huge angular boulder, wedged tight as if trying to jam the
jaws of a monster. And this waterfall *is* a monster. At the very
top it is stained with peat from up the valley, but this gives
way to a column of pure white, broken only when the torrent
hurls itself against the rocks at the bottom with so ferocious
a snarl that spray is flung aggressively in all directions. A pot
of gold, no doubt, but every such pot needs a rainbow, and
this one has it. A hole in the canopy of trees surrounding the
cave allows a slither of sunlight to catch the silver droplets of
spray, and a shimmering spectrum of colour arches like a halo
over this spiritual scene. It is a unique, truly beautiful place.

Chapel-le-Dale: Three Pots of Gold and a Rainbow

I stood, transfixed, before feeling a tap on my shoulder. Dad had plucked up the courage at last and joined me from the bridge. He tried to talk, but was scarcely audible in the cacophony of wind and spray. 'Is that Mohammed's Coffin?' he was shouting, pointing upwards, and I finally interpreted his gesture, and nodded. John Hutton is usually credited as the originator of this name for the wedged boulder. In his *Tour to the Caves* he writes: 'A huge rock that had sometimes been rolled down by the impetuosity of the stream, and was suspended between us and the top of the cascade, like the coffin of *Mahomet* at *Medina*, had an excellent effect in the scene.'

A yawning chamber to the left of the waterfall leads to stream passages which eventually become the flooded links to Jingle and Hurtle Pots, further down the valley. In heavy rain they are almost impossible to enter and certainly no fun if you haven't got windscreen wipers on your glasses. The stream entering the cave as the main waterfall actually sinks into the limestone some way up the valley, and follows a bedding plane until meeting a fault-guided joint, which over time it has hollowed out completely to form the fall, and the pot of gold. It's impossible to keep your eyes off this fall. Your instincts tell you to stand and stare. Your eyes close ...

Returning up the slippery boulders, you are aware of voices and laughter, as the noise diminishes behind you with every faltering step. Peeping through the arch of the bridge – and the steps are pristine, now. The mosses and lichens have gone. A man in a crisp dark suit is holding out his hand to a lady, very slim at the waist, clutching a fan and parasol in the same hand. They smile at you, but human voices *are* sinful here – and they've realized it. You reach the top of the steps and glance back to see them passing beneath the bridge; slowly fading ...

Don't fall in: Jingling Pot's tree allows a knee-knocking view into its awesome depths. *Top right:* The view over Kingsdale from the initial climb up the scars on the west flank, with Whernside just visible on the left.

9. Kingsdale:
A Stroll Along the Pothole Promenade

Grid Reference: SD705785 (Starting Point). A 6 mile adventure.

In a Nutshell: A wild and fascinating glaciated valley; well away from the crowds, containing a large variety of limestone highlights. There are potholes galore, tremendous views to savour, and some of the most interesting geological features anywhere in the country. The adventure involves a high level traverse across an old peat cutter's highway, the Turbary Road, visiting the awesome Marble Steps Pot, with its remote setting and sweeping views of the Lancashire coast. A final treat is a drop through the 'dustbin lid' of Valley Entrance, the most accessible route for cavers into the Kingsdale 'Master Cave'. One visit to 'The Valley of the Vikings' is never quite enough.

Essentials: The best Ordnance Survey map is the Explorer OL2, which covers the Southern and Western Yorkshire Dales areas. A compass is useful in misty conditions if you don't fancy dropping down a pothole. Footwear should have sound grips and wellingtons are needed if you intend to venture into any of the caves. If so, you will also need a strong torch for each person, and a helmet. A cycling or builder's helmet is fine. The weather changes rapidly, so wear or carry waterproofs, as there is little shelter. Children should be supervised at all times and common sense used near all pothole entrances.

Access: Approaching from the east, the A65 bypasses Ingleton, heading for Kirkby Lonsdale. After about 1 mile there is a right turn for Thornton-in-Lonsdale. Go through the tiny village, past the famous Marton Arms pub, and follow the signs for Dent. The road climbs uphill before arriving at limestone and the impressive valley of Kingsdale opens up ahead. Keep your eyes on the one and only farm in the valley bottom, Braida Garth. As you drive along, you will notice a track on the right which turns off towards it. Slow down at this point and glance left. A number of walls come down the steep hillside to meet the road. You need to count three of these walls after the Braida Garth turn off, and you will see a sheepfold in the corner of the field on your left. Immediately after this, on the right, is a parking spot for several cars. Take care not to block the road.

Adventure: Most family beaches have a gentle slope up to the 'prom' – but a little more exertion is needed to reach this one. The 'Potty Promenade' is how I refer to it - quite affectionately - as I like it a lot. Those people with less enthusiasm for holes in the ground may consider you quite potty for strolling along Kingsdale in the first place. There is no tower here – and definitely no waxworks – for this is the real thing; a place where nature's own craftsmanship wins hands down over man's efforts in a subtle, but convincing way – and it won't cost you a penny to see it.

Kingsdale: A Stroll Along the Pothole Promenade

For starters, the valley is a geological masterpiece. During the last ice age, which began some 110,000 years ago, a massive glacier scraped out the shape that you now see. As the ice began to melt, it dumped off a large mass of material or *terminal moraine* at the southern end, to form a barrier across the valley trench. The meltwater therefore had nowhere to escape and a lake formed. Over a long period of time the overflowing water cut out a new exit route which now contains the most famous of the Ingleton waterfalls, Thornton Force. The lake eventually drained to produce the flat valley floor that we see today. The 'dam' is known as the Raven Ray, and the breach is best seen half way through this adventure when there is a seagull's view of it from the 'prom.'

The 'Promenade' is really the Western bench of Kingsdale, on your left as you leave the car. To reach it, walk along the road for a few yards from the parking spot to a gate on the left. Ahead of you now are the cliffs of Shout Scar, oddly named, as a shout is the last thing you'd expect to hear in a place like this. The only sounds, in fact, are the occasional passing car, and you muttering to yourself at having to slog up the slope towards the cliffs, leaving the comfort of your car behind in this lonely landscape. But relax. This is the only bit of climbing you'll be doing all day.

Beware of the Bull

Head for an obvious breach in the cliffs, to the left of the steepest section, and you'll soon be climbing up to the moor above. A gate on the left is the route of an adventure along the 'Turbary Road', used by peat cutters in times gone by to transport their spoils to Ingleton and beyond. However, it is worth a detour to the right first to see Bull Pot. If you are tall, like me, you should have no problems in picking out a lonesome hawthorn on the moor to the north. If not, jump up and down a few times and you'll soon spot the top of it, guarding this beautiful pothole, but take great care as you approach. At the Northern end you will see a remarkable slab of limestone lying right over the shaft itself like a bridge for tiny folk. The shaft is over 11 metres deep, and drops to further 'pitches' at the bottom. It has a particularly beautiful 'fluted' western edge where the stream has been hard at work carving over thousands of years. Keep children under close control as some of the innocent looking boulders hide nasty holes which drop straight into the main shaft. 'Beware of the Bull' certainly applies here. If you look carefully to the east of the pothole, down a small rocky scar, you will see the covered shaft of Cow Pot, and 'Beware of the Cow' would be an appropriate first here, too. Get some imagination, dear farmers!

Appetite whetted, it's time to head back to the gate first noticed on your left at the top of Shout Scar. This gate admits to the awesome Jingling Pot. All these potholes, of course, are a result of water running off Gragareth, the bleak looking hill behind. Gragareth is made up of gritstones, shales and limestones which were laid down well after the main limestone was formed some 340 million years ago. These rock 'sandwiches' of alternating layers, are believed to be a result of fluctuating sea levels. When the sea was dominant, limestones formed from the skeletons of creatures, but when rivers dominated and levels were lower, grit stones and shales were laid down. The sandwiches are known as Yoredale beds, from the old name for Wensleydale, where they are most prominent. Because these Yoredale slopes are steep, water easily runs down the surface before reaching the massive limestone benches beneath. Here it sinks into joints and bedding planes to form the potholes and caves in this chaotic landscape, before emerging when it meets even older,

Watch your step: Rowten Pot, looking across Kingsdale to Ingleborough.

water resistant rocks below. But we'll leave that emergence for now, and concentrate on Jingling Pot.

Jingle Bells

As with Bull Pot, the hole is located by a solitary tree. It can be easily missed if you stick to the Turbary Road, so head onto the higher ground to the right as you close the gate behind you. A few yards to the south west and there you have it. The great thing about Jingling Pot is that nature has provided eccentrics with this kind-hearted tree, which grows in such a way that it allows a bird's eye view straight as a plumb line down the main shaft. Never have I let my children even think about this, as you can't climb back up the 43 metre vertical plunge and say, 'Ouch. That hurt.' If you do lean on the tree, keep your weight to the left, as there are fewer branches on the right to protect you from falling. Listen carefully to the 'jingling' sounds of water playing musical notes on the stones in the bottom. The hole is only a couple of metres wide, and the limestone around the rim is very slippery, so take special care as no-one wants to hear the giant jingle of you hitting the bottom, do they?

The streams approaching Jingling Pot run over beautifully polished benches of bare limestone at the Western end. One stream enters the pot while another twists South West for the interesting Jingling Caves. Follow this stream and you will soon see the first low cave entrance. The water is shallow and the passage only about 10 metres long before it pops up in a shakehole next to a second cave. Children with torches will love it. Send them in at one end and run round to wait for them. The hollow where one cave meets another is probably a collapse feature and the two caves were no doubt once connected. The second cave looks low, but runs for over 200 metres where it meets up with Rowten Pot, our next objective. By all means have a short look in with a powerful torch and helmet, but leave it at that, and return in the future with proper equipment. There are better things to come, so head back for the Turbary Road.

If you see the western benches of Kingsdale as a series of 'fields' below Gragareth, then you have now visited the 'Bull' and 'Jingling' fields and are heading for 'Rowten'. This time, however, there is no searching for little trees. Rowten Pot is overwhelming. Once through the next gate on the Turbary Road, don't let children run ahead. There is a nasty hole in the path which would have made a great Woolly Mammoth Trap, but is really no more than a window into the cave system which runs into Rowten Pot itself. The stream hurries along nonchalantly beneath and enters the great split in the limestone to your left. It is over 30 metres long, and 15 metres wide in the middle. Many walkers don't give potholes a second glance, but everyone stops here. This place is definitely in the pothole top five, and may well even be top of the charts. It dominates Kingsdale 'prom' like the tower dominates Blackpool.

The Big One

A series of boulders at the Northern end ease the otherwise vertical drops to horrendous depths and try their best to make the pot a little less daunting. The boulders are evidence that the feature was formed by collapse, and a very careful traverse around the rim will reveal the stream entering the pot beneath them. It is possible to climb down, especially if you are tall, but I wouldn't advise it. If you do go on to walk around the perimeter of the hole, take it slowly and hold hands. With children, this is certainly a one to one undertaking as the main shaft reaches depths of over 100 metres. Unlike many potholes, Rowten is not hidden in trees and the daylight shaft reveals some beautiful plants which glisten like emeralds on a cloak of white limestone. There is beauty here as well as danger.

Danger is most intense at the 'eyehole', which is a smaller opening at the southern end. Smaller at the surface, that is. There are no boulders or ledges here, so anybody falling in wouldn't even bounce on the way down. It is 67 metres to the cavern at the bottom. Clearly, Rowten's little boy is a far nastier piece of work than his dad ever was. Don't let him fool you.

However, just like Pontins and Butlins, the Rowtens do at least offer some fun for the family. Let the heart rate slow down, wipe away the sweat, and head back for the path. Close to the first hole in the floor is a small lip of limestone where a stream once flowed at the end of the ice age when the main pots were frozen up. Follow this little valley to the west and the entrances to Rowten caves are revealed. A full exploration of the 'wet' entrances involves crawling and forms the basis of another chapter in this book, so we'll leave that for now. Instead, locate the only 'dry' entrance a few metres to the south west in a hollow. This is a beautiful twisting passage of walking height for children and stooping height for their parents. It runs for about 25 metres to an exit near the wet entrances, where children will need a helping hand on the slippery rocks. There is an alternative exit at mid-point which climbs out of a slippery hole onto the moor, and only a good torch and wellies are needed. It's a lovely introduction to 'real' caves for all ages, was the first 'through' cave that I did with my own children, and it really whets the appetite for greater things, believe me.

Pottier Still

Reluctantly leaving the Rowtens behind, a few minutes' walk south along the Turbary Road will reveal another wall, with a rickety stile leading into what I call the 'Swinsto Field.' Just before crossing the stile, a search in the rushes on the right will reveal a pothole covered by rusty iron sheeting. This is Simpson's Pot. It looks nothing, but don't even think about it. It leads into a crawl then drops in a series of underground pitches to a depth of 112 metres. The water finally runs into what is known as the Kingsdale Master Cave, and it is a tricky trip even for seasoned potholers. The Master Cave is the deepest accessible point of the Kingsdale drainage, where water from all the different potholes unites before making its way through completely flooded passages and out onto the surface. There is a secret way into it from the roadside, but we shall leave that to end our adventure.

Following the same pattern, the most interesting features of the 'Swinsto Field' are also on the right just as you are about to leave it. The marker to them is a small pothole at the right hand side of the path, unimaginably named Turbary Pot. Turbary, by the way, derives from the German *torf*, which means peat. I should have mentioned that earlier. Leave the path here and head in a diagonal line towards the field wall, on a sketchy path in the grass. The first shakehole reveals Suicide and Blood Pots, whose names say it all, while the second contains the famous Swinsto Hole, a favourite with cavers, which is a twin to Simpson's Pot and leads to the same exit, through a dustbin lid by the road far below!

Thorney Devil

So many holes can make you weary, so return to the path from Swinsto and take in the fine view of Ingleborough to the east, standing from this angle over a wilderness, like a majestic volcano over a buried city. At this point, as you are just about to cross the wall into the next field, turn sharply left before you do so and walk eastwards in the direction of Ingleborough, beyond where the wall ends abruptly at a corner. The customary lonely tree marks the position of Thorney Pot. This is a beautiful shaft with a garden of crisp vegetation decorating its walls, and it is not too deep to make the heart flutter. Behind it is a superb limestone pavement which has been scraped bare by the Kingsdale glacier, showing the great height that the ice reached. The odd position of Thorney Pot, and the lack of water entering it, indicates an immense age, and it is believed that the hole may have been formed by a stream sinking through a crevasse in an ancient ice sheet, and which sank below the limestone when the ice melted. Whatever its origin, with its guardian tree adorned with blood red berries, set against a backcloth of soft white limestone and the brooding mass of Ingleborough, it is a beautiful feature.

The pavements here are an excellent lunch spot: a

A Three Peaks Up and Under

Other-wordly: The polished 'marble' staircase leading into Marble Steps Pot gives it the majestic name it deserves.

beach at the side of the prom, and a chance to either lie in the sun or curse at the lack of shelter. It is worth considering here that it would need a week in Kingsdale to see all the sights on offer. Having visited some of the best, priorities must now dictate the adventure, and it is inevitable that some sights will have to be missed. There are no hotels or guest houses on this promenade, so one must make the most of a day visit. This must include a visit to Marble Steps Pot, the Kingsdale equivalent of Blackpool's Tower Ballroom, and which more than matches it with its intricate carvings, delicate colours and spectacular sea views. It can be reached in twenty minutes.

Return to the path from Thorney Pot, and enter the next field, where the path runs parallel to a wall on the left. The area is known as Thorney Rigg, after the pot. It contains no features worth a stop, so continue until a further field is reached. This contains Track Cave, on the right just inside the field boundary, and the magnificent Kail Pot on the left after a two minute walk. This is a fenced version of Thorney Pot, and is equally beautiful. A dark chamber can be seen leading off at the bottom, and the rock garden is very impressive. Leaving the Kail Pot field, the path now runs alongside a wall on the right, soon crossing yet another boundary wall, and after about 300 metres on obvious 'corner' is reached where the wall on the right ends suddenly, meeting a wall which runs down the moor from the north west. Magnificent views of Morecambe Bay open up ahead, where the gentle contours of the Lune valley terminate at the Irish Sea. Seeing this makes me feel proud to live in England.

A Path to the Palace
Leave the Turbary Road behind and take a 90 degree turn, following the wall to the northwest over rough moorland, and passing the prominent entrance of Little Pot on the left before a junction with another wall. The wall has a barbed wire top but can be climbed with care as a large wooden post helps matters. However, if your conscience gets the better of you, follow the wall down to the left where a track is rejoined and a turn to the right admits to the Marble Steps field. Climbing the wall is the quickest option, but the latter route takes in the massive Rift Pot with a total depth of 101 metres, so it has its merits. Either way reveals a plantation of mature and wind beaten trees, whose mellow shades come almost as a shock in so remote a setting. Even on an otherwise calm day, the leaves and branches seem to be locked in conversation in such an exposed spot, catching the faintest of breezes from the sea, as if drawing further attention to their presence. A closer inspection reveals what all the fuss is about.

Marble Steps Pot, all 131 metres of it, lies cunningly

beneath: a monstrous 'L' shaped gash in the limestone, where water action has achieved perfection in its sculpture. A series of polished limestone boulders cascading down the safer western end give this stupendous place its name. Even the legendary Wainwright himself, who was not the bravest when it came to potholes, found himself forced to admit that Marble Steps 'looks almost inviting: 'The setting having a beauty in contrast to the desolate moorlands around.' More typically, he goes on to add a warning which seems to be accompanied by a morbid chuckle: 'Anybody falling in is likely to come out, if at all, as a corpse.' While we might doubt any complete disappearance, I don't think any of us would be mad enough to contend the 'corpse' proposal. To relax for one moment when skirting the perimeter on a surprisingly well-worn path is highly dangerous, and a slip unthinkable. Stick to the western corner, or hug close to a lovely old beech at the northern side which gives a great view and makes a fabulous photo. The Eastern end, where the stream sinks, contains two smaller entrances, Lamb Pot and Steps Pot, and the rift leads to a gully dropping 37 metres sheer into the Upper Main Chamber. 'Upper' that is, because there are still another 94 metres to go! Some of the named features below, such as Stink Pot and the Intestines, add further to the horror of the situation, as well as the almost unpredictable flooding which has trapped many a caver.

When the nerves are settled, a slippery but safe scramble down a boulder chute at the western end leads towards the main shaft, and the sheer drop is protected by a boulder barrier. Use common sense here and don't push yourself too far. I have sat my children, with a drink, at the top of this boulder chute, perfectly safe, and taken them down one at a time. Those waiting need never be out of sight or sound as you descend. Once down, pause and look up to see the gnarled old trees leaning like a coven over a seething cauldron. Marvel at the herbs and wild flowers decorating the inner walls of polished smooth rock, and experience the awe at being inside one of the finest potholes imaginable. 'Marble Steps' indicates an air of royal grandeur, and this is indeed a palace among potholes; a place perfectly fashioned for the king of the underworld.

Dropping Clangers

Two more treats before home, and still not a penny spent! Retrace your steps to the Turbary Road, and head back the way you came along it until you are just about to enter the Kail Pot field. Here turn sharply right alongside a wall, aiming for Ingleborough. As long as you keep this wall in sight, you will reach the road through Kingsdale in a few minutes, just north of Thornton force, and it is from this path that you can clearly see the Raven Ray moraine barrier with the river breaching its eastern end. The tricky thing about the path is that there is so much limestone to negotiate. Aim for a ladder stile taking you through into a final field descending scars and then a welcome grassy path, emerging on the road by a hawthorn. The huge boulder on the right as you were descending is the Cheese Press Stone, deposited by the retreating glacier during the ice age, and well worth a visit.

Now it's just a simple matter of walking up the dale to the car, on a quiet road where approaching vehicles can be seen or heard well in advance. It can be dull walking on roads, but not here. It gives you a chance to see the finer details of a dale which aren't seen from the car, and there is the added interest of a visit to Keld Head, where all that water we saw disappearing up on the prom finally reaches daylight. Beyond the first wall on the left, the road curves away from the river, and, at this point, peer over the wall to see the dark and sinister pool. Spare a little sympathy too, for that poor old 'Adam's ale', which has had to plunge its way down Marble Steps and Swinsto, before fighting its way through to here. And how do we know this? Well, determined cave fans have placed coloured dyes up above and popped themselves down here to watch. Apparently, rubber ducks get stuck, if you'll excuse the poetry, but this doesn't deter divers, and the chances are you'll see one in his flippers if it's the weekend. Nod politely to him if you do and, for once, feel *somewhat* ordinary.

Blissfully, as the children are moaning about aching legs, cavers have provided a feature better than any fun house. For years, they were frustrated at not being able to 'come out the other end' from Swinsto and Simpson's, until someone hit on the bright idea of unblocking a small exit which had formerly been blocked by glacial debris. The loose stones and soils kept caving back in, so some bright spark set an oil drum into the hillside and capped it with a 'dustbin lid'. To me, it looks like one of the homes of *The Clangers*; the cult children's television programme of the 1970s. (Remember the Soup Dragon?) Valley Entrance, as all cavers know this feature, is easily reached by a gate on the left, immediately opposite to the Braida Garth turn-off. Follow the muddy path through the ferns to the right, for just a few metres, and the Clangers' home cannot be missed. The drum slopes down at 45 degrees and the slide down into the passage is great fun. With a good torch, even young children can manage it, requiring only a little help with the slippery scramble back out. The passage itself winds off to the left, but it soon meets three pools which are waist deep.

Unless it's a red hot summer's day with low water levels, you will need to wear all the right gear to have a go. The first pool, in particular, is enough to put anyone off, as the roof is so low that only your head may be out of the water! Obviously, prolonged rain can sump the pool to the ceiling, so take special care. It is known as the roof tunnel as it runs well above the main stream passage to Keld Head. It continues for an exciting 300m past a crawl on the left known as the 'Milky Way', before passing under a tall aven and reaching a drop into the Kingsdale Master Cave. Don't be too concerned. Many school children do this trip as routine through outdoor activities centres. They reach the drop, go 'Wow, look at that!', and splash noisily back out, saturated but smiling. If you don't mind a soaking, it's much better than any Log Flume ride, put it that way, and you don't have to queue for hours!

And finally, I don't like to say 'head back to the car', for cars seem out of place in the Viking Valley. 'Return to the starting point' is much better. A leisurely drive then gives you a last chance to see this most secret of dales. The helmets of the Vikings were here well before those of the cavers, and who can blame them for setting up home here? There may be no lights or lasers in Kingsdale, but there is more than enough to illuminate your mind for years to come; I'm sure you will agree to that.

'Oh, I do like to stroll along the prom, prom, prom ...'

Puddles on the riverbank: The beautiful packhorse bridge above Stainforth Force.
Top right: The Happy Valley as seen from Smearsett, with the rugged heights of
Warrendale Knots above Settle in the distance.

10. Smearsett Scar:
A Celtic Walk

Grid Reference: SD820673 (starting point at Stainforth car park)

In a Nutshell: An impressive climb to a fine vantage point which, though of modest height, offers a superb view over Three Peaks country. On the way, there's a visit to the beautiful setting of Stainforth Force, famed for its jumping salmon, and the 'Happy Valley', with its haunting echo. The hidden hamlet of Feizor is also included, while highlights of the return journey include Dead Man's Cave, a thrill for children, and the unique 'Celtic Wall', which hides its mysteries in the distant past.

Essentials: It's best to combine two Ordnance Survey maps for this adventure. The Explorer sheet OL41 'Forest of Bowland and Ribblesdale' shows most of the given route, but the journey from the summit of Pot Scar is best shown on the Explorer OL2 'Yorkshire Dales South' map. Waterproofs and warm clothing are advisable, even in the summer months, as the weather can change rapidly. Smearsett is a short but very steep climb and should only be attempted by the physically fit. You can still enjoy the adventure without the climb, as there is so much to see.

Access: From Settle, the B6479 turns north towards Stainforth close to the bridge over the River Ribble. After two and a half miles turn into Stainforth car park on the right. There is a small charge for parking. Please respect residents and don't be tempted to park in the village.

Adventure: Though Smearsett Scar, known locally as 'Smearside', is a lonely place whatever the season, the waterfalls of Stainforth Force can be Ribblesdale's equivalent of Bolton Abbey in the summer months, so this adventure is best completed, I think, in either spring or autumn. On a hot July day, juvenile Tarzans dangle from precarious rope swings over the plunge pool of the force, while their admiring parents tuck into tuna sandwiches and text their friends from the relative safety of the eroded shore.

Leaping fish are somewhat more graceful than teenagers, and a little more secretive. So if you would rather picture yourself in a David Attenborough documentary than a Tarzan remake, I suggest a trip in October or November when the jungle lords will have retreated, and the river can return to its former glory days, if only for a few precious months.

Leave Stainforth car park and head towards the main road, turning right at the junction and taking great care with the crossing as drivers on here seem at pains to set the new land speed record. Once over, you can kiss the 21st century goodbye for a few hours, and head left down a narrow road, a few yards ahead, which takes you down to the Ribble. The late 17th century pack horse bridge which crosses the river here is a delight in itself, and even more so the view downstream from it, where shelves of limestone offer a perfect spot to sit and contemplate what life was really like before concrete and girders. All around is the sound of falling water, and Stainforth Force, or 'Foss', as some still call it, is easily reached via a gap in the wall on the left. The bridge seems far too perfect to be man's handiwork, and if someone had told you it had been carved by the Ribble itself, you could almost believe it, such is the perfection of the construction and the mellowness of the stone. Man's only other contribution to the scene is usually a gaudy rope dangling from a tree on the opposite bank, from which the little boys dangle on summer days.

Lemmings, Stoats and Salmon

The last of the three small falls plunges into a deep pool. This is the place to stop and stare. Fix your eyes on the falling white curtain, and wait patiently. The jumping salmon show is a real treat for children and even more so for big children, like myself. Don't worry if you find it difficult to leave. I was once staring for so long, completely lost in my own thoughts, that I was oblivious of people around me. Oblivious, that is, until I heard one kind lady say to her husband: 'Do you think he is all right, Dave?' I had to explain that I was only watching the 'little fishies' and had no intention of becoming the lemming that they had suspected. In any case, I told them, life wasn't *that* bad just yet, and there were far easier places to end it in the Dales than Stainforth Force. What about Gaping Gill? Curiosity satisfied, they walked ahead, and in seconds had disappeared over the bridge, without a second look at anything in the vicinity. At least they cared!

Oddly enough, stoats are common around the force, and I have seen them in the lane as well as by the river, even on busy days. According to one angler who has fished here for half a century, they have become accustomed to scavenging fragments of salmon after the fishes have been gutted. 'It's in their bones,' he told me. I once had a mammoth task on my hands here trying to convince Lucy, my five year old daughter, that stoats don't like Jaffa Cakes.

In Search of Happiness

Return to the bridge, and turn left up the lane, heading for the tiny settlement of Little Stainforth. Beyond the buildings, a stile heads left onto an obvious path which skirts a small scar fringed with trees. This path is the gateway to the shyly hidden 'Happy Valley', and as the scar terminates on your right, the valley suddenly opens up at a right angle to it. Ponds are as rare as dodos on limestone so make the most of that which lies to the left of the Happy Valley gateway. In spring, it is usually a teeming mass of tadpoles, but it often dries up completely in summer. The gate into the valley must be climbed, even though there is an official right of way marked on the map, but this barrier, I think, adds to the secretive nature of the terrain to be explored. Small rocky scars on each side enclose a lush green valley floor, dotted with grazing sheep, and on first impressions the scene is so peaceful, so perfect - it isn't difficult to see why courting couples of long ago chose the rather prosaic name. Familiarity, however, doesn't bring contempt – but more a sense of unease.

Sheep aren't usually a problem for walkers, but those of the Happy Valley are *nosey*. As soon as your feet land on the other side of the gate, they will be staring you out; you can bank on that. Now, I know they don't see many two legged mammals in these parts, but there's no need to be so grumpy. To me, they seem to represent the spirits of the Celtic folk who once inhabited a camp at the top of the valley.

Built to last: Huge weather-worn blocks make the Celtic Wall immediately worthy of attention.

Perhaps an entire army of ancient warriors has been reincarnated in wool, in order to stare though their dark masks and check if their descendants really are as bad as the rumours suggest? But this is the *Happy* Valley, remember, so give a big smile back to remind them that we don't all destroy the world on a Saturday afternoon. Some of us even go out to admire it.

The famous echo, too, adds an air of mystery to the surroundings. Wainwright states that 'visitors will be loth to disturb the stillness and serenity of this delightful place by provoking it.' Surely the model fell walker must have been just a little naughty for once in his life? I, for one, can count myself guilty in this respect, because big kids become even bigger ones with their own offspring around, don't they? The amazing thing about the Happy Valley echo is that it can take two or three seconds for your voice to bounce back. The imagination can run riot here. It's like shouting back through the centuries and hearing the cries from another age returning your message, word for word.

The valley, incidentally, was formed by a small glacier, and it seems likely that it is much higher in relation to the River Ribble than in the distant past. The main glacial scouring and entrenching of Ribblesdale during the last 'ice age' has presumably left the Happy Valley 'hanging' high and dry. Its isolation makes it ideal for hunting buzzards which usually put on a great show for the echo-shy visitor. So, if you want to watch raptors at work, I suggest you give the kids a gobstopper and enjoy part two of your David Attenborough documentary. You won't be disappointed.

Scar Face

A wall crosses the Happy Valley at its mid-point, with an ancient gatepost being a notable landmark. Beyond this, the impressive sight of Smearsett Scar looms up on the right, gleaming with white limestone and begging to be climbed. Of the two gateways in the next wall, take the one on the left, and immediately follow the wall corner round 90 degrees on your right, which gives access to an adjoining wall and another stile, leading along the base of Smearsett. The climb up is rewarding indeed, as there is no path, and one must pick a way steeply between boulders and clints to reach the summit. This is ten minutes of real mountaineering, in my view, even though the hill itself is a puny 1192 feet. The sense of exposure is terrific, and the views are sensational. It is every bit as exciting as anything on Ingleborough or Penyghent, though not quite so varied, but the chances are you will have this summit all to yourself. It will be yours to keep.

Close to the ugly Ordnance Survey summit column is a wind shelter fashioned from the plentiful limestone blocks nearby. There seems little doubt that much of the limestone was transported here, and it is believed that the rocks once formed part of a substantial watchtower, maybe even for the Celtic chieftains whose camps can still be traced in the valley below. And what a view they had: Ingleborough and Penyghent look majestic from here. In the distance to the south east, the humped outline of Warrendale Knots, over Settle, dominates the skyline. The shallow grassy trench of the Happy Valley stretches serenely below, but one oddity in the landscape seems to catch the eye more than any other. A detached and isolated stretch of wall can be seen on the summit of the low scar immediately opposite. This wall was unsuspected from the valley below, and is not even marked on modern maps. To the watchers in the tower, however, it will no doubt have been an object of great importance, for this is the 'Celtic Wall' to modern historians – an intriguingly fascinating yet frustrating antiquity, the origin of which is not yet fully understood. Knowing this, and seeing how inviting it looks from here, I am always tempted to jump off Smearsett and hang-glide across to it. However, the wall can wait for an hour, for the ridge walk to nearby Pot Scar is a far more sensible option, and equally tempting.

A Pot Without a Hole
The ridge runs westwards towards another obvious cairn on Pot Scar's summit, passing many interesting outcrops of limestone on the way. Looking back, there is an obvious cave entrance in the face of Smearsett Scar, which in summer is an interesting scramble exercise for the children. In one area, you may notice slabs of limestone jammed between the clints like the dentures of a giant. Take your time here and enjoy it. There is a feeling of being deeply immersed in the best of the limestone country, and, after ten minutes, the summit cairn

Delightful cottages: Feizor, and the ever present water pump. An idyllic setting still here despite the fears of guidebook author and illustrator Alfred Wainwright.

is reached in a moonscape of shattered limestone. Views now open up to Crummackdale and the Norber boulders to the north-west, while the Ingleborough massif very much dominates the scene. Beautiful deciduous woodlands clothe the hillsides, under which the hidden village of Feizor nestles snugly, being just about the only civilization on the adventure so far, and a tiny fragment at that.

The way off Pot Scar is tricky in mist, and sheer cliffs are on the menu here, so take great care. You need to head north down an area of clints and boulders and reach a gateway at the bottom left corner of the field. Once through the gate, follow the wall on your right and, where it meets a cross wall at the bottom, turn a sharp right angle to the left, heading alongside the wall for Wharfe Wood. Where the trees are reached, the path takes another right angle and heads south west towards Feizor. Just over the wall here, on the right, is the hidden valley of Feizor Nick, which contains a number of interesting little caves. In one of these, the ancient skeleton of a woman was recently found with the shaft of a spear embedded in her spine: an enigma for archaeologists to puzzle over. The path soon reaches Feizor, with its delightful cottages, and well-kept village pump which, bless Mr Wainwright, has not yet been moved to an urban museum as he feared it might be. Long may it continue! I've tried and tried to snatch a photo of this pump as a possible watercolour subject, but every time there has been a four-wheeled monster in the way. I'd give a prize to anyone who could tempt the Feizorites out of their village for just five minutes, but wouldn't we all stay at home if life was so idyllic?

Feizor, aside of a recently established (and welcome) tea-room, has no shops or watering holes, and receives only curious stares from many visitors, who, no doubt, feel a bit out of place here with mobile phones and fluorescent anoraks; for this is very much still the haunt of that traditional dalesman, the farmer. Don't outstay your welcome if the kids are being noisy, and head through the village until the *second* of two sign-posted footpaths on the left is reached. Make sure you take the correct path, for the first one will lead you straight back down the Happy Valley and you will miss the highlights of the return journey.

Dead Man's Heaven

The path now runs beneath the rocky outcrop of Feizor Thwaite, passing three notable fields enclosed by limestone walls on the left, before reaching a junction at more open ground. Ignore the branch to the right, which heads for Buckhaw Brow, and keep straight ahead until, after a few minutes walking, a wall is met running up the hillside to the left. Leave the path and follow this wall up the tussocky slope before meeting a gate on your right, just beyond the junction with a cross wall. The gate, after the stiff climb, is always the signal for a welcome gasp of delight at the lovely little cave entrance shyly hidden beyond it. This is Dead Man's Cave, and there is no doubt a reason for such a memorable name, though even Wainwright himself was at pains to discover it. 'There are no dead men in it,' he wrote, with a twinge of disappointment. 'At least, there weren't on the 2nd September, 1968.' There *nearly* was, though, on 27 November 2004. Having begun our walk late due to a snapped handbrake on Stainforth car park, I hurried round at twice the normal speed with a huge rucksack, fading light and three argumentative offspring behind me. Once over the gate, I collapsed into the cave with my trusty flask and about forty minutes of daylight left for the trip back to Stainforth. There was a horrible damp wind biting away outside, and the cave was so beautifully snug. The kids were happy enough, tucking in, but I knew that five minutes in this heaven was all I dare risk to avoid being 'benighted', as the mountain rescue so elegantly like to put it. Not all experiences in the Dales are delightful. That afternoon, I finally understood just how brave Captain Oates really was when he walked out of Scott's tent.

Do enjoy this quaint little cave if you have time. It is a perfectly safe, dry chamber, probably carved out by melt-waters during an early glaciation. Rocks inside can be arranged to make a perfect sofa, and as a dining room it is second to none. It is also alive with history, as the numerous carvings suggest, and was no doubt a convenient spot for courting couples of past centuries.

A Wall Before Hadrian?

Once refreshed, say goodbye to the cave before heading northwards across pathless terrain: keeping the watchful summit of Smearsett straight ahead. Very soon, a welcome blot on the landscape looms up, and the Celtic Wall is at last upon you. This isn't just any old wall, mind you. It is completely detached from others around, being about 20 metres long and nearly 2 metres wide. Compare its structure to others close by and you will see that the individual blocks are huge indeed, and have been so savagely weathered over time as to appear honeycombed in structure. Think how often you watch the news and see the chaos that strong rain and winds inflict on our modern structures. Consider this, and then imagine the incessant hammerings that this wall has suffered over at least twenty centuries, and yet still remained intact. Have we really made such progress?

The wall was once thought to be part of a defensive structure overlooking the camp in the valley below, the outlines of which can be traced on a sunny day. However, it would seem strange not to have continued the wall on if this was the case, and though there is another more ruinous stretch of wall 20 metres to the east, it seems unlikely that the two were ever connected. Instead, local historians have compared the Celtic Wall to similar structures where bodies have been unearthed. Aside of a full scale archaeological dig, we can only ponder. The top class builders may well be beneath your feet, but resist the temptation to wake them. Wouldn't you want a two thousand year rest after carting those huge blocks up here? Leave the boys in peace …

Meeting the Dead

The Celtic Wall isn't quite the last highlight of this wonderful journey. This comes when a slippery scramble down the slope

A Three Peaks Up and Under

Plenty to chew over: There are no bodies in Dead Man's Cave, but it makes an excellent shelter for lunch!

to the north once again rejoins the path below Smearsett, where you can either retrace your steps down the Happy Valley to Stainforth, or, bearing left at the junction, follow a shorter route to Little Stainforth, crossing two stiles over pleasant, rocky pastures. Those who take the Happy Valley route might first wish to bear right as they exit the valley and take the obvious path, (SD810665) leading to what Harry Speight, in *The Craven and North-West Yorkshire Highlands* vividly described as the 'Field of the Dead'. At first, the mounds in this enclosure appear natural, but close inspection reveals otherwise. The first, an anvil shaped construction known as the 'Sheepscar Enclosure', is partly encircled by a 'wall' of weathered stone on its north and east side (SD807664). No doubt a burial chamber of some importance, it has never been disturbed as far as is known. Continuing through this enticing field, an even more prominent mound is encountered on the right, the 'Sheepscar Barrow' (SD 805665) – with a splendid, but little known cairn circle close by. The circle can be hard to distinguish from the surrounding grassland in summer, but once discovered its central 'cyst' or grave chamber will be obvious. It is one of those intricate places only a few will ever encounter.

Finally, the 'Apronful of Stones' celebrated in Speight's classic work, can be reached by exiting the 'Field of the Dead' through a gate, and doubling back along the field wall in a south-easterly direction until the mound's presence is obvious. (SD807663) Marked on Ordnance Survey maps as an ancient cairn, this one was excavated in 1784 and a skeleton unearthed with a single piece of ivory and the tusk of an 'unknown mammal' as recorded by an anonymous writer in *The Gentleman's Magazine*. It is not known if the skeleton was Danish in origin or from a much earlier period. The remains of the excavation can be clearly seen on top of the mound where one large stone may well have been the lid of the burial 'cyst' itself. The place is an enigma. It can be difficult to depart.

Return to the Happy Valley path should be made the same way, as the landscape can be confusing and some paths are unmarked on the map. Whichever route appeals, it is that final glance back over the scars of this spiritual landscape, its small peaks and cairns silhouetted in a late afternoon sun, which will always stay with you and will reinforce your affection for this beautiful part of the world.

Dramatic development: The keyhole at Attermire makes for a splendid and unusual vantage point. *Top right*: Squeezing into the Horsecollar in Attermire Cave can be quite a challenge...

11. Catrigg Force and the Bone Caves: Tottering Through Time

Grid Reference: SD823652 (starting point at the car park by the old school in Langcliffe village). A 6 mile adventure, including an optional trip into mostly dry cave passages.

In a Nutshell: Perhaps the book's most complex adventure, with so much to take in, it may take repeated visits to be appreciated. The route leaves Langcliffe village, climbing the scars to Winskill - of literary interest - before heading to Craven's most stunning waterfall, Catrigg Force, hidden in a wild ravine. The famous erratic boulder of 'Samson's Toe' is passed and finally the celebrated 'bone caves' of the scars above Settle are explored in detail: Jubilee, where human remains were discovered; Victoria, which contained everything from Roman coins to elephants and hippos, and Attermire – probably the most exciting cave entrance of them all, situated high in the cliffs above a breathtaking prehistoric landscape.

Essentials: The Ordnance Survey OL2 map (southern and western dales) covers the entire route. Much of the ground is rocky and loose sections and scree may be encountered, so strong boots with good grips are a must. A compass will be useful if mist descends but the paths are mostly well defined and follow walls and valleys. There are no facilities of any kind and the nearest toilets are located in Settle. Victoria Cave, owned by the Yorkshire Dales National Park Authority, contains warnings about its unsafe nature and *is entered at your own risk. Rock falls are very rare but are always a possibility due to former blasting and excavation.* In particular, discerning explorers should be very careful to preserve the environment and *not touch deposits, loose rocks, stay clear of any boulders and not leave litter.* Powerful torches are suitable for these caves, but a helmet mounted lamp for each person is essential if the full length of Attermire Cave is to be attempted. These can be hired at a low cost from shops in Ingleton, 10 miles away. Children will enjoy Jubilee and the first part of Attermire Cave, but will need one to one supervision at all times. The ledge traverse to Attermire Cave entrance is for confident walkers with a good head for heights. It is a wise idea to have a *complete change of clothes* in the rucksack or waiting in the car, and expect to get very muddy indeed.

Access: One mile after heading northwards out of Settle on the B6479, turn right into Langcliffe village. Opposite the church and village green is a free parking area outside the old school.

Adventure: 'Tottering' fits easily into the fellwalker's limestone language, especially around Ribblesdale. The late Alfred Wainwright's favourite feline was a stray named 'Totty', who was, by his own words 'always tottering around.' Those who undertake this adventure may find themselves not only 'tottering' on the expanses of shattered limestone, but also at the expanses of time through which living things have left their mark on this landscape. If anybody was the ultimate 'totterer' it would have to be Thomas 'Tot' Lord (1899-1965): a man who spent his life roaming these hills; uncovering and preserving the secrets for which they are famed. We shall be tracing his travels on this walk.

Langcliffe's peace is often punctuated only by bird call. It was once under control of the monks of Sawley Abbey, and had a notable leather industry. If you have time to look, there is a fine village green, an old water fountain and a former inn called the Naked Woman, whose famous male counterpart resides in Settle; the name being a satire on the changing fashions of Stuart England. There was, until recently – the 'Big Tree' – an ancient sycamore which was removed for safety reasons; a youngster now taking its place on the village green.

Begin by leaving the car park and turning right along a stony lane. As the path forks with the kennels on the left, keep right between limestone walls, with fine views opening up across Giggleswick Scar and Borrins Wood. Peep over the walls to the right to see lynchets: Medieval field systems that were shaped into terraces for easier ploughing. In front, the quarried face of Stainforth Scar is a prominent feature, frowning down on all. As the cliffs loom closer, the views beyond extend up to Stainforth Hall and Smearsett Scar. The path begins to descend into a hollow, and here glacial drift is plastered along the valley bottom and sides, covering much of the limestone with a soft green blanket. Once through a gate, take the upper of the two paths, a delectable grassy route through ancient copses once known as the 'cat steps'. Reminders of the great Ribblesdale glacier are obvious here: the humps of drift or 'boulder' clay on the left are distinctive, as are the Silurian erratics, like those of Norber – dumped by the melting ice and now cleverly incorporated into the walls.

The Bard of Winskill

Once through a gate next to a lovely old ash tree, the path climbs steeply with the views over Settle becoming ever more impressive. Just as things become tedious, a gate is reached at the top of the scar where the way on, though indistinct, is straight ahead between thorn bushes.

Ignore the overgrown route to the right at this point. Just beyond, a cairn reminds us that even these low hills can become confusing in mist, sensibly preventing people from jumping over the quarry edge on the way down. Now the walls become a mixture of limestone and sandstone: local farmers in the past having hammered away at some of the smaller erratics with their own erratic behaviour! As a small rocky enclosure is reached – there is a beautiful pointed and fractured Silurian 'oddity' on the right – well worth the day's first photograph.

A gateway adjacent to a wall stile reveals a path cutting diagonally across the next field, with the farmhouse of Lower Winskill on the left. Backed by trees and framed by Smearsett and Ingleborough, it makes a great subject for cameras, pencils and brushes – and it abounds with history. Tom Twistleton (1845-1917) lived his reclusive life here as a Craven dialect poet, publishing his anthology 'Splinters Struck off Winskill Rock' – a reference to the famous 'Samson's Toe' that we shall visit later. His surname is well-used in the Craven area – notably at Twistleton Scars near Ingleton – and originates from the Scandinavian 'tun' or settlement, with 'twistle' referring to a river fork or junction. The remote seclusion of Winskill was captured in 'Epistle to W__ L__':

I'm glad to say at Winskill here,
We fra the plague hav yet kept clear
But down at Cleatop Park

Glorious vista: Whernside from the ridge route near Fell Close Rocks; meanwhile the Frog Prince, *pictured above,* seems to lure unsuspecting explorers into the confines of Colt Park Wood.

Mighty respect: The awesome sight of the Mere, *right,* with its outlet into the shafts of Meregill Hole hidden below the camera.

Safe passage: Trow Gill was cut by meltwater toward the end of the last glaciation when the great pothole of Gaping Gill was blocked by ice and debris. Today it remains largely dry.

Lost in time: An old gatepost on the Pennine Way leading to Sell Gil Holes.

Ribblehead Viaduct: A magnet to the eyes, and testimony to the skills of those who toiled in appalling conditions to construct it in the late 19th century.

Mysterious: The upland plateau of Thieves Moss is hemmed in by cliffs at the head of the Crummackdale Stadium.

The Norber Mushroom: Erosion of the limestone pavement beneath has left it resting on a precarious tripod of rock.

Colourful sight: Delightful first impressions at Juniper Gulf, spectacular beyond the entrance pitch. *Below:* Nick Pot's entrance is misleading.

Hidden away: The only clue to the presence of Weathercote is a quaint little door - the entrance, perhaps, to the Secret Garden.

Wind-beaten: The summit of Smearsett Scar, looking to the sleeping lion of Penyghent.

Red signals danger: Rowten Pot sits right by the Turbary Road and should be treated with the greatest respect. The rowan berries add a beauty to an otherwise forbidding scene.

Giggleswick Scar: The Ebbing and Flowing Well has been written about for many centuries - and still shows its ingenious character today.

Historic spot: Attermire Cave's 'keyhole' entrance, high up in the cliff. The remains of a Romano-British chariot burial were found just inside here.

Crashing down: The beautiful Pecca Twins create high drama for waterfall walkers.

Palace of the Giant: The Giant's Prayer Book in Yordas Cave - or was it the Bishop's?
Below right: The bizarre formation known as the Map of Wales.

Stunning: Great Douk is a colourful cave, *above*, as these formations in a side passage testify.

Wild and untamed: Ling Gill is a gorge with massive fallen blocks and exposed situations, the most spectacular gill in Ribblesdale.

Stone on water: A reflected moonscape in Long Churn Cave.

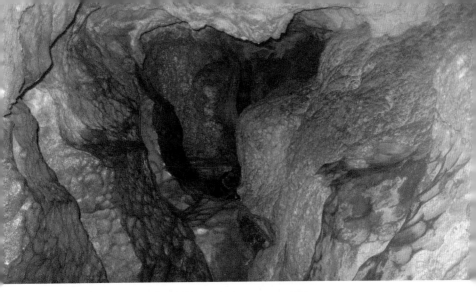

Serpentine: The oxbow in Thistle Cave where Darren got stuck, *above.* I call it 'The Snake'.

Dragon's den: The Main Chamber of Gatekirk Cave, entrance on the left and the abandoned entrance of the Loft, right. A great rib of limestone divides the chamber like the back of a dragon.

Gaping Gill: Britain's best known pothole. Fell Beck drops in a single 340-ft plunge into the nation's largest cavern.

Catrigg Force and the Bone Caves: Tottering Through Time

An Gildersleets and Rarmill Green
An other spots where it he's been
It has made awful wark.

'The Picnic', by contrast, perfectly captures the escapism of care-free days in a karst landscape:

Ower limestone rocks av ling an' bent
Ower hill and slack away they went
Beneath that burning sun
But lang befoor they got t' plaace
Some wiped the heat-drops off their face
An' said that they wor done.

Externally, Tom's home has little altered - but the farm now has a website, promoting its activity centres. A snippet of the 21st century has squeezed, perfectly concealed, into an area where mobile phone reception is as fragile as a limestone puddle. The farmer in charge is another Tom – grandson of legendary 'caveman' of Settle, 'Tot' Lord, more of whom later.

A Catrigg Concerto

The field path ends at a wall stile, where the way ahead lies along the lane to the right. Carry straight on here – but take note of the right hand turn along a lane – leading to 'Samson's Toe', for this will be taken on the return journey. As height has been gained, Penyghent and Fountains Fell take on a brooding dominance, with the Ingleborough massif – not to be outdone – looming up behind Smearside. A fine Silurian erratic is once again passed, resting on the layer of drift to the right, and a gate down on the left then gives a glimpse of what is to come: the snaking Cowside Beck disappearing into a wooded cleft lying on the North Craven Fault.

155

A Three Peaks Up and Under

Hidden delights: The original narrow entrance to Victoria Cave, where Michael Horner made an amazing discovery.

Catrigg Force – formerly 'Catterick Foss' is shyly hidden here from all but the adventurous. Nine times out of ten you will have this scenic gem all to yourself, such is its remoteness from car parks and commercialism. Recently the entire waterfall and its surroundings have been put 'up for sale' by its owner. I dread the thought of a car park ever finding its way here. Just imagine the hand rails and ice cream vans; the 'Catrigg Cornet' with raspberry sauce? Unthinkable! This is a place to enjoy and keep quiet about – so, shhhh – not so loud, guys – keep it under wraps.

The Force is accessed through a gate which is easy enough – but looking down the double fall from the top is risky and great care should be taken. Follow the direction of the watery 'racket' over springy turf and a limestone terrace is reached with a bird's eye view down into the ravine. In wet weather the maelstrom of foaming white is unforgettable – the rocks vibrating with the sheer force of nature's anger –

though it is difficult from this angle to tell that the fall is double as the smaller force is tucked away under the terrace itself. Having survived long enough to take a picture – make your way down the path to the left into a beautiful wooded glen, long believed to be haunted by a 'Boggart.' Here a glance to the right reveals the startling contrast of tumbling white against the somber woodland, the water cascading in a double fall through an hour-glass shaped cleft in the limestone. In drier conditions, it is possible to traverse along the right hand bank on slippery boulders before scrambling across the beck to the opposite side. Here a small cave is developing under the left wall, and the view of twin cascades merging on a higher step before roaring into the plunge pool is one of the wonders of Ribblesdale. Legendary composer Edward Elgar (1857-1934) certainly thought so. Apparently Catrigg Force was his favourite place to unwind when visiting his Settle friend, Dr Charles Buck. There's enough natural pomp and circumstance here, but if only he could have left us with a 'Catrigg Concerto.' Pity, that.

Many visitors are inclined to miss the lower waterfall, such is the drawing power of the upper spectacle. The lip of this second cascade is actually hidden and it requires a few yards' walk down a slippery path on the left of the beck to see an equally thrilling force snarling its way through broken branches into the gorge. Brave souls can, with caution, descend the slippery banking and suspend themselves against a small tree for one of those situations you don't tell your mum about.

What Samson Left Us

Reluctant as Elgar to leave, head back to the gate at the top of the gorge – and the next part of the journey involves retracing your steps back towards Winskill Farm and turning left into the lane previously mentioned (SD829665) – the path to 'Samson's Toe.' If time permits the Winskill Stones themselves, up on the left, are worth a detailed exploration, but no diversion is needed for the famous 'toe' itself, inspiration for Tom Twistleton's anthology title, and one of the most photographed boulders in Yorkshire. Samson required lessons in foot care, as two large 'corns' have flaked off the main stone, which is a fine example of a greywacke erratic dropped onto the limestone during the last glaciation. It has stood there for 12,000 years so is entitled to a bit of athlete's foot. The colour contrast between the 'toe' and its creamy-white pedestal is superb.

Jubilee Celebrations

So far, it's been all rocks and waterfalls: now it's time for the caves. A few yards beyond Samson's Toe, turn right onto the Langcliffe to Malham Tarn road, then after heading downhill for a few yards, bear left onto the Winskill Stones Nature Reserve just beyond a cattle grid (SD835658). The pleasant grassy path curves to the south then begins to swing eastwards, meeting a wall at a ladder stile giving access to the Jubilee Caves. These intriguing little caverns were named by Tot Lord and the Pig Yard Club in celebration of the silver jubilee of George V and Queen Mary in 1935, the year their secrets were uncovered.

Thomas 'Tot' Lord, born in Settle in 1899, was a great local adventurer and lover of the outdoors, and it is thanks to him that many of the finds of the Settle 'bone caves' have been so well preserved. Tot was an eccentric, a one-off personality – more practical than academic, and someone who made an immediate impression on those who met him. Involved in all kinds of trades for a living, he was an enthusiastic amateur who, with others of similar bent, set up the famous 'Pigyard

Club' in Upper Settle and its eventual museum. This treasure trove of Settle relics was later transferred to the now demolished Town Head, Tot's last home before he died in 1965. His love of the caves has made him Settle's most famous son: he even had his portrait painted, has a town trail in his honour – and a pothole named after him!

Tot's impulsive personality meant that warnings from mining engineers over Jubilee Caves being 'ruddy well dangerous' fell on deaf ears. During 1935 and 36, not only were iron age objects discovered, but the remains of *seven* full skeletons were found, carefully tucked into holes in the sides of the cave passages. The renowned anthropologist Sir Arthur Keith dated these back 2000 years to the Romano-British period. The main burial was a man of about 50, 5 feet 5 inches in height, and with evidence of having suffered from rheumatism or arthritis – while four of the other six identified included another man, a girl and two women. Tom Lord, Tot's grandson, and John Howard, (2013) speculate as to whether physical ailments and chronic sickness might have influenced placing of bodies in caves, neither in this world or the next, as people were nervous that these might be passed on to people or livestock, even in death! Many cave skeletons show signs of having suffered similar illness.

Entering the caves with a torch, it is daunting to consider that the crevasses where the walls meet the ceiling were actually tombs of these people, all those years ago. Crouch in the Jubilee Cave passages alone – switch off the mobile phone – close your eyes, and be humbled by the power of past spirits.

A Victoria Sandwich

The greatest of all Prehistoric caves now awaits – and is reached in about ten minutes by walking south-east along the base of Langcliffe Scar. The caves in this part of Ribblesdale are some of the oldest known in the Dales: floor deposits in Victoria Cave alone dating back at least 600,000 years - showing that the cave pre-dates both the Anglian and Devensian glaciations. Albert, the Prince Consort, is the first to catch attention, the narrow horizontal slit of his namesake cave passage lying at the top of a perilous scree slope (SD838651). His cave is not in the same league as his hall or memorial, and is now gated to preserve deposits and archaeological potential – but how great a queen has shared his limestone bed since man has walked the earth!

One man who did walk this way and, by sheer chance, make possible the finest haul of chronological treasures from any cave in the British Isles, was Settle tinsmith Michael Horner (1813-1878). Hunting rabbits one afternoon in the spring of 1837, he became impatient when his trusty hound, having found its way into a small hole in the scar, failed to return. Pulling away nettles, soil and loose boulders, good old Michael worked his way inside and was no doubt 'gob-smacked' as they say in Yorkshire, to see a rising sediment floor containing a number of coins, bones and metal objects. After several visits, Mr Horner had 'sat in the corner' too long with his secret, so he revealed all to his employer, Joseph Jackson, a Settle plumber with a keen interest in history and archaeology. Jackson crawled momentously inside the soon to be named 'Victoria Cave' on 28th June 1838, the very day her majesty was being crowned in Westminster Abbey.

To find this historic entrance, continue along the scar past the distinctive opening of 'Wet Cave' – usually an interesting 'bat cave' for those with a good torch, and a pathway leads up the scree to the gigantic artificial entrance to the lower part of Victoria Cave itself. If possible, ignore this for a moment and climb the excavated spoil heap to the left. Here, in a patch of nettles – is the very hole where Michael Horner's hound made archaeological history, and led us all to a deeper understanding of time and its effects on the way humans and animals lived. Looking at the narrow crawl inside gives an indication of Horner's determination: either that, or all the rabbiting certainly helped his waistline! For the next 30 years both Jackson and Horner explored the cave, removing the sediment floor of what became known as chamber B and finding at first a wealth of Romano-British material including brooches, bracelets, rings, buckles, spindle whorls, needles, and – intriguingly, a number of perforated bone 'spoons' – which have puzzled archaeologists ever since. Why would you have a spoon with a hole in? You wouldn't – as they say in Settle, 'make a reyt decent brew wi' that.'

After 30 years of persuasion a grant was given to the British Association to carry out a full scale dig – and in 1874, having cleared the upper chambers, the team set to work to excavate the lower reaches, blasting the cliff in order to remove the massive amounts of clay and boulders. Looking at the entrance today it is amazing to think that the huge chambers now seen would have once been filled to the ceiling with sediment. The manpower that went into heaving all that stuff out must have been unbelievable! So why go to all the trouble?

Jackson, William Boyd Dawkins and co. must have been determined, as following an Iron Age level containing shards of pottery, they then dug through a huge layer finding nothing, and indicating a massive period of time when the cave had been unoccupied. Eventually they hit on bones of wild horse, badger, reindeer, pig, goat and both brown and grizzly bear. Things were looking up, and there was still more sediment below. All these animals were dated to around 12,000 years ago and had occupied the cave towards the end of the last glaciation. False calcite floors were removed to get at the lower levels, and it was then that the team made a startling discovery. Encased in the sediment were bones over 100,000 years older, dating from a warm inter-glacial period of 120,000 years ago when the Dales lay basking by tropical seas near the Equator - and here were the beasts to prove it: hyenas, hippos, straight-tusked elephants, rhinos, giant deer, lions and bears! All this suggests that the environs of inter-glacial Langcliffe Scar must have resembled a prehistoric safari park.

Tricks of the Teeth
The main artificial entrance gives a clue to the limits of this 'hyaena layer' as it is known – owing to the fact that many bones showed evidence of having been chewed by these animals. Walk inside and keep to the right hand wall. This is chamber D, and at the back, on the right, a hole can be seen leading into a narrow passage some two metres up. This hole marks the level of the 'floor' of the hyena layer and it is possible that the hyaenas themselves used this passage for breeding and raising young – hence its name: 'hyena passage.' Avoid climbing up, as the calcite is very delicate. Instead, look at the back wall where a slot is the entrance to Birkbeck's passage, excavated by local caver John Birkbeck. He was a practical joker by all accounts and, knowing the team were desperate to find human remains, caused complete havoc by leaving one of his own teeth in the sediment – having the cave 'anoraks' in a frenzy of excitement before revealing the hoax. What a great man.

Bearing to the left, and still in daylight, is Chamber A, where wild horse vertebrae with tooled cutmarks dated to

12,500 BC and found near the back wall, indicate that man was in these parts as the glaciers were still melting away. The bones had been gnawed by wolves, and this chamber is also notable for having produced rods of reindeer antler dated around the same time, as well as a Mesolithic antler fragment from about 5100 BC – an incredible 7000 years between the two antlers alone. The passage along the left wall is divided into two by a boulder. Right leads to the very back of chamber A, while left is a thrilling by-pass into the upper series, the original caverns explored when the cave was discovered.

Despite the plundering of the caves, there is still beauty to be seen for those with a good torch or lamp, and who don't mind getting filthy. At the top of the by-pass chamber B is reached, with daylight visible at both the main and original entrances. The latter is such a tight squeeze that Michael Horner's efforts seem even more remarkable, as the passage would have been tiny indeed back on Coronation day! A boulder slope leads to Victoria Cave's most beautiful feature, a stunning bridge of calcite dividing chambers B and C, which reveals its true glory with a crawl underneath and a step up, leading to inspection of the upper surface. Here, the golden tint of the rimstone pools is delicately picturesque, and it is from this area that an engraved javelin-head, dated at 10,900 BC, was discovered by Tot Lord in the 1930s. This is clearly a fragile section of the cave, and great care should be taken not to disturb the remaining deposits and the flowstone features. It is always with great reluctance that I tear myself away from this truly wonderful place, and I always have a last wander round the scree outside Horner's entrance, knowing a barbed antler point, once thought to be a harpoon, was found here in 1870. Both this and the javelin head indicate that man the hunter was in full cry around Victoria cave 14,000 years ago.

A Three Peaks Up and Under

Through the Keyhole

Our 'tottering' continues by descending the scree and heading south with the scars on the left and the 'camel's humps' of Warrendale Knots on the right. The narrow entrance of Brentscar Cave is soon passed, at the top of a steep scree apron. Harry Speight (1892) describes the location of a collection of stones here known as the 'Watch Tower', indicating a look-out post during the Roman occupation. The cave soon narrows and is not worth the efforts of a climb up considering what lies ahead. The route steepens with increasingly impressive panoramas of bare rock on all sides and, crossing a stile, reaches the obvious line of the Mid Craven fault, marking the termination of the limestone cliffs to the left and right. The marshy basin ahead is the location of the former Attermire Tarn itself, unfortunately drained during the last century, while the obvious spoil heaps to the right are the remains of the Settle volunteer rifle corps' shooting ranges, set up in 1860 to train locals for possible war against France. From the ranges, the dominating presence of Attermire Scar, to the east, is magnificent, the white cliffs meeting aprons of scree that would once have reached down to the edges of the tarn itself. The entrance to Attermire Cave can be seen as a 'keyhole' in the cliff along a grassy ledge, and to reach it, as the locals might say, looks 'a bit dodgy' to say the least. No doubt walkers are put off by the daunting location of what must be one of the most thrilling cave locations in the British Isles, but let your love for limestone take precedence here. Attermire Cave is unmissable.

Follow the path that trends diagonally across the screes towards the cave entrance, before scrambling up to the grassy ledge, accessed by steps in the limestone. Great care is, of course, essential, but the ledge is wide enough to keep clear of the drop, and the views are reminiscent of a prehistoric monster movie. 'The Land That Time Forgot' could easily have been filmed here. The final step across to the cave entrance needs particular care, as the ledge narrows and a sheer drop opens on the right, where a waterfall once poured out of this ancient cavern.

Chariots and Treasure
Much has been discovered here. Tot Lord and the Pigyard Club recovered the remains of a Romano-British chariot from the sediment near the entrance, possibly used for funereal purposes, while human bones, jewellery – including looped bronze wire and 'dragonesque' brooches and an exquisite Roman intaglio, have also been found. The heads of Minerva and Silenus, Roman gods of salvation and protection, were depicted on the intaglio, further indicating that the cave was used for death ceremonies. As with Victoria Cave, Neolithic remains, including bones and worked flints, were dug from the lower sediment layers. The location and archaeology itself make this cave very special, but the added bonus of a stunningly beautiful passageway and the challenges involved to reach it promote Attermire, in my view, to 'classic' cave status. It was Tot Lord's most beloved place: his ashes are scattered on the scar beneath, and it is my personal favourite of the many caves in the Settle area.

Old clothes that don't matter are recommended to explore the cave, as well as reliable lights. Being largely dry, the passages are muddy – but the remote location means that even the entrance passage itself can be a convenient changing room! Most will be content to wander 50 metres or so inside, passing beneath a wedged boulder into an uneven passage of increasing height. There is some lovely 'moonmilk' in the ceiling, while arachnophobes and wildlife lovers will have contrasting views of the many cave spiders and tissue moths on show! All is pleasant and exciting until the ceiling suddenly lowers from 40 feet to no more than two. Squeezing behind a flowstone curtain reveals a daunting tunnel, 'the neck' continuing to 'goodness knows where.'

It is best to come back another day if you wish to tackle this obstacle. Having had several attempts to get through in full caving gear, I finally did it one day wearing nothing more than an old jumper, jeans and wellies – realising I had to make myself as slim as possible. Large adults have to go through on their sides, but children will fly through the passage without a problem. The final squeeze is through the 'horse collar' and after twenty feet or so the kidney shaped 'Pool Chamber' is reached, with a sigh of relief. The pool is no more than knee deep and is surrounded by walls of flowstone and calcite. Tot Lord, apparently, was once stuck in the 'collar,' leaving a group of his friends imprisoned in the Pool Chamber behind him, with no way out. Within hours a group arrived and a hammer and chisel were used to free Settle's most intrepid cave explorer!

The Sign of the Lord

The rest of the cave is easy – and a delight. A right turn from the Pool Chamber climbs down a beautiful polished staircase of stalagmite, arranged like pillows, into a spectacular tall rift passage with flowstone walls. Victorian tourists, who unbelievably tackled the 'neck' with tweed suits and candles, have left their mark in graffiti on the wall, which makes fascinating reading. Somehow their attractive script looks almost artistic compared to the efforts of today – which are, thankfully, far fewer. One signature is unmistakable on the right hand wall, where below a 'J. Lord' dated 1849 is the distinctive script of Tot Lord himself, underlined and in capitals, leaving a permanent, undated mark in a cave where he deserves a place in history. I always feel privileged to see it.

Catrigg Force and the Bone Caves: Tottering Through Time

The cave ends in a bouldery cavern less than 200 metres from the entrance, though there is a slot down on the left for more advanced cavers, leading to a trickier length of small passage. It makes more sense to return once more through 'graffiti passage' to the Pool chamber, seeing another wealth of delights in this direction, and then once more tackle the 'neck' before emerging with blinking eyes to that magnificent view over the Craven landscape. Take great care when tired limbs are descending the steps from the ledge, and the scree slope. At the shooting range, the path along the Craven fault should be followed westwards along the base of Warrendale Knots, passing Bivvi Cave on the right. Wainwright (1970) describes its dark entrance as 'so snug and dry a refuge in wet weather that one regrets going past on a fine day.' I doubt you will agree with him once you've tackled Attermire Cave. You'll have braved enough darkness for one day.

The final stage of this memorable adventure is an easy downhill 'totter', leaving the crags behind and approaching the civilized world of Settle in the valley below. Reaching a wall junction at the foot of a steep section (SD824641) a sharp right turn should be taken along the base of Blua Crags towards Langcliffe, keeping left at a junction above a small wood. The road to Malham tarn is soon reached above Langcliffe village, with an easy descent to the starting point. Your first totter may only have been a taste of what was on offer. Perhaps you merely visited the cave entrances for the first time and enjoyed the tranquility of the prehistoric landscape, but the chances are you will want to totter in Tot's footsteps again and again, each time making new discoveries to delight and intrigue. Who can blame him for resting up here indefinitely?

High: A lone explorer pauses by Schoolboys' Tower on the summit of Giggleswick Scar. The great breach of Nevison's Nick cuts through the cliffs below. *Top right:* The impressive cairn, only yards from the edge of the old Giggleswick quarry.

168

12. Giggleswick Scar:
Yorkshire's Rock of Gibraltar

Grid Reference: SD 810640 (Starting point in Giggleswick village). A 4 mile (6.4km) adventure.

In a Nutshell: An exhilarating high-level traverse across a breathtaking exposure of bare limestone, formed on the line of the South Craven Fault. There are attractive woodlands, supporting a wide variety of flowers, birds and mammals, and a range of dry caves to explore, well known for their archaeological finds. The views are outstanding throughout.

Essentials: This adventure involves some rough scrambling so strong boots with a good grip are essential. The Ordnance Survey OL2 (Southern and Western Dales) and OL41 (Bowland and Ribblesdale) maps are required to cover the circuit described. Warm clothing and waterproofs are advisable as the area is exposed and often windy. Take a strong torch if you wish to explore any of the caves. These are small, but perfectly safe and great fun for children. Being dry, however, they tend to be muddy so don't wear anything that really matters! There are one or two exposed areas on the scar where great care is needed, particularly if youngsters are involved.

Access: Leave the A65 for Settle on the B6480. Drive through the town centre and cross the bridge over the River Ribble into Giggleswick. Just after a school and on the left, a lane turns into the old part of the village. Drive carefully down this narrow lane before turning right at the foot of the hill, passing the church. Approaching the impressive old buildings of Giggleswick school ahead, take the next turning left onto a wide lane, and there is plenty of space to park. Take care not to block any entrances.

Adventure: It can be difficult to begin this one - very difficult. So fascinating and immersed in the past is the quaint old village of Giggleswick, that the urge to leave the hiking boots in the car is great indeed. By all means have a wander along the banks of the delightful River 'Tems', as it winds its way serenely through the narrow streets, and don't miss the ancient church of St Alkelda, shrouded in Saxon legend. The famous public school has an almost hypnotic presence about it, with its various buildings blending into the chocolate box atmosphere as perfectly as in a Constable painting. I adore this place, having spent many hours wandering enviously amongst the cottages and up to the beautiful domed school chapel. Rarely do the works of man have so much impression as here, but another visit will be needed to take them all in. In the meantime, we are concerned with creation on a much grander scale. Creation which began as many thousands of centuries ago as to make the Saxons feel like yesterday, and though man has had a pretty good go at destroying it, Giggleswick Scar still stands proud; a resilient bull refusing to fall to its matador.

Giggleswick Scar: Yorkshire's Rock of Gibraltar

The scar differs from Malham Cove, whose unclothed state makes it a stark and magnetic feature of the landscape, being instead shrouded in trees which add to the beauty but somewhat diminish the grandeur when viewed from a distance. A close up inspection is needed. Even the most casual visitor, driving along the B6480 towards Ingleton, or 'Up Buckha' Brow' as the locals refer to it, cannot fail to notice the soaring cliffs on the right, contrasting with a gentler, almost featureless landscape on the left. The cause of this oddity is the South Craven Fault, a gigantic fracture in the earth's crust lying in this vicinity, and along which the rocks have been moving since Carboniferous times. The limestones of the scar itself, to the north and east of the road, have risen upwards along the fault plane, forming the cliffs, while those to the south and west have slipped down. Indeed, so far have they slipped down that a golfer on Settle Golf Club's course at Giggleswick would have to dig down hundreds of feet to reach rock that originally lay on the same level as the cliff-top: as Wainwright concludes, in his *Walks in Limestone Country*, 'something dramatic once happened to the earth in the place now known as Giggleswick Scar.' 'Dramatic' would seem to be an understatement.

Walk back through the village from the parking spot, with the church on your left, and return to the B6480 by taking the steep lane also on the left, past several lovely old cottages. Cross the main road with care, and immediately turn left up a pleasant avenue known as 'The Mains'. Crossing the main road is ten times easier than in the past. Before the Settle by-pass was opened *everything* shot through here: wagons, coaches, caravans, buses, tanks, (only joking) and the road was a virtual death trap. Even back in 1968, when Wainwright penned his classic guide, the horrors had already commenced. Part of the narrative describing a short section of road-walking in his Giggleswick Scar chapter reads: 'In the event of survival, thank your lucky stars.' One can only pause, then, and count the blessings of the Settle by-pass.

The Mains is an attractive place where all the houses are well kept, the birds are in full voice, and the residents don't seem to mind mixing conversation with 'foreigners' walking through their territory. Beyond the houses is the beautiful Lord's Wood, now a site of Special Scientific Interest, and noted for its wealth of limestone-loving plants. In spring and early summer, the rocky slopes beneath the trees are ablaze with colour. The birds-eye primrose, globe flower and columbine being noteworthy, along with several species of orchid, while the smell of garlic is far better than that from any Italian restaurant. Local conservation groups based in the Craven area arrange regular 'flower walks' to the area for budding botanists. As the edge of the wood is reached, pass through a gate onto the fell-side, and, where the paths fork, take the one to the left which clearly doubles back on itself and skirts the upper perimeter of Lord's Wood as it climbs up onto the scar itself. At this point there are superb views across Ribblesdale to Penyghent, and over delectable fields of vivid green turf to the Ribble itself. Above Settle, the great gash of Victoria Cave can be made out in Langcliffe Scar, with her more modest husband, Albert Cave, standing out as a dark slit just higher and to the left. This is a great spot for the camera to come out, and a welcome drink before the stiff climb ahead. Here a monstrosity is reached which could not be of greater contrast to the delicate tranquilities of Lord's Wood.

A Stone-Eating Giant
Giggleswick quarry is the culprit here. Millions of years of nature's craftsmanship have been blasted away forever, to be

replaced by a hole of colossal dimensions. Instead of peering into a 'wild' pothole and seeing nature's playground of boulders and water, we encountered for decades mountains of aggregate, metal machinery, vivid blue buildings and stark red lorries. I try to look on the bright side. I really do try. As a fellow walker said to me when we both peered into it one Sunday morning, 'Settle would not be what it is, and Giggleswick would not be what it is, without this quarry.' The quarry companies at least ensured that their handiwork was largely invisible from the village itself, and from a distance the cliffs could be imagined, I suppose, as a natural part of the landscape. Colin Speakman, in his excellent *Walking in the Yorkshire Dales*, sheds light on the matter in a more convincing way. He describes quarries as being, 'a necessary reminder that the Dales are, in the final analysis, as much a part of the industrial civilization as the motor car or train that carries us there; and to imagine otherwise is an illusion.' Being very competent in conjuring up illusions myself, I must reluctantly agree. In any case, the quarry has recently closed, and nature is once again being allowed to take over: peregrines, my dad tells me, should have a field day!

Ignore a finger post pointing south-west towards Giggleswick, as this will be used on the return journey. Continue uphill with the quarry on your left, skirting the very edge of the 'cliffs' themselves, until the welcome sight of a huge cairn of boulders diverts the attention at last: Schoolboys Tower - another work of man, or, at least, of boys, but strangely magnetic and stubbornly resistant to the nearby industry, even if the western side is slowly collapsing. Presumably, a past generation of Giggleswick schoolboys were responsible for the construction, and it is still possible to clamber over the collapse and stand inside the cairn itself, looking out over the Ribble Valley landscape like a proud

A Three Peaks Up and Under

Away from the madding crowd: Schoolboys' Cave lies high above the main road and is a welcome little shelter.

admiral at the stern. Here, the ghostly shape of Pendle Hill looms in the distance, a first tantalizing glimpse of land on the edges of a vast green ocean.

Having failed miserably to rebuild the tower's battered defences (the Victorians obviously knew better), Schoolboys' Cave provides the next excitement and a first real glimpse of the sheer height of the nearby cliffs. Head immediately west from the Tower, and scramble for a few metres down a steep grassy slope, where a rough path leads to the right revealing the cave, shyly hidden behind a rowan. Children will need a special watch on the path, but although the views down are sensational, all is quite safe. Even so, those who suffer from vertigo will be relieved to escape into darkness for a few minutes. Those for whom both heights and *spiders* provide their biggest fears in life, are, however, in for their worst nightmares. They will have a choice between stepping out of the cave to a hang-glider's view of Giggleswick Golf Course, viewed as if from a New York skyscraper, or stepping inside for a terrifying encounter with *meta menardi* and other monsters of the eight-legged world. Believe me, folks, it's a lovely place.

Joking apart, this is a cute little cave and children will love it. It's also a welcome shelter from the wind, and has no doubt been a place of retreat for many a former schoolboy, before computer games were around to dampen the sense of adventure. Like many caves in the scar, this was probably formed by melt waters during a previous glaciation, and has now been left: high, dry and lonely. Say goodbye to it and head back carefully up the slopes to Schoolboys' Tower, from which an obvious path on short cropped turf can be picked up, trending north-west and running parallel with the cliffs. This is a common hunting ground for stoats, and kestrels strive for a share of the rodent spoils. Continue for a delightful 500 metres (about one third of a mile) until an obvious cave entrance is seen on the right at the top of a scree slope. This is Wall Cave, but the name is no longer appropriate, as the wall across its entrance has now been removed. Children will love the scramble up the scree, and although the entrance soon cuts down, there is an interesting little 'chimney' out to the surface. It is possible to scramble up to the exit above and peer down, though care is needed. Returning to the path, a stile is crossed and Moth and Spider Caves can be seen on the right, the first being a very low crawl not worth getting muddy for, and the second having a larger entrance leading to a passage blocked by a massive boulder. Personally, I'm always impatient at this point to move on to better things, and when a notable dry valley opens up on the right ahead, it is amazing how many walkers simply march past, oblivious to the presence of Kinsey Cave, even though it is clearly marked on Ordnance Survey maps.

Next of Kin

In summer, the passage along the valley bottom is blocked by ferns, and it is necessary to follow a sketchy path along the right hand slope, which needs care. At other times, the easier route may be taken, but only at the last minute is the cave revealed, a large dark opening at the base of an overhanging cliff: clearly an abandoned waterfall from ages past. Named by W. Kinsey Mattinson of Austwick who spent his spare time probing its secrets in the 1930s, the cave is so roomy, sheltered and dry that it would be possible to get a good night's sleep in it, even today. The folk of yesteryear clearly thought likewise. Excavations by Mr Mattinson not only revealed Romano-British artifacts, but also the remains of reindeer, lynx and wolf, not to mention the complete skull of a cave bear.

The finds made their way into many museums, including the Craven Museum in Skipton, where the skull can be seen today – radio-carbon dated to 12500 BC! My children have tried many times to add to them, forming their own collection with owl pellets, a sheep's skull and the remains of a desiccated frog. Not quite museum standard, but shouldn't curators, like cavers, be encouraged to start early?

There are plenty of logs and boulders in Kinsey Cave, making it an excellent spot for lunch, and although the entrance allows light to most parts, it is still fun to use a torch and pick out some of the attractive flowstone features on the left hand wall. The back of the cave cuts down to a muddy crawl, but I have always been reluctant to try it, for fear of coming face to face with a badger, or, dare I suggest it, a sabre-toothed tiger. Try that one as a desperate attempt to keep the children's clothes pristine if you are planning your tea out on the way home.

Taking in the view from the entrance one day, it suddenly struck me that the Kinsey caveman himself would have looked down on more or less the same landscape; but here the similarities surely end. I have often suspected how cheesed off he would be to see me sitting in his private residence, alternating sips of smoked bacon and lentil soup with rich, steaming coffee. That's a bit better than gulping dirty water from a sheep's horn and sucking the marrow from the leg bone of a dead rabbit, any day. No doubt there are some perks of living in the 21st century.

Curiosity satisfied, return down the dry valley to the path, and turn right before crossing a stile into the next field. The limestone scars nearby are very attractive, with some precariously rooted trees adding a further dimension, and yet another opening, Gully Cave, providing shelter, or fun for the children. Once a further stile is crossed, the scars on the left will be seen to have diminished in height, and there is a conspicuous clump of trees clothing the low cliffs. Hidden here are the delightful little Buck Haw Brow Caves. To reach them, locate a small gap in the perimeter wall which leads to a slippery path down, the lorries and cars now hurtling past only a few metres away, seemingly an oddity in such a wild and remote setting. Civilisation is also glimpsed in Scar Top Garage and a former café, once favourite stopping points for motorists before the Settle by-pass was constructed. The caves themselves are little visited today and there are three main entrances. The upper one is attractively clothed in foliage and is a useful shelter, though it is of no great length. A river of stones issues from it before dropping through a remarkable 'window' in the limestone to the bottom entrances. Children should be watched carefully here as the sides are slippery above the sheer drop. The bottom entrances are great practice for crawling into caves, but involve getting muddy and really require some kind of helmet to avoid nasty bumps. The left hand cave is easiest and curves round into a tiny chamber after about 8 metres. The right entrance is most fun, and you may need to clear debris away before crawling in to a perfect little tube, running for some 20 metres into the hillside. Claustrophobics can amuse themselves while the rabbits are running beneath by enjoying the fine view of the limestone window seen from below. Apparently, these caves were once mined as they lie on a barytes string, though operations were never prolific.

I Shall Return …

Now for the hair-raising return leg of the journey. Leave the caves and return along the footpath as far as the dry valley below Kinsey Cave. Instead of carrying on ahead here, turn right towards the very edge of the Scar, where a sketchy path can just be made out skirting the cliffs just above the woods. At one point the path narrows and there is a short traverse across a sheer drop. (SD804656) Children will need one to one supervision here. There is an 'edge of the world' feeling and the view down is breathtaking indeed. The building far below is Huntworth Farm, and the rough ground to its left is the site of the former Huntworth Tarn, which was drained in 1837 and became famous for the discovery of a fully preserved medieval canoe. Carved from a single ash tree, it was considered important enough to be placed in Leeds museum, but ironically was badly damaged thanks to a visit from Hitler's Luftwaffe. Perhaps the moral of that story is 'leave things where they are'. Wouldn't it be great to start a 'Bring Back the Tarn' campaign?

Once over the terrors of the traverse, the squeamish

will heave sighs of relief as the path descends easily to a broad ferny terrace, with a bank of scree running below the cliffs on the left. This is Giggleswick's most popular climbing area, and scarcely a weekend goes by without a sight of the 'rock rats' clinging to the bare limestone. When the ferns below are too high it makes sense to follow the climbers' path across the top of the scree, stepping over an assault course of ropes and tackle bags. We were once engaged in this activity when we heard a cry of 'Coming down, coming down, coming down!' I looked up for a split second to see the dark silhouette of a man, with no helmet, if not intent on killing himself, then certainly one of us! My heart froze, and in that same instant his smiling friend below tugged on the rope, the drama ending with the faller jerking back like a spider on a thread. Nonetheless, he was bruised and shaken, and the poor fellow had to save his two-dozen swear words for later, as there were children present. Since then, I have never walked beneath a climber in the Dales, and my own enthusiasm for rock climbing has, like that very man, plummeted sharply. *I take my hat off to the brave!*

Magical Water

The only exit from the scree is a sketchy path down it, leading to the ferny terrace, and after a few minutes of rough scrambling the way ahead widens out to open grassland, marking the way back to Schoolboys' Cave and the tower. In a couple of minutes a curious horse-shoe shaped 'notch', lined with trees, can be seen on the right. Take care if you go down to it, for the grass is slippery and the sudden drop is every bit as sensational as that of the traverse. This is 'Nevison's Nick', a feature of the Ordnance map that escapes many walkers. John Nevison was a notorious highwayman who was eventually hanged at York in 1684, and there are

A Three Peaks Up and Under

Lovely landscape: A view from the Scar over the former Giggleswick Tarn, where a log boat was uncovered dating back to Medieval times. The downfaulted limestone to the west lies buried deep beneath the present golf course.

many legends about him. Being surrounded by his pursuers after a robbery, his horse is supposed to have drunk magical water from the famous Ebbing and Flowing Well, located by the road-side below. This presumably gave it the great power to carry Nevison in one leap across this awesome ravine, and so delay his mounting of the gallows for a few more years. Presumably, his pursuers were not so lucky, and plunged to a hideous death down the precipice. As my teacher once said, 'The more the gory, the better the story.' Why tell the story of Moses and the Red Sea without having the Egyptians drowning in their chariots?

Nevison's Nick is a signal for a rough scramble up the scars on the left, or it is possible to carry on and scramble up to Schoolboys' Cave, either way bringing you back to

Schoolboys' Tower. From here, trace the path back alongside the quarry until a sign-post points right towards Giggleswick. Follow this, heading downhill with the quarry on your right until the woods are reached, and with a drop over cliffs in front, an iron gate with a spiky top heads right, continuing the footpath to a delightful 'Jacob's Ladder' through the trees and down to the main road. Cave addicts, however, should not miss the lovely Kelcow Caves. These can be found by heading left instead of passing through the iron-gate, and locating a further rickety gate, difficult to open, leading down a leafy slope into the woods. The caves are shyly hidden in the cliffs here: Lesser Kelcow to the right, a small 8 metre chamber, and Greater Kelcow to the left. This has an impressive 9 metre high entrance leading down a winding tunnel for 40 metres, superb for children with torches and perfectly safe. Both caves have revealed human skulls, Romano-British artifacts, and animal remains. They are strangely beautiful considering their proximity to the quarry, and I have often startled deer resting near their entrances, *but* …. (and this is a big 'but' for the timid amongst us) the cave spiders within are *enormous* …..

Reaching the main road, all that remains now is to cross it with care and follow a delectable lane, a little further up and on the left. Bordered with pastures and grazing animals, this heads back to Giggleswick and the waiting car, but if you're like me you'll pause every now and then, taking in the views of the delicate trees, clothing Yorkshire's 'Rock of Gibraltar' behind. Views that will, no doubt, remain with you a long time; though once in the car – there's *still* some fun to be had:

All's Well That Ends Well
No Giggleswick sortie is complete without a visit to the

A Three Peaks Up and Under

Ebbing and Flowing Well, even if, as Wainwright states, 'those who have watched the well for hours without anything happening are numbered in legions.' I was of that same number for years until one memorable April Fool's Day when she was on top form – playing no morning tricks on the observer and merely making fools out of the doubters. Since then, I've been hooked, and rarely drive past without having a peek.

With today's traffic, the one-time beloved walk to the well is dangerous, and it is much better to park on the left hand side of the road just opposite. Take the route from Giggleswick beneath the scar, heading for Clapham and passing the golf course. Just beyond the narrow left turning to Huntworth (SD804654) a tiny lay-by, just enough for one car, will be noticed, with the well a few yards further on the right. Take extreme care when crossing the road as it's like a Formula One racetrack. Choose a day after moderate rainfall and you'll reap the rewards. A dark tide-line around the mossy trough will indicate the well is working, and ten minutes' wait will usually be enough for an eerie gurgling to commence: the depth increasing by eight inches or so in a matter of minutes. No sooner have you 'oohed' and 'aahed' than the level begins its customary 'ebb': the time to look for the legendary 'silver chord' of air bubbles spinning like a submerged silkworm beneath the sparkling water.

As far back as 1612, Drayton, in his *Polyolbion*, related the story of a nymph, chased through the woods by a lustful satyr. In desperation, she prayed to the gods - who promptly turned her into this magical water source, her incessant panting reflected in the bizarre behaviour of the well:

> *Even as the fearful nymph then thick and short did blow,*
> *Now made by them a spring, so doth she ebb and flow.*

182

The final 'unmissable' is the spectacular rock shelter of 'Cave Ha', reached by continuing up Buckhaw Brow and pulling into a lay-by on the right as the road descends to join the A65 Settle by-pass. Known to climbers as 'The Hollywood Bowl' – it is a massive arch of bare limestone, located by a scramble through the trees and only yards from the road. Climbing up into the recess on the back wall, one has the impression of peering through the vast doorway of a great derelict cathedral. This natural 'dome of St Pauls' acts as a sound receptor – picking up bleatings and bellows from all over the area; so don't be surprised if you hear a '*Hey you – gerroff my ruddy land!*' Certainly it was enough to frighten early tourists who associated it with – you've guessed it – the Cave Ha Boggart! The more scientific visitors have, over time, revealed a wealth of material including human bones and Romano-British jewellery, as well as the skeleton of a cave bear. Smaller shelters close by had skeletons neatly wedged into natural grooves in the limestone, while Sewell's Cave, reached after a nasty scramble along the scar to the north – was found to be a depository for human skulls dating from the late Neolithic and early Bronze Age.

Where do we draw the line on Giggleswick Scar? Yorkshire's 'Rock of Gibraltar' offers many days of unique exploration: a marvelously exposed slice of landscape where there is a genuine feel that you're riding the crest of a limestone wave. I envy those who have yet to have their first encounter. Go and enjoy it.

Babbling brook: The River Twiss in sedate mood flowing through Swilla Glen, after its chaotic tumble over the waterfalls. *Top right*: The famous Thornton Force - where the horizontal beds of Great Scar Limestone lie on the Ingletonian rocks.

184

13. Thornton Force:
Rock Music for the Connoisseur

Grid Reference: SD693732: (starting point). An 8 mile (12.9km) adventure.

In a Nutshell: An absorbing exploration which combines a circuit of the famous Ingleton waterfalls with a climb onto the lonely expanses of Scales Moor, noted for its wonderful limestone pavements and perched boulders. The views are unforgettable and there is so much of interest on route that a revisit at a later date is perhaps the only way to see everything to a level of satisfaction!

Essentials: The Ordnance Survey Explorer OL2 map covers the area of this route. Scales Moor is best avoided in mist or low cloud as the footpaths are only sketchy and the views are a large part of its appeal. Despite the waterfalls route being touristy, it is rough underfoot and good boots or wellingtons are essential. Children will need careful supervision. Drops into some of the plunge pools are steep, and lives have been lost here in the past. Be well prepared for an exposure to the elements on Scales Moor, and carry extra clothing as a precaution, even in summer. A fine winter's day is by far the best time to undertake this expedition, as the popularity of the waterfalls can result in a treadmill of walkers at peak times.

Access: Ingleton is best approached from the A65, which by-passes it to the south. Just below the parish church on the main street, a sign-posted lane leads down to the car park for the waterfalls, close to the railway viaduct. There is a charge for parking which includes the cost of the waterfalls walk, and though this may seem expensive, it helps pay for the excellent upkeep of the paths in what would otherwise be an inaccessible locality, so pay it willingly, rather than congesting the narrow streets of the village.

Adventure: There are, from my experience, almost as many types of waterfall-walker as there are cars at the parking spot, but one or two are particularly dominant. The 'Thornton Forcers' – a common species - screech into the car park on Sunday mornings complete with deck chairs and fluorescent green cool boxes. Having paid their money, they don their shades and stampede with panting rapidity up the glens, desperate to get to that 'big one' on the front of the free leaflet. Mission complete, they heroically clamber behind a curtain of spray to impress their better halves, before plunging waist deep in the pool. The 'Forcers' can usually be recognized by their canine companions, who, having emerged from the swirling torrents, invariably shake themselves over other walkers trying desperately to have a humane meal on the bank. I've been a 'Forcer' in my time. Hands up who hasn't?

The 'Ski-polers' are another abundant lot. These differ from the 'Forcers' in having a more consistent speed , after spending about half an hour in the car park tucking their socks into their trousers; while flexible high-tech water bottles dangle conspicuously from their rucksacks (which, it should be added, generally cover everything but their boots and ankles when viewed from behind). They are less voracious in their eating habits than the Forcers, pausing only for an anxious glance at the watch and a nibble from a super high energy glucose bar (hands up if you're a Poler, then – don't be shy!). They plough relentlessly through this classic novel, in danger of missing the very meat of the story.

Whose Fault is it?
This is really a story of the Dales rocks, laid out, page by page. The car park itself is built on a thin layer of sedimentary rocks covering the coal which contributed to Ingleton's prosperity in past centuries. The remarkable thing here is that coal is a relatively young geological product. It was formed in late Carboniferous times, when the thin layer of gritstone covering the area was overlain by swamps with plants and huge trees. Yet here, the coal is actually lying *below* the limestone which dominates the scenery in front, and is so far below the gritstone summit of Ingleborough that to suggest it once lay above it seems ridiculous indeed.

The novels of nature, however, are far more unpredictable than those of man. The coal's odd position has resulted from a slippage, over millions of years, along the South Craven Fault. The line of the fault is passed as you leave the car park and enter a dramatic limestone gorge named Swilla Glen. It is strange to stand on this line and think that millions of years ago, you would have stood hundreds of feet above your current position. You may also wonder what the limestone is doing down here, level with the village of Ingleton, when the majority of limestones in these parts seem to be high up on the valley sides in Kingsdale and Chapel-le Dale? The answer is exactly the

A Three Peaks Up and Under

Hanging walls: Dipping beds of Great Scar Limestone in Swilla Glen.

same: for less than a kilometre upstream is the North Craven fault, down which this huge block of Great Scar limestone, with the slates and greywackes beneath it, has slipped over immense periods of time. Take a careful look at this limestone as you enter Swilla Glen. Not only is it impressive, with walls towering hundreds of feet on both sides, but a glance to the right, across the River Twiss, reveals that it is dipping below ground at a steep angle, as if a giant has been trying to force it underneath.

The reason for this is what lies below. The basement rocks beneath the limestone are ancient slates and sandstones known as the 'Ingletonian' rocks, and earth movements have not only shifted the once horizontal beds to a vertical position, but have also 'buckled' them into a wavy structure like a giant length of corrugated iron. The base of the limestone in

Swilla Glen has been laid down on the slates at a point where a large 'crest' in the undulating rock once touched the surface of an ancient sea bed. Therefore the base of the limestone is concave, and it can be seen so curving steeply away on the river bed. The two Craven Faults have also effectively 'trapped' this great slab of limestone in Swilla Glen between them, and their movements have further contributed to this great upthrust, or *anticline* in the rock. Got it so far?

Swilla Glen ends at a sharp bend in the River Twiss, and observation of the left bank at this point will reveal a small cave. This is merely a failed attempt to extract lead, but to its left a distinctly *diagonal line* can be traced in the rock strata. To the south of this line is the limestone of Swilla Glen, while the ancient slates lie along the way ahead to the north, clearly higher than the beds of limestone. The diagonal 'line' is a minor fault alongside the actual plane of the North Craven Fault itself, hidden by vegetation but reached by a short scramble through the undergrowth. It is along this line that the rocks we have just passed have been slipping since Carboniferous times, while the rocks to the north have lifted upwards to provide a setting for the fine scenery in front. The limestone was lifted, too, of course, but most of it has been worn away by river and glacial action to leave the older greywackes (a type of sandstone) and 'slates' exposed instead. The Great Scar Limestone is in fact not met again until Thornton Force is reached, about a kilometre upstream.

A Wrinkle or Two
In this direction you can see, on the left, an old slate quarry where the Ingletonian rocks can be studied in detail. Some of them have a greenish cast, and it's a strange feeling to handle rocks that are amongst the oldest objects on this planet. You can even see lines and patterns on them which are not, as my

son imagines, 'old ladies' wrinkles', (though this is as good a way of remembering their great age as I know), but instead were probably caused by rippling water currents as rivers washed into the Iapetus Ocean some 500 million years ago. Trying to get your head around that one is enough to make you have wrinkles yourself.

Carrying on, the rocks are now greywackes, shales and 'slates' which, if you remember, were once hidden by limestone. As already described, their beds are almost vertical due to the aggressive earth movements after their formation. This series of alternating layers has provided an adventure playground for the Twiss, which has worn out the thinner greywackes and shales to leave a series of spectacular 'steps', down which the Pecca Falls plunge; the pools, of course, being composed of the less resistant rocks. The falls are undoubtedly beautiful, even with the necessary handrails and hordes of people draped over like bearskin rugs with their digital cameras. I cannot help, however, admiring the works of man too, for the Victorians clearly went to great lengths to tuck their paths ingeniously into the cliffs here and reveal what would have been an otherwise inaccessible view for so many. Well done, lads.

The lower fall is followed by the Pecca 'Twins', and finally, the lovely Hollybush Spout, which usually exists only in my imagination, for I have yet to take a photograph that isn't over-exposed or too dark. See if you can do any better. It seems as though the fall is getting revenge on the species that finally revealed its identity and disturbed its peace, by playing shy to the camera. Oh, well, there's always next time.

Next up is the 'football stadium' of Thornton Force itself. I say that because the amphitheatre of this great natural landmark is usually thronged with the 'Forcers', and even the 'Polers' take a break here. If it's summer time, the Forcers will

Mind-blowing vision: On Twisleton Scars, weather-beaten trees cling precariously to the Great Scar Limestone.

be laid out on the rocks with newspaper and tanning lotion, while the Polers will be having a swift sample of the glucose bar and a check at the GPS, with a sit down being the last thing on their minds. It's rather like two opposing sets of fans in a natural arena, only with no violence between them and with the Forcers overwhelmingly out-singing their rivals. Was I imagining it, or did I really see a bunch of Polers retreating over the waterfall followed by a chant of '*You're not singing anymore?*' Yes, I must have been. A tea hut between Pecca Falls and the force adds to this commercial atmosphere, selling half-time pies and bacon butties for the travelling faithful, and providing a rare luxury for rock fans who don't need to bother undoing the rucksack for a nibble.

Less of the people-watching and more of the rock music! Thornton Force, with or without the crowds, is one of the finest geological wonders in Britain. The River Twiss

191

plunges 46 feet (13 metres) over a lip of Great Scar Limestone which, let's remember, once continued to the plane of the North Craven Fault below Pecca Falls, before being eroded away by the power of the water. The limestone, with clear horizontal bedding, resembles the top layer of a sandwich, and a thin layer of pebbly 'conglomerate' rocks form the 'butter' in between, representing a land surface before the sea levels rose allowing the limestone to be laid down. Once horizontal itself – the ancient base of this 'sandwich' has been buckled by earth movements to form a massive 'u' shape beneath the surface; the southern limb of the 'u' lying at the quarry, with the northern limb touching the surface beneath this famous waterfall. This downfolding of the rocks is the opposite of the feature we met at Swilla Glen and is known to geologists as a *syncline*.

There is a huge block of limestone close to the path in the plunge pool, which looks as though it once plugged the lip of the present waterfall. The scramble onto it is easy for tall people, though children will need a hand. From this vantage point, the force is seen in its true splendour. Many think of this as the archetypal Dales waterfall, though in my opinion that of Weathercote Cave, about three miles to the north-east, is the finest of them all.

A Handful of Time

A scramble behind the fall should not be taken lightly. The vertical bedding means the slate outcrops in sharp plates and wedges, and the spray from the cascade makes for a slippery surface. Keep as close to the cliff as you can. The reward is a fine curtain of silver passing nonchalantly before your eyes, though it is likely that other eyes will be following yours, for this is rarely the place for quiet contemplation that it would once have been. As you scramble back to the path, a last treat for inquisitive youngsters is that well practiced 'Hand-Span of Time.' Place a thumb on the slate and stretch out your hand so your little finger touches the limestone above. The distance between thumb and finger represents about 170 million years of geological time. Such is the immense period between the formation of these layers of rock, demonstrated here by a trivial creature whose tiny lifespan would have to be multiplied some two and a half million times to cover that distance. Think of that, and wonder at the complete insignificance of your own existence.

The path swings around Thornton Force to the left, and enters another area of fascinating geology. The river is now seen cutting through the eastern flank of an enormous grassy mound, stretching ahead upstream to the valley of Kingsdale. The soil is often exposed at the surface, and close examination reveals loose clays and small rock fragments, as if a bulldozer has been clearing the edges of a building site. This, actually, is not far from the truth, for the bulldozer in question here was a massive glacier which scoured out Kingsdale's 'u' shape during the last 'ice age', beginning about 110,000 years ago. As the snout of the glacier pushed ahead, it 'shoveled' an immense amount of debris from the valley sides and effectively blocked the river's former route, creating a natural dam in the process. As the ice melted, a long narrow lake is believed to have occupied Kingsdale, the deepening water finding its way over the dam and cutting this new exit, a few hundred metres to the east of its former route. The debris pile dumped by the glacier is known as a *terminal moraine*, for it effectively terminated the progress of the ice. It is known to geologists, and marked on Ordnance Survey maps, as the Raven Ray: a name no doubt connected with the Viking settlers, who occupied these remote valleys centuries ago.

A Three Peaks Up and Under

About the size of it: The handspan of time beneath Thornton Force - with 170 million years between thumb and fingers!

A Door to the Moor

Leave the Raven Ray by crossing a footbridge over the Twiss, which leads to a track linking the Kingsdale road with an old Roman road through Chapel-le-Dale. From the track, the attractive limestone benches of Kingsdale can be glimpsed to the north-west, giving further indication of just how far the limestone at the beginning of the walk actually slipped down the Craven Fault plane. Follow the waterfalls route by turning right down the track, with the impressive outcrop of Twisleton Scar End to your left. Buzzards can often be seen hunting around this area. After about 300 metres a watch should be kept on this left side for a grassy track which zig-zags in a north-westerly direction up the hillside (SD699753). The path cleverly avoids the steepest section of the slopes, and with good reason, too; for this is the start of the Kirkby Gate, an ancient packhorse route which linked Ingleton with Kirkby-Stephen. At the top of the slope, the path follows a quaint little 'nick' in the limestone, and emerges on the lonely plateau of Scales Moor. The views of Ingleborough to the right are truly magnificent, and from here it can be seen proudly resting on its plinth of limestone, the supreme commander of this majestic landscape.

Scales Moor seems bleak and uninviting at first, a treeless wilderness stretching in a monotonous ridge to its termination at the summit of Whernside. The lack of people, after the experience in the football stadium, can further reinforce this hostility. Don't be put off, however, for there are treats in store here that few people ever see. The path heads across the limestone at Ewes Top, and although it is a little indistinct in parts, a series of wooden markers help in direction finding. There are also three distinct landmarks that invite inspection. The first, set into the wall on the left, is the 'Standing Stone', a boulder which can feel jolly proud in its stubborn refusal to move being the chief reason for the positioning of the wall in the first place; and rightly so. It's been here for the last 10,000 years. Why should it move now?

Two other rocky companions sit out on the limestone pavements to the left, bordering the edges of Twisleton Scars. Here an equally impressive boulder will be noticed, and close to it is a beautifully constructed cairn; man, no doubt, doing his very best here to match the works of nature. Stick to the path before the Standing Stone and yet another natural marvel is met. This is the 'Fluted Pothole', of no great depth, but whose sides have been worn by water action into beautiful triangular plates of limestone, giving the impression that a giant has been having a go at making an ornamental bird bath, before leaving it with a hole in the middle. Having admired his handiwork, and greeted the Standing Stone, head right (south-east) across the limestone to the second boulder, which is probably the most photographed object on these moors, and known as 'The Obelisk'. Like the Standing Stone, it has been dumped here by the retreating Chapel-le-Dale glacier during the ice age. So finely is it balanced that it seems as though a tiny shove will make all the difference, but maybe only if you're blessed with big ears and a trunk, and I'm not. I find The Obelisk so fascinating that I once used a whole roll of film on it, capturing it at every angle, with King Ingleborough behind, proudly watching over his tiny prince like a doting father. Look carefully at the precarious balance of this boulder and think of what has taken place since he last moved. Think of the great events, the wars and the battles that have shaped our history, and through it all he has kept his feet rooted firmly to the spot: amazing.

The nearby cairn offers a similar stunning view of Ingleborough, with the coaches and ice cream vans of White Scar Caves with the ugly gash of the old Ingleton slate quarry being the only effect in a glorious panorama. From the cairn, return to the path which passed the Standing Stone and follow it for a further delightful mile, taking your time by detouring right occasionally to enjoy these limestone pavements, which have a liberal decorating of 'erratic' boulders dotted here and there. Many of these are gritstones which originate from the Ribblehead area to the north. The path is tricky to follow, but keep a look out for a ruined sheepfold in front, remarkable in being constructed from both shales and limestones. At this point veer to the right and walk due south across the pavements until the wall on the edge of Twisleton Scars is met. Head right (south-west) along this wall and enjoy this fabulous high level promenade across the very best of limestone country. It's impossible to get lost, as the wall heads straight for Twisleton Scar End, passing the cairn again, and returns you to the second leg of the waterfalls walk, and civilization.

Halcyon Days

Peering over the wall and down the cliffs, a distinctive little wood will be noticed in the valley bottom, enclosed by a wall, and to its right is a farmhouse with a wall running up the hill immediately in front of it. This is Springcote Farm, a special place to me, for it was here that I camped as a seven year old and had my first ever glimpse of this magnetic mountain and its surroundings. Recent research has shown that the British were at their happiest in 1976. I'd certainly go along with that. This view, then, is very similar to the one I had through the flap of a two man tent, and whenever I see it again I drift back to being seven, in that seemingly endless summer with my long hair, flared pants and trainers: Dancing Queen' blaring out on the radio ... trying to be Allan 'Sniffer' Clarke ...

Once the cliffs of Twisleton Scar End are reached, swing right to return to the 'nick' in the limestone again, before zig-zagging back down to the lane. From here there are usually fine views of the Lancashire coast. Turn left, onto the waterfalls route, and continue until it crosses Oddie's Lane and passes Beezley's Farm. The coloured coats of the Polers and the Forcers will be here again to keep you on track, as well as the many signposts. Now there is no more map reading to be done, you can relax and enjoy another series of beautiful cascades, beginning at the Beezley Falls, where the path drops into a wooded glen and joins the River Doe. This river has had an interesting life up to this point, for it has plunged into Weathercote Cave at Chapel-le-Dale, where it is known as Chapel Beck, before gathering the water from all of the famous Ingleborough potholes at God's Bridge, about 2 miles (3.5 km) upstream. After leaving the waterfalls, it

Power shower: Snow Falls seem to hang suspended in the woodland like a cornice waiting to topple. They are a beautiful sight.

changes name again, to the River Greta, before joining the River Lune on its way to the sea.

Foaming Felines

The Beezley Falls have an upper and a lower section, and their geology mirrors that of the Pecca Falls in the first glen. The upper fall is a wide cascade into a dark plunge pool, while downstream a narrow column of rock keeps the Rival Falls apart, though still allows them to spit their foaming spray at each other. In wet weather they aggressively merge together like two snarling white tomcats locked in violent combat. All of this is observed from the safety of quaint steps cut into the steep sides of the ravine, which eventually narrows into the spectacular rift of Baxengill Gorge. Here a viewing platform, splendidly and imaginatively situated, gives a breathtaking vantage point over the River Doe, its peat-stained waters crashing between the cheeks of bare rock. At such a perfect spot, it's strange to think that the active and ugly Ingleton quarry is only a few metres to the east, hidden by the trees, or perhaps don't think of it at all, and concentrate instead on the beauties of Yew Tree Gorge, terminating at the beautiful Snow Falls.

For many people, these are the final highlights of the walk, as abandoned slate quarries now dominate the scene as far as Ingleton, but one last wonder awaits the adventurous 'Rock Fan'. After a footbridge crosses the Doe, follow the path on the opposite bank through the woodlands until a stream is met gushing down the hillside on the left (SD701747). A clamber down the banking at this point will reveal the delicate, almost lace-like cascades of the Cat Leap Falls, where the tributary of Skirwith Beck takes a ceremonious last plunge into the Doe. This stream has just had an even more exciting time in Skirwith Cave, above the Hawes Road to the east, which opened to the public in 1964, but closed a decade later, quite literally, when its entrance collapsed; quarrying operations no doubt weakening in a few decades a good few thousand years of natural sculpture. It can be entered – and has gorgeous formations – but loose boulders reserve it to the realm of the fully equipped caver.

The path now continues through the old Mealbank limestone quarry back to the main street of Ingleton, the route to the starting point being well sign-posted. The final notes of this rock classic have now sounded. Your little car is shivering in the frost, and all around it is emptiness: silence. The Forcers and the Polers left ages ago. Where have you been till this time?

If only they knew.

They told me of this narrow way
That wandered in from light of day;
Of chambers, pitfalls, goblins there,
Of wonders waiting everywhere:
With silent awe I heard the tale,
I then resided in the vale
This Monarch mountain overlooks;
I threw aside my pen and books,
And said, 'no longer I'll forego
The things I so much wish to know.
Robert Paine Hudson (1857-1923)

Book Two
UNDER

Before You Go Under:
Some Important Notes on Caving

IN contrast to book one, **Under** takes you away from your comfort zone and into some of the fascinating cave systems of the Yorkshire Dales. The caves are listed in order of difficulty with the most accessible caves first, so that you can gradually ease yourself in. Before you get the jitters, or rush for the entrances, you need to consider several things:

Firstly, caving may not be for you. You may have visited the show caves of White Scar, Ingleborough and Stump Cross and been content to end matters there. You may have no wish to go wading in water, or stripping out of ringing wet clothes on a windswept moor. If so, fair enough. But there will always be some of you who have been enthralled by the experience and wish to don the helmet, lamp and wellies so that you can see for yourself what all the fuss is about.

The important thing to remember is this: though experienced, I am not a *seasoned caver* by any means. I have explored caves with ladders, in large groups, and spent hours underground – but the sights, for me, have always taken precedence over the sport. *True cavers*, in the sporting sense, dangle down potholes on ropes, using complex equipment which requires a good amount of specialist training to be fully mastered. True cavers challenge themselves by dropping down vertical underground shafts, known as 'pitches', requiring practical knowledge, confidence and above all, teamwork. The caving adventures which I shall describe in this book have no pitches in the routes I suggest: only one or two simple climbs up and down requiring a little care. *What they do have, inevitably, is water – a lot of it – and complete and total darkness.* It is these two aspects of 'wild caves' which perhaps strike most fear into people contemplating a first time exploration. Many people when talking of caves, think of confined spaces: *'You wouldn't get me in there. I'm claustrophobic.'* Nobody would force, or even encourage an absolute novice to go crawling in a cave, and these adventures merely offer the option for those who may wish to have a go. For the most part, these caves have walking or stooping passages, and their beauty should be enough to counteract any fears.

Having experienced at first hand, and with my family, all the thrills and spills of novice caving in the Dales, I consider the following advice to be very important before you go underground:

1)   **You must have strong, reliable, artificial light for each person.** Torches are useful only in shorter caves such as Yordas. Avoid small torches with non-rechargeable batteries and stick to the larger kind which you can recharge before the trip. Make sure you know exactly how long the batteries last. I was once in Borrins Moor Cave with my children when one torch cut out completely with no warning. After that, I never bothered with torches again, and opted for the comfort of caving lamps. Torches, in any case, do not leave the hands free, which is annoying.

2) Caving lamps are expensive, but definitely worth it if you are really keen. The best examples have a Nicad battery which is mounted on the back of a caving helmet. A two way switch gives a choice of a main beam, which uses more power, or energy saving LEDs, which use less power, but give a dimmer light which is still very pleasant. The LEDs can also give light for over twenty hours, so all worries of being left in the dark diminish. Some cavers use what is known as a carbide lamp, in which a chemical reaction keeps a flame burning on the helmet. They are wonderful to look at, but to novices are complicated and best avoided.

3) Don't forget the joys of borrowing! Lamps can be hired, at a very small price, from Bernie's Café and Caving Shop and Inglesport, which are next door to each other on the main street of Ingleton. These venues, by the way, also offer excellent food, including breakfasts in the company of other eccentrics. This makes the lamp hire trip all the more worthwhile, and saves you the bother of leaving lunch boxes outside the cave later on.

4) Make sure you have a helmet. If you are carrying a torch, a cycle or builder's helmet is better than nothing. Again, there is no substitute for the real thing, but if money is tight then hiring from Bernie's or Inglesport is the key.

5) Wear the correct clothing. I always have several layers on top and an old cagoule that doesn't matter. Breathable material is important as caving can be hot work. Waterproof trousers are essential, and they should be pulled down over Wellingtons, rather than tucked in. Almost invaluable are **wet socks** made from neoprene, like a diver's wet suit. They are

Bottom's up: Clambering through the Portcullis going to Sand Cavern, Gaping Gill

available form shops in Ingleton and can be ankle or knee length. Once filled with water they insulate it inside your wellingtons so walking in a cold stream suddenly becomes a warm bath! They can make all the difference to children enjoying caving or not, and are well worth the investment.

6)   Take a *change* of clothing, and don't forget a *towel*. In most cases, you will not get wet through to the underwear, but you never know! I always take my spare clothing to the cave and hide it under some convenient dry rock, or in a dry part of the entrance itself, in a waterproof rucksack

7)   Know where you are going and what to expect. Take a pencil diagram of the route into the cave, and keep it in a clear plastic wallet, tucked into the inside pocket of your cagoule. If you use pen, your diagram will run when it gets wet – so be warned!

8) Go in numbers – not alone. Three adults are fine in the caves I mention. When children are involved, two adults to a single child and beyond that use common sense and a lot of it!

9) Use even more common sense. Do not climb, or let children climb, where it is at all risky. If you are at all unsure of the depth of water, test it yourself first by wading across. If it's too deep for the kids, carry them over carefully or turn back. In some caves, **water over the wellies is inevitable.** Try to get used to this. It's worth it to see the wonderful underground scenery. Always walk in front when children are around, and never let them go first. Tackle only what you are happy with. If you don't like crawling, then don't crawl. It's as simple as that.

10) Get an accurate, up to date weather forecast before you enter a cave. It's much better to go during a spell of settled, dry weather. Flooding is one of the hazards of caving. I have yet to meet it, because I have been careful. With children, I have to be careful. So do you. When you arrive at the cave, if rain looks imminent – don't kid yourself that it might fine up. **Stay out – and go for a walk instead.**

Final And Most Important Point of All:

Always, always, **ALWAYS tell somebody where you are going**. You should in all cases leave, with a responsible person, the names of the caves you are intending to enter, and the time that you expect to arrive home. That way, **Cave**

Rescue can be contacted in the event of an emergency. (*See appendices*) Remember that it only takes a second for an accident to happen, whether above or below ground.

And absolutely finally...

Cave Conservation: Don't be a Bull in a China Shop!
I love limestone and would not dream of snapping off a stalactite or stalagmite. Nor can I see the point. Remember that caves cannot be repaired and try to leave them as you found them. The best motto is one I give to my children when we go in a fancy shop: 'Look with your eyes, and not your hands.' Enough said.

Ready to Go, Then?
We're nearly there, aren't we? Just make sure that, when you park your car in a remote spot, you remove any valuables. Cavers are obvious targets for thieves, even in a place which seems so far removed from today's world.

If you follow all the rules above and stick to the adventures in the following pages, I can promise you that your experience will be nothing short of enthralling. Chances are - you may wish to take your interest further, and join one of the many caving clubs in the area. You might even become one of the 'true cavers' I mentioned earlier. If you do, then helmets off to you!

Can you see him? Yordas the Giant looks down on all. His cheeky face can be seen at the top, with his hand brandishing a club and the calcite forming his coat of mail. *Top right*: Looking through the window into the Chapter House.

1. Yordas Cave:
The Palace of the Giant

Grid Reference: SD 705791

In a Nutshell: A superb, former show-cave with very easy access including a huge chamber, probably the largest the general public can reach without any 'gear'. Interesting formations such as the fallen pulpit, a strange pinnacle of rock, the 'Map of Wales' and the 'Ram's Head' are on the menu here. The highlight, however, is the 'Chapter House': a plunge-pool through a natural window in the main chamber, into which thunders a spectacular and beautiful waterfall. This cave is first on the list as it is the easiest of the lot to enter – and the best introduction to caves for children, and nervous parents!!

Essentials: Three things are an absolute must here: wellies, waterproofs and artificial light. Torches must be powerful and reliable. Lamps can be hired from Ingleton at a low cost, and as it's so close – why not? In any case, helmets are essential if you want to visit the Bedchamber and avoid bumps at the entrance.

A Three Peaks Up and Under

Access: Thornton-in-Lonsdale is a small village off the A65 about 2 miles west of Ingleton. It is signposted from the main road. Drive through the village and take the road signposted for Dent. The road climbs steeply before reaching the Great Scar Limestone and there is a conspicuous boulder perched on the edge of the scars on the left. A lonely valley (Kingsdale) opens up ahead with one noticeable farm standing out like a sore thumb in the middle (Braida Garth). Continue along this straight road for another 2 or so miles until the first plantation of trees is seen on the left. This is Yordas wood. There are convenient lay-bys on the right. Take care not to block the road. The roadside gate below the wood is the way on, and the cave is now on public access land.

Adventure: The remote position of Yordas cave has saved it from the coach parks and the ice cream vans. The cave has never had any fixed lighting, although in the 18th and 19th centuries it was one of the best known sights in Yorkshire. It seems to take an eternity even today to reach it, picking a way cautiously along Kingsdale in the car, and praying that nothing massive will come the other way to force a stiff-necked reverse. You have to marvel, therefore, at the Victorians in their classy clobber - calling at Braida Garth farm to pay for a 'tour guide' with his improvised light of a long stick containing a row of candles. Mind you, they didn't have satellite television and text messages to bother with, and were probably better for it – bless them. The earliest account of a visit is that of the Reverend John Hutton in his *Tour to the Caves* (1780) where he writes of stopping at what is now the Marton Arms in nearby Thornton: *'To procure a guide, candles, lanthorn, tinder box etc..'*

Even then, the cave was well established on the

tourist itinerary, as Hutton continued: *'On the right was the Bishop's Throne and on the left the Chapter House, so called from their resemblance to those appendages of a cathedral.'*

Housman (1800) relates the darker side of the cave's then recent past, recounting how, *'about half a century ago, a lunatic escaped from his friends at or near Ingleton and lived here upwards of a week in the winter season, having previously provided himself with cheese and other provisions.'* To avoid being traced across the snowy ground this wily refugee had the bright idea of removing his heels from his shoes and fastening them to his toes so it appeared someone had recently exited the cave rather than entered it! Wouldn't it have been easier to walk in backwards?! Housman then adds, with typical poignancy: *'Since that time, a poor woman, big with child, travelling alone through this inhospitable vale to Dentdale, was taken in labour, and found dead in this cave.'*

Among the most notable early visitors were the Bronte sisters, having time off from their notorious education at Cowan Bridge. A little cave exploration seems to have been one of the few excitements in a harsh regime of dunces' caps and wicked punishments. Emily Bronte was enraptured by the lonely Haworth Moor, so it seems likely that the Three Peaks will have had a similar effect. Many assume that the 'Fairy Cave' of *Wuthering Heights* is good old Yordas itself – and knowing where Emily went to school, why shouldn't they?

From the parking spot, a glance across the normally dry streambed to the east will reveal 'The Apronful of Stones' – a prehistoric burial cairn now protected from floods by a retaining wall. Several skeletons have been unearthed from the much-disturbed site, and the circular structure of cobbles is well worth a visit if time permits – having its own eerie atmosphere. It is believed to date from much earlier than the

A Three Peaks Up and Under

Experience to remember: The unforgettable sight of the Chapter House Waterfall - one of the very few easily accessible underground waterfalls in Yorkshire.

Norse settlers who bestowed many of the names around this secluded dale: 'Yordas' its-self deriving from 'Jord aas' or 'earth stream.'

A Great Hall Beckons

Close the field gate as there are sheep around, and avoid the mini gorge before the wood straight ahead, by taking the grassy slope to the right. This descends to another gate into the wood itself. The heart begins to beat rapidly with excitement on seeing the forbidding rectangular entrance with a well-worn path leading down to the cliffs on the left. When it was a show cave this was a 'no go' area unless you were prepared to pay: early photographs and engravings showing an arch at the entrance resembling a stone fireplace. This arch has only recently been removed, and this gives things a more

212

natural, undisturbed look. It also gives more room for the giant of Norse legend, Yordas himself, to get down on his hands and knees and crawl back into his lair – once again ready to feast on the bones of any little boys who dare to walk inside his palace. Parents, you have been warned.

Don't just saunter straight into the cave looking for giants. Doing so could result in a bump, if you don't have a helmet, as huge rock 'teeth' hang from the ceiling on the way in. James Carr (1876) wrote of 'rocks of an uncommon size hanging from the roof as if by magic, or like the suspended coffin of Mahomet.' Keep looking up, until the teeth have disappeared, and then quickly downwards before you slip on your bottom, as the floor dips without warning. The cave is now a thick gluey mud, but only for a few steps. Shine your torch or lamp ahead and you'll see a floor of pebbles with a shallow stream running across it from right to left. If you've got this far without a bang or a slip, or without being eaten, you must see the rest. Relax here. Listen to the noise of the stream and the hidden waterfall. It can be a little bit spooky glancing back at the teeth now silhouetted in the entrance. But the re-assuring thing is this: You have now come down the entrance passage, or the 'lobby', as I like to call it, and you are standing safely in the Great Hall of Yordas. Carr, in his *Guide to the Caves,* suggested that: 'were it tiered after the model of the amphitheatres of the ancients, it would vie with the Coliseum of pagan Rome.' Many have stood inside Gordale Scar, underneath Malham Cove, or on the summit of Ingleborough – but how many have stood inside the Great Hall of Yordas? How many, in fact, know where it is? And what's more – nine times out of ten you'll be the only people inside. You'll have the cave all to yourself for the next hour or so. No rushing. No queues. No coaches or ice cream vans: wonderful.

A Three Peaks Up and Under

Make sure you do halt on first reaching the pebbles, because it's a good place to get your bearings. You are standing in a chamber about 55 metres long and 15 metres wide. Shine your light up to the ceiling and take in that beautiful rock architecture. It can take about half an hour for your eyes to get fully used to the dark in the giant's palace, and only then do you really appreciate the size of the place. To your left, the stream disappears through a low archway, but we'll leave that till later. All the noise is to your right, and this is where the fun lies. Up above, the Ram's Head gazes down on the scene, a natural gargoyle peering over an awesome nave.

Carry On Screaming

I'll never forget the first time I took the young Oldfields here. We'd walked from Thornton Force over the Turbary road, passing Rowten Pot. I'd a job on my hands getting the two girls anywhere near Rowten Caves, but as Yordas was the climax of the expedition, and as I was carrying butties, bottles and torches – I was determined to get them in. It didn't help that I'd been telling them stories about the giant in the car on the way. After some consideration, Emily decided she'd go for it, as long as we held hands. Joe decided anything that Emily would do, he would do – which left Lucy – who decided there and then that she wasn't going to be eaten by any giant. I quickly checked for food, a great temptress. One packet of squashed 'cheesy thins' left. Joe and Emily then had the face on while Lucy tucked into her pre-caving dinner, or maybe the 'last supper', as she saw it. Could I succeed? Could I bribe my four year old into braving the darkness with a packet of cheesy thins?

No chance! If Yordas himself didn't wake up at Lucy's arrival, then just about every other living organism in the

Don't wake him up: The entrance to Yordas Cave, where the Norse giant reputedly waits to devour small boys!

cave did. Every bat, moth and cave spider must have wondered what the heck had hit them that autumn afternoon. One thing I would say from the experience is that Yordas is a very safe cave. Structurally safe, I mean by that. I'm pretty sure Lucy's dramatized screams could have provoked an avalanche in the Alps. To think that – only three months later, she waded through Long Churn Caves to the amazement of onlookers. Children develop so quickly.

Keeping right and following the direction of the noise, you come to the 'top end' of the Great Hall. On the left wall you will notice now a strange flowstone formation which looks rather like an ugly witch with her mouth open. The water is at its most rapid close to this feature, and if you view it from the other side it has an uncanny resemblance to the map of Wales, as it has indeed been named for many years.

A Three Peaks Up and Under

People used to say my grandma had 'legs like a map of Wales', but I don't think they were quite so twisted and contorted. Often, you will see the remains of wax candles on the Map of Wales – left by those who try to make the cave look like Notre Dame.

Selfish Giant

Opposite the Map of Wales, at the top right corner of the Great Hall, the roof is at its highest and the cave itself is in the form of a high sub-chamber known as an aven. Carved into this is the famous 'Bishop's Throne' and it's a delight to climb up into the recess and sit surveying the cave you've just conquered. Just beneath, a massive pillar of limestone, 'The Pulpit'- has recently collapsed: something old Yordas himself might have been responsible for. Tourists posed on top of it for generations; me included, and he'd no doubt had enough of it! Only his prayer book now remains – a delicate wafer of limestone tucked into a cavity behind the fallen Pulpit. Surveying all this with satisfaction is the great man himself. Shine your light to the right of the 'Bishop's Throne' and a suit of chain mail stretches 60 feet to the sneering face of the formidable ogre, his left hand outstretched in triumph. If the thought of giants is too much – then why not opt for gentler company? Facing the 'Bishop's Throne' is a mass of flowstone resembling an obvious shell and with a protruding head on the left side, peering down to the 'Pulpit'. I call this the 'Holy Turtle.' He appears to be seeking grub – but is just too high to offer an apple or a piece of lettuce: shame.

Through the Window

The climax of any cathedral is the altar, but in Yordas Cave the pride of place lies elsewhere. Leave the throne and make your way to the opposite wall, to the right of the Map of

Wales. Shine your torch towards the noise and you'll see a curious window at the back of the main chamber, shaped like the top of a blacksmith's anvil. It has been worn smooth by the passing of Brontës, Oldfields and other famous visitors over the years. Step through, and you are in a small chamber with another similar window – a last piece of wrapping paper before the prize. Pop your head through that second window and hold your breath. If you have children with you it's quite safe to lift them up and stand them on the 'window ledge', as the pool is not too deep in normal circumstances, though in exceptional rain it does overflow and flood the cave. I lifted Lucy up here after the cheesy thins, the thundering water drowning out her screams of giant phobia. Even Joe was apprehensive.

This is the Chapter House: the smooth chamber indeed resembling one, with pillars of flowstone stretching up on all sides as far as the eyes can see. Over a well-worn lip in the rock the water leaps in a magnificent cascade of silver spray which fills the senses. It's the kind of place to change the emotions over a few seconds. I have felt a shudder here, and the fall has almost frightened me. I have felt excited as I have waded through in my wellies and let the water fall over my head. I have, within the same visit, just stood and stared for ten, even twenty minutes at this awesome sight. It's quite safe to step into the pool and let the spray catch you, noting a small passage leading out of the pool on the right, capturing the overflow. Step into the passage and a delightful walk through the running water leads back into the main chamber. This 'Choirboy's Walk', as I like to call it, is thrilling for children. Let them do it alone if they don't mind getting a little water over their wellies. If not, leave them with a torch in the Chapter House pool, and there's a lovely little window at mid-point in the passage through which you can gurn at

Silent sentinel: The Ram's Head has gazed down on all who pass below for thousands of years.

them. The passage is a cute little introduction to the complexities of caving, moving from a huge chamber into a narrow canyon.

And So to Bed

The final stopping point is one that is best left until last for a simple reason. It will finally convince the kids that the whole thing about giants is a load of stuff and Yordas.

On seeing the crawl through to the Bedchamber, Joe at once remarked, 'Hey, there's no way a giant could fit through there, Dad.' I tried to tell him that it used to be bigger, and flood debris had filled it over the years, but he wasn't convinced. Then Emily and I tried telling him that Yordas only went to bed in there when he was a kid, and they didn't think of building him a larger bedroom …

To get to the Bedchamber, retrace your steps down the

Great Hall, which will now be fully fathomable as your eyes will have adjusted, and you will see the stream disappearing into the archway we mentioned earlier. It's possible to crawl through here to the Bedchamber if you don't mind getting very wet, but if you look to the left of the archway an inviting little notch between two smooth mud banks leads to an easier crawl. For this, helmets and waterproofs are really important. It's a good introduction to crawling in caves and it's no more than a few metres before the Chamber is reached. As with the aven, the ceiling is high with silvery water drops decorating it, but there is no bed, no carpets and no decent place for a night's sleep. It's also possible to climb up into the chamber on the left, but take care on the right where the chamber drops over a short 'pitch' into the stream passage. Beyond is Yordas' Oven, which is too tight and narrow for the casual visitor, and is not, apparently where the giant cooked his little boys, but where he cremated his victims! Enough said.

Back into daylight, and to finish your visit a wander up into the trees will reveal a dry limestone gorge – Yordas Gill. Clambering over the rocks will reach the point where the stream vanishes into a small 'sink'. A tree trunk is wedged inside to help potholers reach the bottom and eventually the top of the Chapter House waterfall, but don't bother trying to descend. Save that for years to come and the company of experienced cavers. Also keep well away from Yordas Pot itself, further up the gill, where a tree trunk spans an obvious fenced shaft, again leading into the giant's palace.

Yordas Cave is the best introduction to a really 'wild' cave for both adults and children. You don't need to be as cruel as I was, and chances are you'll leave with a vivid picture of some magnificent limestone scenery emblazoned on your mind. But a parting word of advice – a packet of cheesy thins can be just as useful as a pair of waterproof trousers.

Opposites attract: Lovers about to kiss in the canyon passage of Great Douk Cave. *Top right:* The spectacular entrance to Great Douk Cave is many people's first real caving experience.

2. Great Douk Cave:
When the Mites Go Up

Grid Reference: SD 747770

In a Nutshell: One of the finest underground adventures: beginning with an exciting climb up a small waterfall into an impressive cave entrance. For a novice explorer, Great Douk offers the longest danger free cave passage anywhere in the Dales. There are no hidden drops or loose boulders to worry about, and the optional long crawl in water is, luckily, at the very end of the cave. It doesn't interfere with the adventure, but can become a real challenge for those willing to have a go. This trip contains something for everyone. There are cascades, rapids, pools and small chambers, as well as some beautiful formations. Children will love the experience of passing underneath an open pothole as they wander through the cave passage. Great Douk is a day to remember.

Essentials: Helmet mounted caving lamps are essential here, in order to negotiate the climb up the entrance waterfall. These can be hired from Ingleton at a low cost. Waterproofs and wellies are a must of course, and a towel and change of clothing are recommended for each person. Avoid heavy rain and check a reliable forecast before exploring the cave. Expect to get wet feet, even in wellies, but that's part of the fun. As with all stream caves, do not venture in alone: a party of three or four is recommended.

Access: Leave Ingleton on the B2655, heading for Hawes. This road follows the impressive valley of Chapel-le-Dale, and after three miles the Hill Inn is reached on the right hand side. A few yards further on there is a small car park on the left. It is often busy in fine weather, so aim to arrive early. There are also usually a few spaces on the opposite side for smaller vehicles. Great Douk Cave lies in a hollow on the Ingleborough side: a fifteen minute walk from the car park.

Adventure: In April, 1981, I was a humble lad of twelve with a decision ahead of me that would help to change my life. I'll never forget it. I was at Whitehough Camp School near Pendle Hill with a group from school, and we were cleaning the fluff from under our beds for the dreaded daily inspection. Suddenly I was aware of a dark shadow behind me. It was 'Jetbomb' Phillips, our Chemistry Teacher, who fancied himself as a bit of a sergeant major. After labelling the underside of my bed a 'spud plantation' he turned to me with a look of disgust.

'Right then, Oldfield. Is it caving or canoeing tomorrow?'

The fact that, at the time, I could swim 5 metres of 'doggy paddle', largely governed my choice.

'Caving, Sir, I suppose.'

He promptly ticked me off on the list. 'Be outside the barn after breakfast tomorrow for kitting up, Oldfield.'

'Sir.'

'And by the way, Oldfield ..'

'Sir?'

I can still see the look he gave me all these years later.

'How can you tell a *stalactite* from a *stalagmite*?'

'Don't know, Sir.'

There was a peal of raucous laughter behind the curtain. He grabbed at my shoulder.

'Now think about this, Oldfield, and I don't want you to forget it. It's dead easy to remember that *when the mites go up, mi lad ...*'

His timing was perfect.

'Then the tights come down.'

So ended my first lesson in speleology: to a crescendo of applause from the audience, and an exit from the star performer.

Magic Bus

I'd thought caving was the lazy option, and that all caves were like Speedwell Cavern in Derbyshire, with pretty lights and fancy coach parks. Jetbomb clearly had other ideas. My strongest memories are of the bumpy mini bus ride to Ingleton which seemed to go on forever, and of my mate, Kirk, promptly throwing up all over my caving suit on arrival. Next, we were through a hole in the limestone and I recall a queue of 14 kids and 3 staff, with Jetbomb at the helm, crawling on their stomachs in freezing cold water. I had one heck of a miserable time. My battery, or 'acid bottle', as they called it, kept slipping round to my stomach, I could scarcely breathe, and the smell of sick in such a constricted passage was the final torture (Kirk was in front of me, by the way). To cap it all, we all had a number that we had to call out every 5 minutes to make sure we weren't missing. I was number 13. Jetbomb said I deserved it.

A Three Peaks Up and Under

That was my first experience of Great Douk Cave, but I must add that once the shock of the crawl was over, I was mesmerized by the rest of the trip, and it has influenced me to return many times since. What's more, it's quite possible to enjoy a good day out without doing any crawling, so if that's not your idea of fun, you can always go in at the bottom entrance and turn back when your nerves finally crack. Whatever your plan, it definitely makes sense to visit both ends of the cave at some stage as the top entrance, Middle Washfold, is fascinating in its own right. For convenience, however, we'll tackle the easier option first, and consider the complexities of the crawl later on.

Cross the road from the car park on to the Ingleborough side, where the mountain looms up menacingly and is a magnet to the eyes of all walkers and cavers. Go through the gate into a field containing an obvious lime kiln, with impressive views of the U shaped valley of Chapel-le-Dale opening up ahead. Follow the Ingleborough foot traffic over two stiles, noting the boulders scattered around left by the retreating glaciers during the last 'ice age'. At the second stile, a glance up the wall to the left will reveal some obvious deciduous trees partly hidden by a limestone outcrop. Say goodbye here to those heading for the high ground, and turn left for the trees which shelter the huge crater of Great Douk. A step in the surrounding wall leads down to an easy path into the depths, but do take care with children on the scramble down, as it can be slippery and tree roots can trap unwary cavers. As you descend, you will hear the torrent of water resurging from the cave, as yet out of sight, while two points of interest are the boulder-strewn surroundings and an obvious 'hole in the floor', where cavers have been trying for years to detect the further adventures of the Great Douk water, once it departs from the main cave. Keep children well away.

Door to the underworld: Great Douk's upper entrance is through a distinctive limestone pavement at Middle Washfold.

A glimpse down the shaft shows two ladders disappearing into the darkness. The water descending into the cobbled floor here has been dye tested to emerge between Hurtle Pot and Weathercote - about 1 km to the west, but no diver has yet made it through the constricted passages. Keep the fingers crossed, then, and keep the brave souls descending!

Before rushing off to the cave mouth, it's worth considering just how this impressive hole in the ground, with its towering cliffs and shattered rocks, came to be here in the first place. Great Douk is actually aligned on a fault, and movements of the rock strata over many years have caused a once great chamber to collapse, leaving a huge roofless cavern – or more technically a *collapse doline*. The waterfall, which is responsible for the wall of sound around you, will have once flowed into total darkness, and into a much deeper chamber, before it was choked with boulders and rubble.

A Three Peaks Up and Under

However, so impressive and accommodating is this waterfall entrance that all the 'what ifs' of the past can be forgotten. I'm always surprised that the picture postcard shops in Ingleton don't include Great Douk as a subject. An immense bed of Great Scar Limestone rests crudely on the supporting rocks beneath: the full bedding plane between them exposed as an inky black fracture. The stream has hollowed out a joint in this lower layer to form the cave passage, so that it now effectively emerges between two distinct 'cheeks' of rock. The resulting impression is of the petrified mouth of a giant spewing out the stream in an attractive, gushing little force; one that is actually far easier to climb than it looks.

Switch on the lamps then …. And let's go!

From the Bottom Up

The full length of the passage above the fall is just under a kilometre: the last 100m or so being a flat out crawl, so even if you turn back when you reach that point, you can still enjoy the trip both ways. Remember that some cave features that are missed in one direction can easily be seen in others.

Take care on the fall. With children it is best to lift them to the first 'step' in the force, after which they can scramble up and wait in the safety of the passage, though older children should have few problems. The fall is great fun because it wets you through before you start, and prepares you for the soaking ahead. At the top, on the right, a 'sofa' of limestone provides a convenient waiting spot while the other members of the party tackle the climb up.

Before your journey begins you will notice, on the left, an eye hole which is, in fact, an alternative entrance into the system. The inlet here links to Southerscales Pot, but it is passable only to divers. Forget that, then, and proceed carefully up the fine passage. Soon you will reach a small chamber with a high ceiling, and on leaving it the passage once again narrows before an interesting climb up into a small aven on the left is reached. The climb up is fairly easy, and worth it for the fine bird's eye view of the stream passage below. Continuing up the main passage, many large collapse blocks add to the variety of the scene, before daylight is seen ahead, and another of Great Douk's secrets is revealed at Little Douk Pot.

Seen from the surface, this pothole is one of the dullest in the Dales, but from down here it is quite beautiful. Don't rush ahead, but spend some time brushing your face against the hanging gardens of moisture-loving ferns and delicate mosses which add a little luxury to this subterranean world. When I was a naïve youngster on the trip with Jetbomb, I splashed with hurried curiosity below this cave 'window', unable to ask any of the staff what this 'big hole' above me was. I later told my Mum, who wasn't to know any better, that I'd been inside Gaping Gill (the name rang a bell, you see). Wishful thinking indeed!

Greeting the Duchess

A passage leads off to the left of the pot with a climb up, but it has a dangerous drop down into the stream and is best avoided. Instead, leave daylight behind and continue straight ahead, where the pools are just over knee deep in parts. Don't try to avoid filling the wellies. Get it over with now, as there is worse to come. A curious feature nearby is a pretty little bridge of flowstone across the stream passage, which it is necessary to pass beneath. Next there's a feature which cannot be missed. Protruding from the left hand wall is the obvious 'face' of a woman, complete with a fine head of hair, ghostly complexion, and a distinctively pointed nose and chin. Back in 1981, one of our lads christened it 'Maggie

A Three Peaks Up and Under

Let's get wet: The long crawl into Great Douk is absolutely guaranteed to fill your trousers with water.

Thatcher', no doubt very topical at the time, but unless you're a staunch Conservative you might prefer my own 'Lion Duchess', as feline limbs are clearly more discernible than a blue suit (goes well with the Great 'Duke': get it?). When travelling in the opposite direction, the Lion Duchess is easily missed.

Water in the Wellies

Beyond the Duchess, the passage narrows to a splendid tall canyon, and the noise level escalates quite dramatically at the approach to the 'Jacuzzi Rapids'. These I named at the suggestion of my son, Joe, who'd encountered a posh bathroom in his school reading book and finally met his dream with these plunge pools. A series of small cascades drop in steps and are a delight for children. We've often gone back and done them several times, just for the fun of it, but if you don't want to get too wet, here's your chance to practice a little 'bridging'. The canyon is only narrow above the pools, so you can simply wedge yourself into the walls by spreading your arms and legs over the water, and be *as thoroughly boring as it is possible to be.* Get that water over those wellies!

It is always with some reluctance that you will leave the rapids, but as you do so, look up into the high ceiling to spot some remarkable wedged boulders which look poised to fall on your head at any minute. After this, the canyon continues, though less noisily, until a sharp right angled bend is met at an area which I call the 'Silver Wands'. This is approximately Great Douk's half-way point, and the ceiling is worth a careful inspection. It is an exceptionally smooth bedding plane, its surface broken by just a few stalactites, whose tiny droplets of water glisten serenely in the light of your lamp. After a further sharp bend, a different kind of cave formation becomes prominent on the ceiling. This is the delicately soft 'moonmilk', which is a welcome contrast at this point to the walls of bare and scalloped limestone. Continuing, the height of the ceiling increases, and the first of a series of flowstone 'curtains' which I have christened 'The Drapes', are a wonderful sight on either side of the main passage.

Beehives and Bottoms

Further on, there is an 'oxbow' on the left, which marks the former route of the stream before it cut its present course. Children will love clambering through, as it's at a slightly higher level than the streamway. As it rejoins, there's an attractive 'pillar', where a stalactite and stalagmite have merged over many years. After this, things become really exciting, and the flowstone 'curtains' protrude so much that they almost touch each other. A formation on the right looks just like a miniature version of the Beehive in Ingleborough Cave, and it is necessary to duck underneath it, which is thoroughly good fun. Children can enjoy a free comedy show at the Beehive Duck. For them, it's easy, but self-respecting adults, who have waded and bridged with determined dexterity to this point, invariably lose it all here in a few seconds. A quick bend down and the wellies are full, the socks hold enough water to wash up in, and the bottom sports the trademark dark patch, perfectly round, which will later tell the watching world, 'I tried to be a clever clogs in Great Douk and now I've got a soggy bottom to prove it.' You have been warned.

Now you've survived the little experience, (maybe you are getting used to wearing wet underwear for the first time since you were potty training), the remaining features may not seem so appealing, but they are some of the finest in the cave, and make excellent photographic subjects. The way ahead passes another flowstone feature, 'The Wasp's Nest', before meeting the beautiful flowstone 'Curtains', and 'The Claws' on the right, which will be obvious once you see them. There is then an abrupt change in the character of the cave. Ignore an inlet coming in from the left, and keep straight ahead, up an obvious 'step' in the floor which enters a dry passage with the ceiling lowering considerably. A few metres on is the 'Giant's Hand', probably the most memorable single feature in the cave. A grotesquely shaped flowstone formation, the extremities of which resemble the fingers of a mythical beast or monster, its colours show up well on photographs and it is a compulsive halt on the expedition. With a little use of the imagination, the rock immediately opposite takes on the appearance of a dolphin or swordfish. You can have hours of fun fitting your own names to this strange display of cave sculpture. One more intricate example

Easy does it: Tackling the waterfall at the entrance to Great Douk Cave.

is a few metres further on, in a little recess on the right of the passage. Here, just opposite an inlet coming in from the left, is the 'Last Supper', complete with flowstone and calcite figures sitting around a crude table. It is small and likely to be missed by those with blinkers. Can you spot it?

Finally, on the right, an inlet soon leads to a 'sump' which links to Middle Washfold Sink. This is important as it marks the spot to turn back for all but the most adventurous. Looking ahead now, the ceiling is lower and the passage contains gently flowing but very cold water. If you're all up for crawling, then, and are undeterred by such obstacles – read on.

Creepy Crawlies

The passage ahead may seem daunting, but, if this is any comfort, it's only about 28 metres (just over a swimming pool length) to a welcome 'hole in the roof', leading you out of the water to better things and the eventual exit. An inlet immediately on the left is the water finding its way in from the 'wet' entrance at Middle Washfold. Unless you want to inflate your underwear with water, I suggest you practice a 'spider' technique, by bridging your body over it. After that, you can carefully avoid the water in most places by crawling along the ledges at each side. As if to tease us, nature has kindly removed these ledges a few metres further on, to coincide with the deepest, coldest stretch of the entire crawl. Once through that, you've nearly done it. Look ahead for a conspicuous trio of stalactites dangling from the ceiling. When you reach these, you know you can't be far from that hole. The passage seems to be narrowing down even further, but breathe deeply. You've come this far, now. There must be no turning back. Give, as I always do, a whoop of celebration when you spot that elusive hole: the golden key to the journey's end. The first time I found this with the children, we hugged each other as though we'd just conquered Everest!

Stand up carefully and pop your head through the 'manhole' or 'flue' as I call it. Your route now is immediately left, through a very low, but dry passage. You have about 5 minutes to go. After less than 10 metres, a junction is reached following a crawl under a huge slab of limestone. The ceiling is now higher, and movement is thankfully easier. According to trip reports from caving clubs, many cavers have difficulty finding a way out at this point, but it's quite simple. Ignore the right hand branch and once again bear left, into the 'horseshoe', a splendidly curving passage of hands and knees height, which makes me imagine myself as a spider, crawling through a 'u' bend in the plumbing on its way into the bathroom. Once the horseshoe is completed, mass jubilation breaks out. Daylight is seen ahead for the first time since Little Douk Pot, and a very welcome sight it is, too.

Don't allow that daylight to spoil the journey. You still need to find the surface in safety, and remember that sunlight encourages the growth of algae, making the rocks here far slippier than underground. A step up into an obvious exit, worn smooth by a former stream channel, and you are suddenly standing on a gleaming limestone pavement. Be very careful not to get too carried away with the feeling of elation, as the clints of Middle Washfold are invariably slippery. Sit down, relax, and feel on top of the world. You deserve it.

From the Top Down

Middle Washfold Caves are Wainwright's 'enchanted place'. 'I am always loth to leave,' he wrote in his later days (1991). 'I have always found Middle Washfold to be a place of fascinating interest.' No doubt you will, too. You have just emerged from the 'dry' entrance, easily distinguished from the others by an absence of water (of course), and by a quaint 'cap' of weathered limestone which acts as a cosy little canopy over the doorway into Great Douk. The 'wet' entrance is a few metres to the east: hidden behind the sheepfold after which the caves are named. This can be entered, but it is narrow and uncomfortable, and the route through to Great Douk has shingled up. The third entrance, the actual sink itself, is marked by a Rowan tree which makes a lovely foreground object for a photo of Ingleborough, rising beyond. There is an alternative entrance just beyond it which can be entered, and, as Wainwright chuckles 'adults with girths not exceeding 40 inches may confidently insinuate themselves in the narrow fissures.' Knowledge of the entrances here will prevent you from 'going in the wrong

A Three Peaks Up and Under

The Lion Duchess: Half human - half feline, the Lion Duchess is a distinctive feature of the Great Douk stream passage.

hole' if you care to tackle Great Douk from the top down. In addition, Middle Washfold makes a wonderful picnic spot on a summer's day, when caving is not on the agenda, but there is a simple desire for the spiritual peace that the limestone country can provide.

For those then, who wish to follow in the footsteps of the great 'Jetbomb', and go through from the top down, this simple set of instructions can be memorized to help you on your way:

> *Under the canopy,*
> *Into the 'shoe',*
> *Beneath the boulder*
> *Down the 'flue'*
> *And 'well done, you!*

Not quite Shakespeare, but it helps to remember this as you head for Washfold - following the path around the top of Great Douk's main hole, before crossing the pastures to where the limestone provides a welcome break on the moor. (SD747764). Once the 'through trip' has been completed, it will give you confidence to go on and tackle more intricate crawls, but a word of warning is necessary here. Great Douk's waterfall demands great care when going down. The trick is to *face the water*, slowly feeling around for the convenient step at mid-point. When children are involved, come down yourself first, and, having directed them to the step and covered their fall, you can quite easily lift them the remaining couple of metres to safety.

And to show for it all? A few pints of water in the wellies; a stiff back, chapped fingers, wringing out of sodden socks and underwear, and, I dare say, shivering behind some wind swept boulder as you peel off the filthy clothes, muttering to yourself that there's no way you'll ever be so mad again. But, oh, *what memories*! Surely it has all been worth it?

Door to beauty: The entrance to Browgill Cave where curtains of limestone appear
to have been drawn back to let the light stream in. *Top right*: Massive fallen blocks
litter the floor and make a chaotic scene inside the wild ravine of Ling Gill.

3. Old Ing and Browgill Caves: Rompin' Under Ribblesdale

Grid Reference: SD801768 (starting point at High Birkwith). A 2.5 mile (4km) adventure (not including the caving).

In a Nutshell: A visit to a very special area of Upper Ribblesdale, and two contrasting, but exciting, cave systems. Old Ing is just about as wet as a novice cave can get, with plenty of pools and cascades making for great fun, while Browgill is a little more intricate with climbs, squeezes, crawls, and a noisy and unforgettable underground waterfall. There's a chance to absorb the limestone scenery between the two caves, with miniature gorges and natural bridges to enjoy. All in all, if you are well prepared, it should be a 'rompin' good time.

Essentials: These caves are a little more challenging than most covered in this book, and if the adventures described are to be undertaken, helmets, lamps and full waterproofs are essential. A change of clothing is a must, and wellies should have good grips and a firm fit. Plenty of food and warm drinks will be welcome as there is no doubting that you *will* get very wet indeed. A SETTLED WEATHER FORECAST is paramount as both caves can flood rapidly. Old Ing as far as described is unsuitable for children due to deep pools but they can enjoy the first 100 metres at the cost of wet feet. Children at Browgill's entrance will need careful supervision on the vertical ribs of sharp rock. If already used to caving, and with correct supervision, they will enjoy the challenge of reaching the waterfall chamber.

Access: Approaching Horton-in-Ribblesdale from the south - drive past the main car park on the left. Where the road turns a sharp right angle over the River Ribble, take a turning on the right onto a lane just before the bridge (SD 807727). The lane is narrow, but well surfaced and with passing places. Continue along this lane for 4 km (2.5 miles), passing over a ford before the hamlet of Newhouses, and taking care on a tricky cattle grid which warns that you must 'cross at your own risk'. High Birkwith is a cluster of farm dwellings at the termination of the lane. Beyond the buildings is a gate on the right leading to a rough track, with a small conifer wood to the left. Park on the grassy verges on the right of this track, but do not block access for farm vehicles, and take care to shut and fasten the gate behind you.

Adventure: High Birkwith is such a perfect little spot. The farmsteads have a 'time stood still' atmosphere and there is plenty of bird life. Pheasants scurry in and out of the conifers while herons soar over the tree tops on their way to the tarn in the valley below. Before donning the helmets and wellies, take in the fine view across Ribblesdale to Simon Fell and Park Fell, the satellites of Ingleborough. Below them, an isolated clump of trees marks the position of Alum Pot, perhaps the most impressive pot hole in the country, with the

Old Ing and Browgill Caves: Rompin' Under Ribblesdale

Gothic impression: Fangs of limestone huddle over the entrance passage to Browgill Cave like a coven of witches.

famous Long Churn Caves just above. Eventually, this seemingly bleak and unfriendly landscape becomes a wonderland to the better acquainted, with both sides of the dale containing a treasure trove of exciting landscape features. Wainwright ventured to declare Upper Ribblesdale as being among his favourite places on earth. For any true lover of wild places, it is difficult to disagree.

Another advantage of High Birkwith is that there are no passing cars to whip past as you change into your caving gear, and you can take all the time in the world: lovely! I always carry a snack and drink up to Old Ing in a small tackle bag, and return to the car for a leisurely lunch on the rocks nearby, before going on to Browgill. It is a little more sheltered down here from the wind, and sometimes I change into a clean pair of socks at the car as it can be awful walking with so much water squelching in the wellies.

Leave the car and walk up the rough lane ahead, with the conifer plantation on your left and a hidden gorge to your right, having no access, which carries the water from Birkwith Cave down to the River Ribble. Ignore the finger post on the left for 'Nether Lodge' as this is the route to Browgill. Instead, continue ahead towards Old Ing Farm until a wall is met on the right, along which the Ribble Way runs towards Horton in Ribblesdale. Take this path alongside the wall until it crosses a stile and passes along the top of the noisy entrance to Birkwith Cave, hidden in the small gorge to your right. At this point (SD804768) the paths fork. Ignore the Ribble Way straight ahead, and instead take the rocky path to the left, worn smooth by generations of eager cavers and divers. The landscape now looks unpromising, and the names of its features even more so. To the right is Rough Hill, and rising gently to the left with a wall running over its flank is the pitifully named Dismal Hill. Couldn't somebody hassle the Ordnance Survey with a petition to have this name changed? Maybe that could be an ambitious project for my retirement.

A Dismal Shudder

Old Ing Cave lies between these two hills and just to the left of the path, so it's quite easy to locate. The first caves on the left, before the path swings round to the east, are the Dismal Hill Caves themselves. Who would want to enter these with a name like that? There are plenty of reeds and rushes about. Why not 'Windrush Cave'? *Very* romantic, Stephen! Perhaps the name is a fortunate deterrent, for though the caves are easy to enter, the route drops down two nasty climbs needing ropes, and the flood risk is also very high: far better to shudder and continue. A short distance (200 metres) further on, the much friendlier Old Ing Cave is located in a shakehole on the left and is identified by its easy walk-in entrance; no other cave in the vicinity having this feature. (SD807768) The first time I visited Old Ing, I was struck by the lack of water at the entrance, but appearances deceive, as you will soon discover. Check that sky for one last time, then. No approaching thunder clouds? Good. A trip to the 'sump' and back will take about an hour, so judge the sky with this in mind. You can never be too careful in this game.

The cave has three distinct sections. The first, which is suitable for accompanied children, runs for 158 metres to a sharp right hand bend, where another stream, Rough Hill inlet, enters on the left. From then on, in the middle section, things become very wet for about 170 metres to a small chamber, and finally a tall rift passage heads to the sump, which can only be passed by divers. Be careful on the slippery path down into the cave, which immediately opens up into a wide passage, with the stream entering on the left from a bedding plane. The first notable feature is a fine natural archway with an oxbow passage to its left, which children will enjoy. The passage then continues with a shelf on the left along which the timid may scramble to avoid the water. Then, as the route swings left, there is a clamber over boulders which mark a former rockfall, and another bridge is seen ahead spanning the first of many pools. This is the point where the wellies generally fill with water and it is perhaps wise to get that over with now, for there is worse to come. Following another pool, deeper than the first, are two huge slabs of rock leaning precariously over the passage and it is necessary to pass underneath them. The bottom then joins the feet in the 'saturation society', and prepares for the adventure ahead. The canyon widens considerably and the

Danger sign: Browgill Cave floods rapidly and should only ever be entered during settled weather.

sound of rushing water indicates a small cascade, before a sharp bend to the right concludes this first easy section. *Children should not be taken beyond this point unless they are fully equipped and accompanied by experienced cavers.* Intrepid adults may continue …

'Take My Breath Away'

Now the pulse quickens and excitement builds. At the sharp bend you will see Rough Hill inlet increasing the volume of water in the cave, and the sound ahead now is of watery turmoil. There are some lovely 'curtains' of flowstone as the passage continues for a few metres before the stream cascades into 'Breathtaker Pool'. A rope has been rigged on the left wall and the trick is to catch hold of it, feel around with your left foot for a rib of rock at the near edge of the pool, before striding across and finding another rib with your right foot.

In a way, it is similar to Double Shuffle Pool in Long Churn Cave, except that here the water is moving, and in my opinion is even colder. For most adults the crossing of 'Breathtaker' is straightforward enough, but I'll never forget my first time. Only when the water was above delicate parts did my breath fully disappear, and, having experienced it, I can assure you that plunging into the sea at Morecambe on a grey December morning is far easier. In some places below the cascade the water must be over 5 feet (1.5 metres) deep, so be prepared if you let go the rope!

Slump at the Sump

Continuing, and knowing you have to come back through the 'Breathtaker', can be a little discomforting, but there is nothing worse as the passage proceeds, and in fact it becomes great fun once you are already soaking. A series of rocky ribs in the floor separate more deep but very narrow pools, which are easy to stride across, before the cave becomes even more interesting. Up on the left is a dry oxbow passage that is a tricky climb up, but is easy to descend on the return journey, so ignore it for now. The oxbow conveniently by-passes the main route ahead, which is a waist-deep, curving canal leading into a small chamber, beyond which the oxbow reconnects. This canal is very cold, but freezing of delicate bits can be avoided, luckily, by spreading the legs out onto shelves in the shallower water at each side. Once in the chamber, floored by a shallow pool, the second and most difficult stage of the journey is complete. The final stage, for about 85 metres, is an impressive tall rift passage in shallow water which eventually leads to a sinister looking deep 'sump' pool, where the water foams and bubbles menacingly, as if enticing you onwards. Experienced divers can actually continue through to more passages here, but it is absolutely out of bounds even for most cavers, so feel proud on reaching the sump, and head back to daylight. A return journey is always easier when you are familiar with its features, but do try by-passing the canal by using the oxbow. The drop back into the canal is good fun, and the water just over knee deep. Another soaking won't make any difference, will it?

The Drastic Fantastic

Once daylight is reached, return to the car with squelchy wellies to bemused stares from any walkers nearby. If time permits, a visit to Birkwith Cave's entrance is very rewarding. Follow the sound of rushing water to the head of the gorge passed on the outward journey, and a stile gives access to a slippery path down to the cave entrance. Take great care on the path, as at mid-point there is an exposed drop into the river below, and children will need careful support. The low, dark entrance has a beauty of its own, and makes a perfect photograph – the water from Old Ing and Dismal Hill emerging in a scene of undoubted beauty. Anyone considering entering should bear in mind the 'no nonsense' advice given in *Northern Caves*. *'Warning,'* it says, *'floods drastically: novices liable to be flushed out!'* These guys have a wonderful way with words.

Food is the priority now, and the best place to put fuel in the tank is a two minute walk from the car, a short distance along the path signposted for 'Nether Lodge', where an old ash watches over a trickling stream, and farmy fragrances fill the senses in an invigorating way. I once spent twenty minutes here trying my best to get out of a pair of wellies, which had sucked to my feet with the Old Ing water inside. As desperation was reached, one boot suddenly gave way with a sickening rush of brown liquid that promptly swamped my remaining sandwiches and all but ruined a good day out. If you are a budding lunchtime welly-emptier then take my advice and keep the butties in the rucksack.

It's All Down to the Maker

Having 'eaten for England', as they say in Yorkshire, continue along the Ribble Way ahead, crossing a stile where several walls meet into another delightful field, where the path runs alongside a wall on the left. In a few minutes the sound of water beckons, from where the path will be seen to cross an attractive limestone gorge, the water tumbling through a square window underneath. This is God's Bridge, and it makes an equally suitable lunch spot. It is also great fun to scramble down the cascades into the small cavern which soon emerges into daylight. By ignoring the window out to the surface on the right and following the water to the left, it is possible to emerge and then rejoin the cave at the dry entrance, thus completing a fun figure of eight circuit. Children will love God's Bridge, but remember that the rocks here are exposed to light and so are far more slippery than underground. There are also some steep drops in the river bed beyond the bridge, so careful supervision is important.

Browgill Cave, our next target, lies upstream at the head of the limestone gorge, but do not cross the ladder stile to reach it. Instead, leave the path and follow the wall just before God's Bridge to the right, which runs alongside the gorge for 200 metres. A lovely old lime kiln will be seen decorating the opposite bank, but all thoughts then shift to the magnificent cave entrance, revealed at the last minute beyond a cluster of delicate small trees, the walls of the gorge adorned with ferns and ivy. I consider Browgill to be the most beautiful cave entrance in the Dales, and its interior certainly as thrilling as anywhere a novice is capable of reaching. The water resurging here last saw daylight as it dropped down the shaft of Dry Lathe Cave, better known as Calf Holes, about 500 metres to the south east, though the underground flow is much further due to the meandering of the stream-way. Calf Holes – well worth a visit – is impressive, but cannot be descended by casual visitors and requires rope or ladder techniques. It is much more satisfying to enter here and progress as far as the experience and nerves allow. A trip to the underground waterfall will certainly be enough to thrill most people.

Closing the Curtains

Wade in the shallow water keeping to the right bank of the stream where there is a ledge for support, then pass through the easy pools at the entrance. The view back out is stunning, with the curtain-like swathes of jagged rock framing a perfect picture of trees and shrubs reflected in silvery light on the stream's surface. The impression is of peering through the porch of a vast cathedral, and as progress is made, so the curtains seem to close and the aperture becomes the window of a more humble place of worship. It is always difficult to leave this scene, but comforting to know that it will be there to greet you on the way out.

Browgill's floor needs special care due to the sharp 'ribs' of rock that have been formed by water dripping though the shallow ceiling. The water rushes through these ribs and at times it is necessary to wedge the feet in narrow crevasses. As the light diminishes, a distinct shelf on the left makes a convenient escape from the water. It is an easy hands and knees crawl, until finally a shine of the lamp ahead discloses what appears to be a low crawl into nowhere. Don't be put off. This section is only very short, and as far as crawls go it's quite a luxury, being largely dry and free from sharp ridges. In no more than two minutes of crawling, with the

Old Ing and Browgill Caves: Rompin' Under Ribblesdale

Calf holes: This is where the stream sinks into the limestone, before making its way through to Browgill Cave.

stream on your right, a walking passage is again reached by passing underneath a flowstone curtain. Glance back at this feature as you emerge into the passage beyond. The 'curtain' resembles the portcullis of a castle and it is easily remembered as the signal for the crawl to begin when returning. There is little fear of getting lost in Browgill.

All thoughts now switch to the magnificent passage ahead. This is in effect a huge oxbow and was the former route of the stream before it found its present course. It rises to over 10 metres (30 feet) in height, and I call it 'The Nave'. The ceiling is unusually level, and massive blocks litter the floor. The first of these requires a careful scramble, and the floor between contains nasty cracks and crevasses in parts, so do take care. Excitement mounts as the passage closes in. At first, it would have been possible to drive a bus through it, but it soon narrows to a squeeze. The main excitement, however, is the almost sinister rumble of water ahead, seemingly vibrating the narrow walls of The Nave as it begins to approach the Waterfall Chamber. The walls now are worn beautifully smooth like marble. The temptation is to rush ahead, but suddenly the attention is captured by an oddity in the surroundings. Dangling invitingly down a natural 'staircase' to the left is a knotted rope marking the climb up to the top of the waterfall where an ingenious little 'banister' of rock prevents a fall to the right. The climb is not an easy one for small people, and you must remember that coming back down is even trickier. It leads to the stream above the fall, and later, via a contortion known as 'The Sausage Machine' – through a series of passages to Calf Holes. Only the fit and agile should attempt the climb, and it is best to enjoy what you have seen so far and return with happy memories. Many caving clubs use Calf Holes as their first novice trip, but remember that all beginners are accompanied by experts, and there is a big difference between an expert and an Oldfield.

The Dungeon Master

The climax of your trip will make up for any feeling of incompetence. The underground waterfall in Browgill is probably the finest that a novice can reach in the Dales without any special equipment. There is a sense of achievement on reaching it. Most people *wouldn't dare*, you will say to yourself. A special memory will be yours to keep, and usually yours only, for the fall is an awkward little beggar to photograph, the chamber being too large and the spray too forceful for the average camera. A word of warning is, however, essential. Just beyond the Staircase, before the passage descends into the chamber itself, is a nasty drop on the right which I call the 'Dungeon'. Anybody falling in would need Cave Rescue to pull them out, and that is no joking matter. I often wonder how many people must have fallen down here as they rushed through to the waterfall. A good way to deal with the drop is to provide a human shield to it so other members of the party can pass in safety. The Dungeon is underneath the right hand wall, and it would be far easier for children to fall in than adults. The trick is for the tallest member to wedge his back into the wall just above the drop, and to spread out his legs to cover all the gaps. I have found this 'human star' to be a handy improvisation when conducting people across.

The final obstacles to the waterfall are a series of boulders descending into the chamber. One sloping block on the left provides a comfortable slide down, and then you can relax and take in the quite magnificent spectacle. The cascade plunges in an aggressive tumult to the chamber floor, from a lip of rock about 6 metres (20 feet) above. It is not so much the height as the sheer volume of water that once again takes the breath away, and also the knowledge that, in the heaviest rain, the chamber floods completely and overflows along the Nave itself. Comforting thought, isn't it?

All that remains now is a safe return to the entrance, taking great care at the dungeon, and watching out for the portcullis to signal the crawl out. Before leaving, I always like to pause on a welcome little sofa of rock beneath the staircase climb. Strange it is how we're all creatures of habit. Out comes the flask of coffee from my trusty little tackle bag, and so I sip in contentment, smoothing my fingers over the polished walls, and listening to the eternal rumbling of the industrious little river, weaving its magic in the darkness.

In Awe of the Daw
High Birkwith merits several visits – and 'surface' cave exploration can be every bit as enjoyable as a trip to the

underworld. From Birkwith Cave (SD804769), the Ribble Way can be followed southwards to meet the Pennine Way at Sell Gill Holes. The path here occupies a natural bridge spanning a dry entrance to the west with another, swallowing Sell Gill Beck to the east as it meets the Great Scar Limestone. These caves are very popular with intermediate explorers practising ladder or SRT techniques as they are easy to access, roomy, and relatively short. For surface explorers, they are a place to linger – taking in the expansive views, watching descending cavers, or experiencing one of the best examples of an active stream rushing off the Yoredales and vanishing into the limestone.

Return to High Birkwith can be made along the Pennine Way, passing two contrasting potholes, both meriting a place on the Ordnance Survey map. Jackdaw Hole, in a clump of mature trees to the left of the path, makes up for in width what it lacks in depth – being an animal trap befitting of its cunning name. A precarious tree at the western side offers a view down into the 'pit', resembling the lair of a mythical beast with boulders, bones and various rusting metal objects littering its floor. It's easy to conjure up visions of cackling black birds greedily pecking away at whatever is lured into the confines of this formidable opening. Continuing northwards from the hole, a wall comes down to meet the Pennine Way on the right, beyond which we encounter a very different pothole. Penyghent Long Churn is a wicked, banana-shaped rift swallowing a stream at its eastern end, and being narrow enough to jump across at the west corner. This is a classic limestone feature, presumably younger than Jackdaw Hole, and falling to a depth of 90 feet (30 metres), with a notorious reputation for serious flooding. Couches of heather and ferns help to mask the severity, but keep children and dogs well away from this one. At the northern end of the same enclosure are the entrances to Red Moss Pot, for cavers only – before a diversion (SD811762) is made alongside a wall on the left and back to Birkwith.

Linger On

And so to the final temptress: and the greatest of them all. Following the path northwards about a mile from Old Ing, an attractive pack-horse bridge spans the beck at the head of Ling Gill: a place of untamed beauty – even savagery; displaying a wildness that makes 'Wuthering Heights' in the novel seem tame in comparison. Here the waters of Cam Beck drop into a formidable gorge, with towering cliffs, hundreds of feet high and largely obscured by trees. In the hands of Natural England as a nature reserve – there are no paths – nor are there ever likely to be. Access can be gained by permission but the route through is an assault course of massive boulders, fallen trees and deep pools. At one point the only way on is actually through a hole in a limestone boulder! Waterfalls and small caves are in plenty – and this is the kind of place you take a risk to visit – but which will remain implanted in your memory for a lifetime. Only swashbuckling adventurers with steady feet and the agility of a mountain goat should seek permission – and fine weather is essential – for the gorge has no way out in flood conditions – responding aggressively to intruders. Each and every step in Ling Gill has to be planned and observed as if future existence depends on it, but the scenes that unfold are magnificent.

All done, then? I think you can agree we've had a 'rompin' good time – and I hope this exploration has whetted your appetite for more adventures in this lovely part of the world.

Gorgeous grotto: Stalactites and flowstone in the passages of Lower Long Churn Cave. *Top right*: The top entrance to Upper Long Churn Cave, leading to the water chute into Doctor Bannister's Handbasin.

4. Alum Pot and the Long Churn Caves: An Appointment with Dr Bannister

Grid Reference: SD783757 (parking spot at Alum Pot Lane, Selside) about 1 mile (1.5km) from the caves.

In a Nutshell: Fabulous fun in the classic 'novice' caves of the Dales, and a chance to see at close hand the most spectacular pothole shaft in the UK. After admiring Alum Pot, the exciting stream passage of Upper Long Churn is followed up to 'Dr Bannister's Handbasin', a superb underground pool and waterfall. There's an optional trip through 'Baptistry Crawl' via the 'Font' – and then a chance to test your nerves at 'Double Shuffle Pool', barring the way to the famous 'Cheese Press.' There's not a dull moment from start to finish!

Essentials: The Long Churn Caves require helmets, lamps, suits and wellies, all of which can be hired from Ingleton. Take a towel and full change of clothing for each person, and expect to get very wet. Food and drink should be in plentiful supply. Choose a period of settled, dry weather as the caves carry a significant flood risk. The area around the caves is exposed moorland and can be bitterly cold for wet cavers in winter, so pick a spring or summer Day with no thunderstorm risk. Upper Long Churn is suitable for supervised junior-aged children provided they are fully equipped.

Access: Selside is a small hamlet on the B6479 between Horton-in-Ribblesdale and Ribblehead. From the south, drive through the hamlet and turn immediately left (SD783757) onto a stony lane, tucking your car in near the wall on the left side. You may need to drive some distance up the lane as this is a busy spot, so take great care as there are sharp rocks that don't care for vehicles. It is always best to arrive as early as possible. Please heed the warning signs about not leaving valuables on show. As Alum Pot and the caves are on private land, a small charge (50p per person) is payable at Selside Farm, reached by exiting the lane back onto the road and turning right towards Selside. The farm is the first building on the left. Take great care as there are blind bends on the road.

Adventure: *'It is, without doubt, the most terrific natural opening in the ground that is known in Britain.'*

So stated Harry Speight in *The Craven and North-West Yorkshire Highlands* (1892) when describing Alum Pot, Ribblesdale's most awe-inspiring limestone feature, and with justification – for even the most intrepid and experienced outdoor adventurers draw breath when gazing into this monster. Here is the piece-de-resistance of all potholes – exposed appallingly for all to see, and with little imagination needed to confront the obvious: step over the safety of its surrounding wall and you are risking your life. A slip – and it's all over.

Dramatic as this is, it is comforting to know that the

surrounding caves are some of the friendliest in the Dales, visited by countless school parties and outdoor education groups, their mini-buses usually taking up the best parking spots on the lane. The Long Churns are Britain's most popular 'wild' caves, but – and a **word of warning** here - like the humans who explore them, their moods vary. In settled weather they are a delight to splash through, especially when the sun is beating down outside, but in rain they can be, and have been, lethal. Much is made of caving accidents but remember that more are recorded from the Long Churns simply because of their popularity – just as there are more accidents on the M6 than the M90. *Never* enter these caves in rain, and especially not when there is a risk of thunderstorms. Choose a fine, settled day and you and your family can have some of the best outdoor fun there is to be found in England. These caves are wonderful and remain, despite the ever-increasing visitors, visually stunning.

Having called at the farm, proceed up the lane until a stile is reached, with a sign reminding you that you should have paid at this point. Ignore the route to the left, heading for Sulber Nick, and continue ahead towards a distinctive plantation of pines, isolated on the plateau above. The trees mark the position of the pot, but no-one lost in the mist could ever wander into it anyway as there is a high limestone wall surrounding the hole. If anything, the trees add to the sinister prospect of what lies beneath. As the pot looms closer, a notable dry limestone valley opens up on the right, with evidence of abandoned waterfalls. This, it is believed, was formed at the end of the last glaciation by meltwater when the caves and pot were plugged by ice. Alum Pot is one of the oldest shafts in Yorkshire, initially formed some 600,000 years ago and predating both the Anglian and Devensian ice ages. When the limestone was first exposed by erosion and earlier glaciations, water rushing onto it from the non-porous Yoredale rocks met a major joint of weakness, very slowly beginning to carve out the chasm we see today. Clearly, a massive waterfall once did most of the work, but later glaciations exposed more and more of the limestone pavements to the west, so that the water eventually found its new route through the Long Churn Caves. Only a modest fall now makes its way down the pothole, except in flood conditions.

Once the surrounding wall is reached, this waterfall can be heard cascading into the pot at the southern end. The stream seems gentle and carefree before the plunge, unaware of the fate that awaits it, and a wire fence wisely prevents sheep and thirsty dogs from following it into the bowels of the earth. Albert Mitchell (1912-1985), founder of the Craven Pothole Club, went this way in October 1985 when it was his wish to have his ashes scattered into the stream. An amazing fact about Alum Pot is that the water, instead of resurging in the dale below, actually appears again over a mile away at a deep and murky pool known as 'Turn Dub,' (SD797749) having passed *underneath* the River Ribble! Albert, a greatly respected man, clearly went where no caver had ever been before.

Hell's Bells

Children and dogs should here be kept, as Wainwright often warned, 'under lock and key', but there are always adults who wish to see the pot in detail and frighten themselves silly. The best view from the path is along the axis of the shaft from the southern end, close to the fall. Speight's 'terrific' hole is 130 feet long, 40 feet wide and drops to over 290 feet at the deepest point: not something to be messed with. For this reason, the decaying ladder stiles crossing the wall have not been repaired. The famous jackdaw's-eye view, plumb-line straight down the shaft, is obtained from an ash tree rooted into a lip of limestone and standing precariously on the very edge of the abyss. Cavers use it as a belay point for the main descent of the pot, but they are roped up and experienced. Lesser mortals can, *at their own risk*, skirt the outside wall in a clockwise direction to the second ladder stile, where the wall can be crossed to a grassy terrace on the north side, a reasonably safe distance from the edge and offering great opportunities for the camera. Continuing around the perimeter, the ledge gets narrower and rockier, with a tangle of tree roots leading to the little ash tree itself. Be very careful not to dislodge loose stones and never throw objects down the shaft. In July 1936, a Leeds school teacher, Miss Mabel Binks, became the pot's first tragic fatality when she was hit by a boulder falling from above. Whether the rock was in fact dislodged deliberately was never ascertained.

Only those with steady feet, confidence and a great head for heights should proceed to the tree, clutching the trunk for a view to rival any in Great Britain. A hundred feet down, the shaft narrows to an evil-looking black gash encircled by a wide ledge, across which 'The Bridge', a massive slab of moss-covered limestone, has fallen and wedged itself at an angle. In summer, views are shaded by rich vegetation with the The Bridge only just discernible, but winter reveals all, and the column of water encrusted with icicles and frost can be magical. A dark shadow in the north wall indicates where cavers usually appear part way down the hole, having avoided a straight descent by coming through the Long Churn Caves. Their route, down the underground 'Dolly Tubs' pitch, requires a ladder or rope, and follows an abandoned passage into the pot, as most of the water now makes its way in through a horrendous series

A Three Peaks Up and Under

Amazing sight: The magnificent stream passage in Upper Long Churn.

of drops inside Diccan Pot, the innocent-looking entrance to which lies in a field to the north-west. We'll be heading that way later.

Three Men in a Tub

John Birkbeck (1817-1890) a Settle banker, and his best buddy, William Metcalfe, of Weathercote, were the first to attempt the route in through the Long Churns in 1847, carrying, according to Boyd-Dawkins: 'nothing other than ropes, planks, a turn-tree and a fire escape belt.' Cold and increasing water levels prevented them reaching the bottom, but they returned a year later, this time straight down the main shaft, using a windlass supported on two baulks of timber, from which a shielded bucket was suspended. The unpredictable weather again hampered progress, and it was not until 1870 that the inseparable duo, Britain's first real potholers, accompanied Professor Boyd- Dawkins and a group of ladies to the very bottom. Navies working on the Ribblehead viaduct placed a massive gantry across the shaft, and the group were lowercd in pairs, again in a shielded bucket, with guide ropes to prevent the bucket from tipping them out on the way down! Struggling and soaked to the skin, the group made their way to the final sump pool, where the water vanishes underground before its journey under the Ribble.

My first descent several years ago was much less eccentric, but equally dramatic. As last but one down of a group of cavers, my rope became entangled on the Dolly Tubs pitch and I spent seemingly forever getting down the 40 foot drop. Eventually unclipping myself, I realized the others had already gone ahead down the 'Greasy Slab' pitch leading on towards 'The Bridge.' I found myself wandering through the arched 'window' completely alone, onto a ledge half way down Alum Pot – with the sun streaming down the shaft forming a rainbow in the spray and a massive cloud of steam issuing out of the depths around me. The horrors of 'The Bridge' and the final descent had yet to come, but that initial walk out into the cauldron of light, spray and sound was something that will never leave me. Albert Mitchell had the right idea when he chose his resting place.

Having survived, follow the path clockwise around the wall on the outside of the pot, and a path strikes up the field to the north-west, heading for some obvious enclosures. The first cave entrance, swallowing the stream down on the right, should be seriously avoided. This is Diccan Pot, previously mentioned, the present main route for most of the water into Alum – and a place of terror for the early pioneers who attempted it. Many have been the rescues from here. Just inside, past a pool, is a 40 metre crawl to Lower Long Churn, but this is too tight for the average beginner, and Diccan is far better viewed from outside. Beyond the pools are a series of massive drops into the lower reaches of Alum Pot under the full force of the water – so daunting that the pot wasn't 'conquered' until 1932, by members of the Gritstone Club. The Long Churns themselves lie in the enclosure above and there are three obvious entrances. The first is a gaping hole formed by collapse of the now abandoned passage, and following a short dry section it leads downstream towards the Dolly Tubs pitch and Alum Pot. The second, beside a thorn bush, is the upstream entrance to Upper Long Churn – the friendliest of all; and finally, over the fence to its right is the narrow exit from Wilson's Cave, emitting a stream over boulders and looking anything but inviting. On a summer's day this cave is great fun. Its entrance lies on the pavements above and, after dropping down a pair of underground waterfalls a wonderful limestone bridge is reached, spanning a small chamber. The cave then lowers and deepens, soaking all parts of the anatomy until emerging from that nasty looking exit. 'Wilson' – whoever he was, clearly had no problems with hydrophobia!

Appointment Looming

'Doctor Bannister's' is on every novice caver's agenda from this point on, and is reached in twenty minutes or so by taking the safe looking thorn-bush 'doorway' into the limestone. Lights on, from this point, folks! This is Upper Long Churn, and at first the 'doctor's corridor' is warm and dry, the stream having long-since taken a new route, soon to be obvious. Be really careful on entering as there is a sinister hole down on the left; in effect a pothole beneath a cave, and it is wise to keep to the right. The stooping passage can be awful on the back at first, but it gradually heightens to walking size, where the stream is at last met, scurrying off down its 'new' route into Lower Long Churn along 'Loop Passage'. We'll see where it goes later. Our concern now is to follow this delightful water upstream. It is usually not more than ankle deep until meeting a series of pools, and it is worth getting wet feet at the very least to experience this classic cave. Some lovely golden gour pools are passed at shoulder height on the right, before a large rock formation protrudes over the passage looking, to my children at least, like a pizza – though mention has been made of a swimming flatfish. In any case, this indicates a passage turning off to the left, 'Cross passage' or the 'Baptistry Crawl.' It is hands and knees crawling and pops out 91 metres away in Lower Long Churn. Halfway along is the 'font' itself, where you have to duck below a stalactite into a pool for a full-bodied soaking. The idea is that you rename yourself for the rest of the adventure as you plunge in. Last time I tried it, the water was like anesthetic to my lower half and what I muttered at my 'baptism' isn't printable!

That Sinking Feeling
Continuing along the main stream-way, an oxbow, or abandoned stream passage, is passed on the right and children will enjoy the by-pass, linking with the main stream further on. There is then a lovely pedestal of limestone splitting the entire passage in two where the stream has carved a route either side. A further optional oxbow is reached on the right and this one is at a higher level, so a climb up is necessary. It marks a former flow level of the cave and shows the amount of erosion that has taken place at least since the latter period of the ice age. The oxbow reconnects at a small chamber, and then the fun really begins. As if testing the willpower bit by bit, the cave presents a series of pools and cascades for the intrepid souls amongst us. The

first, knee deep, will be over the wellies – the second will refresh those parts the other pools can't reach. Enough said! The fun is increased by watching first-timers, up to the waist and in a state of shock, realizing they still have to climb up a cascade to escape the on-setting hypothermia. If, like me, you can't resist adding fuel to the fire, just remind them gently that they must come out of the cave the same way they went in. It's always a classic, that one.

The third pool, the 'water chute,' is peanuts when you're already soaking, and the ceiling becomes higher, with Milner's Inlet, a small passage, leading off on the left. A link to November Hole, a horrible flat-out wallow through a muddy canal, can be seen on the right, and then stooping is once again necessary. The sound of rumbling water intensifies with every step, and the heart quickens. The passage widens out at last into a lofty pool chamber, Dr Bannister's Hand-basin, with a 4 metre waterfall roaring into the void. Fine misty spray particles at once cloud the caving light. The cascade demands attention, and at first the full extent of the pool beneath it is not immediately obvious. At most it is five feet deep, and a surrounding undercut, where flood conditions have been further eroding the bedding plane, offers shelter from the spray and an exciting underground picnic spot. The 'doctor's waiting room' is what I call it. The top entrance to the cave lies just above the fall, and in sunny weather daylight can be glimpsed to prove it.

Doctor Who?
In normal conditions the climb up the waterfall is, for tall people like me, easier than it looks. First, wade into the thigh-deep water, and the trick is to bridge the cascade with your knees and wedge your bottom into the right hand side of the chute. Got that? Easy, isn't it? Then alternate shuffling with

bottom and feet will soon have you at the top, where care is needed as sudden light can make the rock slippery underfoot. Coming down the fall into Dr Bannister's is tricky without a rope, and it is best to head back over the moor to the original entrance. Many a coccyx has been injured by those plunging carelessly into the pool. Those not wishing to impress better-halves or youngsters should have the common sense to return down the passage for a second soaking in the pools. By now, you will probably be beyond caring! Don't forget, however, that nasty little slot on the right just before you emerge into daylight.

No-one knows who Dr Bannister was, when he lived, or why he had any connection with Long Churn Cave. In his *Tour to the Caves*, as far back as 1780, the Reverend Hutton mentions 'a round pool of pellucid water from three to twelve feet deep known as Dr Bannister's Handbasin.' The depth may be exaggerated, but there is little doubt from the writing that, even then, the origin of the doctor was beyond living memory. And why a 'handbasin'- when there is enough water here for a swimming pool? Was Dr Bannister a giant of local legend perhaps? Was he a local 'witch doctor' with compulsive hand-washing tendencies or, and this seems a more likely possibility – could he possibly have been the first known cave explorer in Yorkshire? It is an intriguing question that will never be answered.

Do the Double Shuffle

To round off the day, a short venture into Lower Long Churn is irresistible, but only in settled weather. Having emerged at the 'dry' section, take a breather before stooping into the low passage in front, where the roar of the underground stream can be a little scary after few seconds in the outside world. A fine cascade is seen coming in from the right – the same water that we last saw taking the 'loop passage' just inside Upper

A Three Peaks Up and Under

Long Churn. The passage follows the stream to the left through a few knee-deep pools, until the water does its disappearing act yet again – turning off to daylight in a few metres before its horrendous tumble through Diccan Pot. Don't follow it out to daylight, but instead take the now abandoned 'dry' passage up on the right, admiring the many small stalactites and flowstone formations. All is relaxed – a doddle, even, for a few glorious moments until nature bars the way with the notorious 'Double Shuffle Pool'.

At first this patch of dark water, merely ten feet across, looks nothing – especially after a trip to Dr Bannister's, but the approach, from a few feet above, is very awkward. It is great fun for those who don't mind a soaking – and by this I mean above head height for most people – but terrifying for the faint hearted, and the termination of the journey for most beginners. You can, however, have great fun watching the many visiting parties trying to cross it – for nature has provided, as if sympathetic to cavers, a tiny knob of limestone, protruding just an inch or so above the murky depths. The trick, for tall people, is to grip the side of the passage with the left hand and simultaneously slide with the left foot onto this tiny knob, moving left onto dry land by quickly changing feet and stepping across. Sounds easy? If you miss – you're in up to the chin, and believe me, it's an experience never forgotten. Far better to attempt it with an experienced group of cavers, and don't risk it with your own children. Remember that young people, however confident, feel the effects of the cold far more quickly than adults.

Tummy Testing
Beyond Double Shuffle lies the slightly shallower 'Plank Pool' – both these pools having been bridged by wooden planks long ago so eminent Victorians could cross them easily. After

that, the cave drops down a slot in the floor to a lovely domed chamber, known as St Paul's at least since the 18th century – before the option of the claustrophobic's nightmare opens up on the left – the celebrated 'Cheese Press.' Here a gap between bedding planes of only 40 cm or so provides a real challenge for aspiring cavers, or at least the motivation to start slimming. I well remember my head and helmet being too large to go through it, so I took my helmet off, holding it in front of me, and can still recall the crushing sensation somewhere in the middle – the rock seeming to bend my ribcage like the drawing of a longbow. The crawl is only about four metres long, and can take anything from forty seconds to, dare I say, four hours. There are tales of novices being stuck in the middle and needing a shot of fairy liquid to get things moving! Once you have been 'cheese-pressed' the cave then leads onto the Dolly Tubs pitch, needing ladders and rope to emerge, after a forty foot climb, half way down Alum Pot, and that mind-numbing experience I mentioned earlier.

Though thronged with visitors, being in many respects the 'Blackpool' of the wild caves of Yorkshire, the Long Churns are deserving of their popularity and still remain, with their 'parent' pothole, hauntingly beautiful. As you lie by the car with your family trying their best to pull off a water-filled 'wellie' and the sheep chuckle at you parading round in your underwear looking for a lost sock – you have crossed an important frontier. You will have joined the thousands whose love of the wild places and the underground world began with a trip to Alum Pot and 'an appointment with Dr Bannister.' Few hours in your life will have been better spent.

Hole in the wall: The entrance to the cave is snugly hidden between the ruined barn and the limestone scar behind. *Top right*: Bruntscar Farm, behind which lies one of Whernside's best-kept secrets - for the price of a donation to the local church.

5. Bruntscar Cave:
The Hole Behind the Barn

Grid Reference: SD745778 (starting point at Chapel-le-Dale). The cave is approximately 1 mile from the parking spot.

In a Nutshell: A unique cave situated behind the ruins of a crumbling barn on the lower slopes of Whernside. The cave is a 'hidden gem' and cannot be seen or even suspected from the path, but access is available to all who are prepared to put a donation in the 'church collecting box' at Bruntscar Farm. Great fun can then be had in splashing through the beautiful passages, climbing three lovely waterfalls and admiring some fine formations. As a bonus, the handsome little Gatekirk Cave is visited on the return journey, where a large chamber can be entered before a crawl into 'The Tomb.' This adventure would make a fine day out combined with a trip to the Chapel-le-Dale potholes, Yordas Cave, or perhaps some of the caves of Ribblehead, but it can still be enjoyed as a full day out in its own right.

Essentials: Helmets with lights are essential, as climbing is involved in both caves. These, together with waterproof suits, can be hired at low cost from shops in Ingleton, where early morning breakfasts can enhance the day's experience. Ordinary waterproof trousers will suffice, but expect your underwear to fill up with water very quickly! Wellingtons are a must, as is a change of clothing and a towel. Children will enjoy these caves, but should be carefully supervised at all times, as the text indicates. FINE WEATHER is very important, as with all stream caves, so make sure you obtain an accurate forecast, and don't forget that all important church donation.

Access: The caves are reached by a pleasant walk from the parking spot, as described. This is either one of two lay-bys on the left of the B6255 Hawes Road, 3 miles (5km) north east of Ingleton, a short distance above the Old Hill Inn. Cars may also be tucked in on the opposite side, close to the water treatment works.

Adventure: The legend goes something like this: a man wakes up, haunted again by that strange rumbling sound beneath his farm that has been plaguing him for some time, only now it is louder than ever. Exasperated, he knocks up two trusty farm workers and the intrepid trio head for a small fissure immediately behind the barn. A few hours with spades, crow bars and pick axes follow, and the resulting rubble is cleared away to reveal a magnificent cave, so far untouched by man, and adorned with every kind of delicate formation.

An alternative version relates the story of the farmer, rather too indulgent with alcohol, seeking a space big enough to store his extensive wine collection, and fancying that the 'hole behind the barn' might be expanded with a little physical effort. In the event, not only does he discover a 'cellar' large enough to contain all the wine in England, but, in his excitement, all future indulgences with the bottle are put on hold. There is potential here, he thinks, for a show cave: potential to boost his income by drawing the same tourists who come to Yordas Cave and Weathercote. And so the rest of his days are spent, putting in steps, strengthening the entrance, naming the features: working tirelessly on a project, which, in the end, never fully materializes.

On and Off

What we do know for certain is that the cave was 'discovered' around 1865. In his *Yorkshire's Hollow Mountains*, W.R. Mitchell refers to a certain Joseph Carr, a prominent 19th century local writer who was among the first to enter the cave and see such features as 'The Devil's Bridge', 'The Egyptian King', 'The Organ', 'The Belfry' and even 'John Bull', England's own version of America's 'Uncle Sam.' The discoverer, and presumably the man who christened the features, was a Mr Kidd of Blue Hall, a frequent visitor to Bruntscar Farm, whose name not only evokes images of swashbuckling piracy, but whose enthusiasm seems to have been bordering on fantasy itself. After being shown around the cave by Mr Kidd, Carr wrote that 'there are even plans to widen the narrow passages and thus render it comfortably accessible to all classes of sightseers, while it is also under consideration to make such improvements that the stream may be turned on or off at pleasure.' Ideas like that suggest that Kidd, when he met the writer, had already had a few too many.

To see what all the fuss was about, leave the parking area and walk carefully down the road towards the Hill Inn, keeping in single file as the traffic is always in a hurry here. Just before the old school house, turn right into Philpin Lane.

A Three Peaks Up and Under

A short distance along on the left is a barn, converted into a welcome 'snack bar' for Three Peaks walkers, but open usually only at weekends. Ignore the footpath branching off to the right and continue on the tarmac lane, through lovely pastures, until a track is met between two farms at the base of Whernside. The track can be seen continuing ahead, twisting its way in an ugly eroded scar up the side of the mountain, and it is usually the accepted route of descent on the Three Peaks Marathon. Here you will receive curious stares from walkers, who wonder what you're doing here when most other astronauts seem to rocket round Ingleborough. You tell them, 'There's a cave behind that farm, just there' and they nod, politely: '*Very* interesting! Have you heard this, Gertrude? Yes, behind this barn here? Well, I never. You learn something every day,' before the inevitable conclusion follows: 'You wouldn't get me in a cave.' And off they go, leaving the wonders ahead of you all to your little selves.

Someone's Knocking at the Door
Broadrake is the farm to the right at this point, with Bruntscar itself lying off to the left. It is unlikely the surroundings look much different from Kidd's day, the eastern end of Bruntscar Hall, dated 1689, standing amongst quaint old buildings and beneath whispering trees, as if keen not to give away the subterranean secrets of this remote little dwelling place. Take note of a small gate leading into the front garden of the hall, and proceed along the track, past the ruins of the old barn, there being nothing at all to suggest the cave hiding behind. The next building is Bruntscar Farm itself. A strange feeling suddenly grips you here. Are you really knocking on a door, asking a farmer if you can look into his secret cave, hidden behind a spooky ruin? This is like a scene from Enid Blyton's

Bruntscar Cave: The Hole Behind the Barn

Pot-oilers paradise: A rib of limestone dividing the Main Chamber in Gatekirk Cave.

Famous Five. It's *spiffing* stuff, folks - just requiring that lashing of ginger beer. They are lovely people at Bruntscar Farm, a far cry from the few farmers who, as Mike Harding states, refer to cavers as 'ruddy pot-oilers', and they are only too keen to let you inside, providing, of course, you know the risks.

Having parted with your offering for the lovely church of St Leonard, retrace your steps to the gate, heading into the front garden of the hall. Walk behind the hall and you will see a tiny gap between the old buildings and the scar behind. A squeeze through this gap, watching out for a rusty hook on the wall, and there you have it. The entrance to Bruntscar Cave: shaded by trees and clothed in damp mosses, liverworts and ferns. Before the entrance, to the right, the steps intended for the tourists and built by Mr Kidd, are just discernible beneath the luxurious vegetation. The rusty iron headboard of a seemingly ancient bed has been tied at the bottom of the steps, presumably to prevent sheep from being too inquisitive. It's interesting to imagine this to have been the bed in which Kidd slept on the exciting night when the cave was discovered. At least, I used to say that to my kids when they were little.

A Tapering Tunnel

Take care on the slippery clamber down to the entrance. Just inside, an iron gate is met: Mr Kidd's way of preventing a public free-for-all in the days when stalactites were common garden decorations. It is easily pushed open, and the inviting passage is about two metres high and wide, with only a trickle of water, until the stream is met disappearing under the right hand wall just a little further in. My friend once received a nasty bang to her head at the entrance when we ventured inside with just a torch and no helmets, so take particular care here. Once the stream is met, the passage narrows into a beautiful tapering arch, where the stream has cut through a major joint in the limestone. Mr Kidd no doubt had his own name for this feature, extending ahead in a straight line towards the sound of falling water, though Carr doesn't mention it. You'll no doubt want to think of one, as this is as attractive a section of stream passage as any you'll find in the Three Peaks area.

Just after the 'tapered' section ends, the canyon turns sharp right to the first waterfall, and the excitement begins. A narrow spout gushes into a plunge pool from a rocky lip about a metre up, where a second small fall is seen in the light of your caving lamp. Between the two is a small plunge pool hollowed into the rock in the shape of a bowl. Was this Mr Kidd's 'font'? If so, then presumably some kind of climbing aid must have been offered to the Victorian ladies, whose dignity would otherwise have been destroyed forever by a climb up the cascade. Some authors state that this fall is 'easily overcome.' If you're a beginner, I would argue otherwise. Certainly it's easy to lift children up into the font, but then they become a barrier to their heroic parents, trying their best to climb up behind. I once muttered all sorts to myself in trying to get up here, eventually collapsing on top of Joe with my underpants full of ice-cold water.

The second of these 'twin' falls is much easier, and is great fun on the way back. It is much more of a 'waterslide' than the first, being less than a metre in height. Children can scramble up it and lead on in front, as the passage ahead is straightforward, though narrow. In a few metres it leads to another waterslide, this time lying in a small chamber with shelves of rock bordering a knee-deep plunge pool. This is a great spot for a rest, and a chance to photograph the fine 'organ' formation, decorating the waterfall to the left. 'Ladies and gentlemen of taste and leisure', so often mentioned in the earliest guidebooks, didn't half 'rough it' compared with your tourists of today, who walk down galvanized steel pathways in White Scar Cave in their jeans and trainers.

Bridges and Belfries

Above this cascade, easily overcome by a 'step' in the middle, is 'The Devil's Bridge', a mass of calcite spanning the narrow passage which is easily missed, and what I presume to be 'The Belfry'. This is where the passage opens into a small chamber decorated with flowstone and a few large but damaged stalactites. Glancing back, the flowstone has formed a series of gleaming white 'pillows', arranged in a cluster like a peal of bells set into the little aven. These are similar to the 'mushroom bed' formations in Ingleborough Cave, but are

Sylvan setting: The beautiful entrance to Gatekirk Cave. It lies amongst mature trees and can be entered safely in settled weather.

much more exciting without the tourists, hand-rails and electric lighting. There is a third little waterslide beyond, but unless you have tried a few caves before, this would be a sensible point to turn back. You can then have great fun plunging down the waterslides, admiring all the features on the way out that were not easily seen in the opposite direction.

If you're feeling brave, then the remainder of the cave is a hands and knees crawl, generally great fun if you like that sort of thing, especially where masses of flowstone and the occasional stalactite force occasional flat-out crawling in the cold water. There is nothing hazardous here apart from any obvious change in the weather, so consider what the sky was like outside, and be realistic.

Never Been Up

Returning to daylight, it doesn't take much to ring the doorbell of the farm once again and give a quick word of thanks. This, of course, will familiarize you for any future visits. Here, I discovered that, despite living inches from it, the farmer's wife had never actually been into the cave herself! Dalesfolk tend to display this kind of nonchalance as far as their homeland is concerned. My dad's old friend, Stanley, a sheep farmer from Chapel-le-Dale, could not for the life of him understand why we had traveled forty odd miles to climb Ingleborough, and calmly stated that in three score years of sheep farming in the shadow of the mountain, he had found no reason, as yet, to venture as far as the summit. *'Bin up on't slopes fer a ewe or tooow,'* he used to tell us in his broad Yorkshire twang. *'Nefer actly bin on't top.'*

A warm drink, dry clothes and the car may well dominate the thoughts at this point, but if you are game for more adventure (and those who have paid to hire a suit usually are), the next port of call is Broadrake Farm, a short distance along the track to the north east, where permission should be sought for an exploration of Gatekirk Cave. This superb little resurgence cave is hidden away off the path and can be quite tricky to reach. To locate it, take the path south east from Broadrake, following it until a ford is met crossing the usually dry riverbed of Winterscales Beck. Immediately after the ford, the path almost touches the riverbed itself (SD745789), and here the bed should be crossed to a fenced area of shakeholes containing small trees and vegetation. A stile admits to these holes, one of which is the upstream entrance to Gatekirk Cave. It is a narrow squeeze down through rather dodgy-looking blocks, accompanied usually by an intimidating roar of water far below. This water is next

A Three Peaks Up and Under

seen at a far more accommodating entrance, but one that can only be reached by following the streambed down and clambering over an awkward sloping fence into the attractive woodlands beneath. A careful scramble down reveals the water gushing out of a wide but low cave mouth, perfectly decorated with mosses, ferns and mature sycamores; rivalling Browgill Cave in Ribblesdale as the most beautiful cave entrance in Yorkshire.

A Limestone Tomb

The water is knee deep at the entrance, which leads almost immediately into an impressive and very active chamber, floored by massive boulders, and with a small waterfall entering from a narrow passage on the left hand side. Further left, over a metre up, daylight can be seen through an abandoned exit known as The Loft, presumably the course of the stream before it cut its present route. The Loft is best entered from the outside, as the slide down into the stream is much easier than the climb out. Several species of bat are known to roost here, and special 'bat detector' instruments can often be seen placed outside the cave. Escape from the water is accomplished by clambering onto an obvious shelf on the right hand side of the chamber. This gives fine views of The Loft, and of the curious 'bulbous' stalactites liberally decorating the ceiling of the chamber. From the shelf, hands and knees crawling along a normally dry passage reveals a most startling sight. Protruding across the scalloped floor, perfectly carved by water action, is the figure of an Egyptian Mummy, lying on his side, the gleaming face presumably having been polished white by imaginative cavers, determined to terrify others. They certainly put the wind up us on our first visit, prompting us to refer to this passage, ever since, as 'The Tomb.'

A 'through trip' can be achieved in settled weather by following the stream in the main chamber past a cascade at floor level and into a dry passage on the right, the crawls at 'The Tomb' also linking to this passage. A scramble through blocks then emerges through the tight upstream entrance visited earlier. In its present state it is best avoided, and when the stream is in spate it is highly dangerous, so it is best to return through the main entrance. I have seen the water in Gatekirk Cave become a dangerous torrent after only a few hours of moderate rain. Yet it is the awesome power of nature at work that makes a visit to this little cavern something to relish.

For a squelchy-wellie return to the car, retrace your steps across the dry river bed above the cave to the footpath below Broadrake. A short distance further down the path a surfaced lane is met. Almost immediately, leave the lane here and turn right along a clear path through fields, meeting the beck again at Haws Gill Wheel, before emerging once more on Philpin Lane, close to the waiting car – and warm clothing.

And for the prudes amongst us, a final word of advice: keep your boot open when getting changed at the parking spot. The parcel shelf will at least screen the passing public from the horrors of encountering you 'in the altogether.'

That just wouldn't be the 'done' thing, would it?

Hobbit home: The intricate limestone sculpture around the entrance to Cuddy Gill Cave, bedecked with ferns and looking like scene from Tolkien. *Top right*: Runscar Cave's most obvious entrance is an archway at the base of a small cliff.

6. Thistle and Runscar:
A Rabbit Round Ribblehead

Grid Reference: SD766793 (starting point at Ribblehead lay-by). A 4 mile moorland wander on pathless terrain including some exciting caving.

In a Nutshell: A memorable day exploring some of the fine caves on Batty Moss, close to the famous Ribblehead viaduct. First - an interesting little 'through trip' along the passages of Runscar Cave, followed by a return through the parallel Thistle Cave, with a chance for some more strenuous activity. To round off the day's enjoyment, a trip into Katnot Cave is on the menu, situated in the lovely Thorns Gill - famous for its flowers and river scenery.

Essentials: Though Thistle and Runscar can be explored with good torches and hard hats, much more comfort is gained from wearing a caving suit, lamp and helmet, available for hire in Ingleton. Otherwise, good waterproofs and wellies will suffice. Take a complete change of clothing and a towel for each person, with plenty of food and warm drinks. The Yorkshire Dales Explorer (OL2) Southern and Western areas map covers the caves, though their individual names are not marked. A compass may be useful if mist descends, making the parking area invisible from the cave entrances.

Access: Ribblehead lies between Ingleton and Hawes. Leaving the A65, follow signs for White Scar Cave, and take the B6255 along Chapel-le-Dale for 5 miles, (8km) until it meets the B6479, just beyond the Station Inn. There are plenty of parking spaces on the right. As an alternative, Ribblehead can be reached from Settle via Horton-in-Ribblesdale on the B6479.

Adventure: No matter what the weather, you are rarely alone at Ribblehead. The Station Inn does a roaring trade; families throng the banks of the clear streams with fishing nets, picnics and barbecues; scores of bikers cast off their helmets and collapse into the rushes by the roadside; grandparents thumb through newspapers in the front seats of their pride and joys, their attention occasionally shifted to the mountains in their midst: whose summits are no longer so accessible, but whose profiles are unchanging, relentlessly drawing the eye. Photographers screech to a halt and jump out, camera, tripod and all, as the clouds break for one brief moment and the impatient sun threatens to smother Whernside. All is a hive of activity; yet there is nothing that nature has provided here to create all *this* commotion, or so it seems. The moors look bleak: even boring. There isn't a tree for miles. Whernside hardly seems to qualify as a peak, and looks just like any other lump in the landscape, with even mighty Ingleborough at sufficient distance to warrant a few miles travel down the road for a better view. No - nature is clearly the loser here: for once, and once only in the Dales, it is man whose works have triumphed over the surroundings, turning an otherwise inhospitable wilderness into a veritable Mecca for the masses.

A Loo With a View

The magnet, of course, is the mighty Ribblehead viaduct: all 440 yards of it, sprawled across Batty Moss like an invincible dragon; stubbornly resistant to all weathers, and to all attempts to stop the trains of the Settle / Carlisle Railway from crawling across its back. There it stands, robust and proud, a fitting monument to the 2000 plus 'navvies' who slaved away on these moors in appalling conditions to create it. All eyes fall on this magnificent construction, perhaps the finest work of man in the Yorkshire Dales. The Station Inn nearby even advertises 'A Loo With a View' so that regulars can remind themselves, when nature is calling, just what drew them to these parts in the first place. Built between 1870 and 1875, with a maximum height of 104 feet, the viaduct has so many admirable qualities that it is possible to forgive the quarrymen who blasted away the nearby Little Dale for its raw ingredients. Unrelenting Yorkshire rain turned the moss into a quagmire for years on end, and it was necessary to sink the foundations to a depth of 25 feet, in order to prevent the whole thing from sinking. Hence, the job took a lot longer than was anticipated. Men gathered with their families in the shanty towns of Sebastapol, Jericho, Jerusalem, Salt Lake and Belgravia, occupying their spare time by fighting and drinking themselves to death: that is, if smallpox, malnutrition, or general exhaustion had not already overtaken them. The tiny churchyard of St Leonard at Chapel-le-Dale was extended to become a mass grave: countless others lying unconsecrated on the moor.

Curious visitors are often content to wander beneath the arches, or to pick their way amongst the obscure ruins of the shanty towns, before returning to their vehicles and heading off to the Ingleton Waterfalls or the delights of

A Three Peaks Up and Under

Hawes. In doing so, their attentions are often shifted away from the viaduct by a most unnatural sight, prompting them to mutter 'Where did *he* just appear from?' The barren moor, as if by magic, is suddenly dotted with hordes of tiny goblins moving towards the parking spot, some in red, some in yellow, most appearing from apparently nowhere. These are not the ghosts of the dead, coming back to haunt the people of today. These are more like little spacemen, aliens, people of the 25th century: certainly, in *this* landscape. Their colours don't belong.

Visitors arriving earlier in the day may have witnessed a group of these multi-coloured misfits on their outward journey. In doing so, they will probably have noticed them heading for a small cliff, situated to the left of a conspicuous area of limestone pavement on the moor, and just visible from the parking area facing Whernside. (SD765796) If this cliff isn't obvious, then effort should be made to locate it by jumping up and down in the parking area until it is spotted, for this is the key to a full day of exciting underground adventure for all the family

Batty and Boggy

The next task, easier said than done, is to reach the cliff by a walk across Batty Green. If the viaduct beckons first, it makes sense to follow the obvious path towards it, beginning at the road junction close to the Station Inn and the quaint little Batty Wife Cave. Once an open shaft that has since been filled in, it was here that a Mr Batty met his estranged wife to talk things over – only to reignite the rift between them and promptly dump her body in a hole that has borne her name ever since. The cliff and pavement can then be reached by turning eastwards across the moor, once the masonry has been sufficiently marveled at. This route has its advantages, as a direct route to the cliff encounters treacherous bogs, swamps and other nasty things, the crossing of which, no doubt, provides hours of entertainment for the observing motorists. 'Whoops! He's in again, Fred!' is no doubt a typical utterance from the ringside spectators here. It isn't just the viaduct and the sandwiches that they come for.

Whichever way the cliff is reached, the first sight of a large stream gushing from an impressive cave entrance at its base, before plunging once more underground beneath a bridge of weathered limestone, is something totally unexpected; something likely to set the pulse racing after the relative monotony of the approaching walk. This is Runscar Cave, and the nature of the stream here is its main giveaway. Running parallel to it is Thistle Cave, and many visitors confuse the two. If you are standing at a small cliff adorned by a prickly little bush and a low cave entrance with no water emerging, you are actually at Thistle Cave, and need to be a few metres to the east, along roughly the same contour. I find a few visits generally help navigation become easier.

Child's Play

The 'cliff entrance' to Runscar Cave is probably the most suitable stream cave for children in the whole of the Yorkshire Dales. It is always wet enough to be exciting, the pools are deep enough in parts to be good fun, and there are no confusing passages to get lost in. However, sudden downpours can swell the stream to a dangerous current, and I have seen the cliff entrance actually fill to the ceiling allowing no way in. Make sure the day is settled before going ahead and a great time will be had by all. It is, of course, possible to venture into the downstream entrance, climbing carefully beneath the bridges of rock into a stream passage. However, this soon leads to a low crawl in water and an uncomfortably wet exit into daylight, and so is perhaps unsuitable for the absolute novice.

Entering the cave in the cliff face is always exciting. It is necessary at first to adopt a 'gorilla' walk or a hands-and-knees crawl. The passage is low, but wide, with attractive terraces of limestone providing natural sofas to lounge around on until everyone manages to get in. It also pays to let the eyes become adjusted to the dark at this stage. The way on is a sheer delight: 122 metres of twisting canyon passage with attractive moonmilk formations decorating the ceiling. Children will love splashing through the pools and mini cascades, and nowhere is the water more than knee-deep. After twenty minutes of fun, daylight is seen ahead and the passage emerges up a bouldery slope to daylight; the temptation to go back and do it all again being extremely strong. Immediately ahead now are a confusing array of small entrances beneath boulders, some of which are too precariously balanced for comfort. This is the upper part of Runscar Cave, probably best left to more experienced rabbits. There is one short (33m) through section of passage that can be negotiated, requiring effort to emerge from a hole at shoulder height, but after that things become constricted and, indeed, dangerous, as the way on penetrates beneath the boulders to reach the intricate Scar Top Cave.

Thistle Do

For a far more appealing alternative, return to the large Runscar entrance you just emerged from, and walk about 75m northwest onto the bare moor, where patient hunting should reveal a large, funnel-shaped shakehole, its muddy sides usually well churned by hordes of visiting goblins. This is Thistle Cave, and a careful slither down the hole leads to two entrances, both of which are superb. The upstream entrance, to the right, looks a little daunting at first as it requires a flat-out crawl to get in, but don't be put off if you are wearing a caving suit and helmet-mounted lamp. The trick is to stand at the lowest point of the shakehole and then enter head-first. A slither beneath an array of badly damaged stalactites, and you are inside, where things become immediately easier. The stream has cut a trench out of the floor and this makes a refreshing walk after the intricacies of the entrance crawl. Decorating the ceiling are some impressive stalactites, becoming more prominent as the route progresses. It's great fun splashing through the stream, and almost a disappointment when after only 80m or so, the cave comes to an abrupt end at a chamber. I'll never forget two dozen members of the Craven Pothole Club taking lunch here on one freezing March Saturday with a degree of well-seasoned nonchalance that suggested they were in any other Ingleton café. Such is the world of the caver, and long may it continue!

Splash back down the stream-way and return to the narrow entrance. You've done it once, so the nerves will be calmer, though exiting is more difficult head-first as there is an abrupt drop to the streambed to be negotiated; somewhat easier for tall people with chimpanzee arms, like me. The first explorers of this cave had to break through a stalactite barrier and beauty has been sacrificed for man's insatiable curiosity. I can never crawl out of Thistle Upper Cave without feeling a touch of guilt. Considering the vast amount of school and outdoor centre traffic that congests these caves, it is incredible that there are, fortunately, still some lovely stalactites to admire. Let's all try our utmost to keep it that way.

Superstar
Now take the easier downstream entrance to Thistle Main Cave. Like Runscar, this is a delightful twisting canyon,

A Three Peaks Up and Under

Worth investigating: Katnot Cave, explored by the Reverend Hutton, lies on the bank of Thorns Gill, and carries an active stream.

though it is perhaps more attractively decorated. There are many fine cushions of 'moonmilk' in the ceiling, and, following an abrupt 90 degree bend, several abandoned oxbows that children will love to explore. The cave runs for about 150 metres and is perfectly safe, though the exit requires a flat-out crawl into the daylight, where a patch of nettles waits cunningly to test the strength of your caving suit. A few metres before the exit, on the left of the passage, is an oxbow that my family have unofficially christened 'The Snake', and with good reason. Children will slither through this easily, but for adults it's a different game altogether, as we found out on a recent caving expedition. Heading down

Thistle and Runscar: A Rabbit Round Ribblehead

Thistle passage, my friend, Darren, and I encountered 'Hoggy', a well-seasoned member of Craven, popping head-first out of the oxbow with (we couldn't help but notice) no small amount of huffing and puffing. 'Well, if *he* could still do it,' we reasoned, 'why not give it a go?' Five minutes later, with each and every part of my anatomy appallingly contorted to fit into the snake's twisting stomach, I thought decidedly otherwise, though I wasn't telling Darren that. 'I'm nearly through,' I gasped out (instantly promoting Hoggy to 'superstar' status in the same breath) while managing to add, menacingly: 'Piece of Cake, pal.'

The inevitable, of course, followed. Darren, who, dare I risk saying, is a touch larger round the middle than me, found it more than a full cake to say the very least. We spent an alarming twenty minutes trying our best to encourage him that 'what goes in – must come out.' Hoggy was screaming 'take your --------g helmet off!' down one end of the Snake, while I was shouting 'Move your leg about a bit!' down the other. What Darren was shouting is, needless to say, unprintable.

Leave Your Helmet On

Immediately opposite the exit of the Main Cave is the most daunting entrance of the lot: that of Thistle Lower Cave. A tight flat-out crawl beneath a bedding plane is bad enough at the best of times, but with a floor of sharp cobbles it becomes agonizingly uncomfortable. Claustrophobics will have a nightmare here, but true rabbits with decent gear should not miss the opportunity to have a go. Keeping to the right inside, a passage is met after about 6 metres, swinging off to the left and dropping into the stream, with the ceiling increasing in height only very slightly. Comfort is provided, however, by the most beautiful formations: glistening silver stalactites and calcite curtains, surprisingly well preserved. Clearly, flat-out crawling is not on most people's Ribblehead menu, and thankfully so. About 90m in, the passage is lined by mud banks for a final 40 metres of crawling in water towards the last horrifying obstacle: a tiny exit, so small that most heads won't fit through with a helmet on. Mine won't, anyway, and I'll never forget my ceremonious exit from here on my first visit with the Craven Pothole Club. Several of the younger members, perhaps no older than ten or eleven, had made short work of the crawl and, unbeknown to Darren and myself, were waiting patiently outside for the 'big lads' to pop out. I made the mistake of shouting back to Darren, 'I'm taking my helmet off!' and believe me, that is a mistake in caving circles, where removal of the hard hat is a sure sign of a man who can't master his manoeuvre. My head and shoulders popped through the hole to a torrent of ice-cold water from above and my first thoughts were, 'Whassat?? Waterfall? I can't remember a blinking waterfall!'

I was right. There never had been. Instead, perched on the rocks above was a cackling coven of juveniles, calmly filling their helmets from the stream and baptizing all who were daft enough to emerge as I did. One girl, (Jenny, if she's reading this) discovered it to be a most convenient place to empty the murky contents of her wellies. Fortunately, Darren was waiting for that one.

The Hanging Gardens
Other underground adventures wait for the intrepid explorer on Batty Moss, but these are perhaps best left for another day. One of these is Cuddy Gill Pot, easily located by climbing onto the clints above Runscar Cave's top entrance, where tall people should just be able to make out the top of tree (yes, that's right – a *tree*) about 200m to the north-east. Smaller

people should jump up and down a few times or at least walk in that direction until they spot it. Cuddy Gill is worth finding as it's one of the very few pothole shafts that ordinary people like me and thee can actually climb down in relative safety. It's also a haven for a variety of wild flowers. 'The Hanging Gardens of Batty Moss' may be a far cry from those of Babylon, but any floral display at Ribblehead is more than welcome. A stream emerges from Cuddy Gill Cave at the base of the shaft before sinking into rubble, and a short walk (about 60m) across the moor in a north-westerly direction should reveal the cave entrance itself. (SD766799) Like Thistle and Runscar, it is easily explorable for 150m or so, but it is dank and gloomy, lacking the beauty of its neighbours. It also fills to the roof in flood, which is just about enough to put anyone off. I tend not to bother.

Taking the Tube

Immediately west of Thistle and Runscar Caves, and closer to the viaduct, is the much more interesting Roger Kirk Cave, one of the entrances of which can be spotted easily from the road, close to an old lime kiln. Roger Kirk provides sport for the more experienced caver: no special gear is needed, but the passages are low, requiring intricate squeezing and crawling. The top entrance lies in the vicinity of Roger Kirk Rocks, marked on Ordnance Survey maps, and is a small drop into an initially dry passage. This soon becomes a natural assault course and eventually follows the stream into a horrifyingly low tunnel with about a head's-width of airspace, known simply as 'The Tube'. *Northern Caves* pleasantly informs us that 'this is best tackled on one's back – and in normal weather presents no problem.' I wouldn't like to castigate the scriptures of the Holy Bible of caving, but on one blistering August Bank Holiday I did try it on my back; then on my front; then on my back again. No one way was better than any other. Both were *awful*: no amount of gorgeous cave passage beyond could make up for the amount of water I swallowed, but I lived!

Those who *have* braved the Thistle Lower Cave may want to head back to the car and clean clothes without delay, but others with greater staying power and a feel for cold water should not miss the short detour to Thorns Gill: one of the finest sights in the Yorkshire Dales and a place beloved of all those adventurous enough to have discovered it.

The Thrill of the Gill

The secretive location of the gill, hidden away from the eyes of all by-passers on the Hawes Road, plays a large part in making it so special. Wainwright, in his final book, *Wainwright in the Limestone Dales* (1991), debates whether or not every Tom, Dick and Harry should be allowed the privilege of eroding this beautiful spot: 'There is currently an unresolved contention by the landowners that there is no public right of way along the gill, and they are probably right.' Even today, current Ordnance Survey maps don't show a Thorns Gill, and there is certainly no indication of a footpath. Before visiting, it is probably best to enquire at Far Gearstones Farm. A few extra minutes out of the way will definitely be worth it.

From the Runscar area, head back to the B6255, cross it with care, and walk eastwards alongside the road for half a mile (0.75 km) until a gate on the right gives access to a path adjacent to a sheep pen. The path crosses a grassy hillock and in a few minutes descends to the remarkable packhorse bridge of Thorns Gill, barely a metre in width but of sufficient height to make any fall over the edge not worth thinking about. Presumably, the packhorses were sure-footed enough, but I certainly wouldn't let anything take *me* across apart from my own two feet. Take care with youngsters here. After crossing, descend to the right onto rocky terraces overlooking deep pools, with an unforgettable view of the bridge itself, its delicate nature being all the more apparent from this angle. The graceful arch merges so seamlessly into the limestone cliffs on each side of the gill that it appears to be a work of nature: surely man can't have produced anything so impressive, you will tell yourself. At its narrowest point, barely 8 inches of weathered rock hold up anything that passes above. I have witnessed a dozen members of the Craven Pothole Club, who have seen wonders most of us could only dream of, marveling at this bridge for half an hour or more – such is the perfection of its construction. The great irony, of course, is that to construct any bridge in a beautiful location today causes uproar: to damage or remove this one would destroy the beauty of the gill itself, just as to remove the viaduct would destroy Ribblehead. Each of these works of man is a true masterpiece. One is a snarling dragon, sprawled across the moor for all to behold, the other a delicate damsel.

Turn upstream (left) at the bridge, keeping to the right hand bank. In the field above are clusters of interesting limestone boulders, dropped off by melting ice sheets at the end of the last glaciation. One is mushroom-shaped and makes a fine subject for the camera. The stream flowing through the gill here is christened Gayle Beck, originating to the north and eventually, of course, becoming the River Ribble further downstream. Follow the edges of the gill and cascade, until a stream is met crossing the route. This emerges from Katnot Cave, the entrance to which is situated a short distance ahead, at the base of a small cliff overhung by a customary tree. This cave is one of the best for beginners in

A Three Peaks Up and Under

Yorkshire. As long as the weather is fine there are few hazards, though you are likely to get wet enough to require a complete change of clothing.

Rocking Reverend

The cave has an easy walk-in entrance, but the floor soon slopes upwards onto a rocky cone indicating recent falls from the ceiling. There are some unpleasant rocks still dangling, but thankfully the worst of these have fallen in recent years. From the top of the rock pile, the floor slopes down into a comfortable walking passage and soon reaches a chamber, remarkable for its collection of signatures. These have been made, not with hammer and chisel, but with the plentiful supplies of red ochre deposited on the walls of the cave, likely to leave stains on your caving suit far more persistent than a spaghetti bolognese ever could. Sceptics, of course, will question the legitimacy of 'J. Caesar 55 B.C.', but some have clearly withstood the passing of centuries. Katnot was a great favourite with pioneer cave explorers of the past, and one man who may well have daubed his name on the walls (presuming a man of the church would do such a thing when his friends weren't looking) was the Reverend John Hutton, author of *A Tour to the Caves in the Environs of Ingleborough and Settle* (1780). He leaves us a valuable insight into the terrors of caving with a candle: *'We had not gone out of the sight of day before we were obliged to wade up to the mid-leg.'*

One has to ask, how would the Reverend have coped, chin-deep in a wetsuit, with today's caving fraternity? He goes on to further describe the cave beyond the chamber, where a series of small cascades are encountered: *'The different notes made by the rill in its little cascade and reverberating from the hollow rocks amused the ear with a new sort of rude and subterranean music.'*

After passing a choked branch on the left, Katnot continues as a magnificent stream passage for about 300 metres, perfect for the whole family to enjoy a caving experience together. Eventually, the roof lowers sufficiently to force uncomfortable crawling in water, great fun for those willing to have a go, but horrifying for candle-bearers in tweed suits, like Hutton: *'Perhaps if we had mustered humility and fortitude enough to have crouched and crawled a little, we might have come to where the roof again would have been as high as we should have desired.'*

Wishful thinking, Mr Hutton, but actually, it wouldn't. And what he could have said, in far fewer words, was that he didn't want anyone catching the local vicar with a squelchy bottom. Get to the point, Reverend. Come on!

Retrace your steps along the Katnot passage once you've had a wallow in the water, and pray for a bit of sunlight to warm your shivering body once you get out. There are two choices now. One is to head back to the car by retracing your steps down the gill to the bridge, while another is to continue up the gill to Holme Hill Cave, situated beneath a scar on the left bank of the beck close to the road (SD785802). At one time a show cave, there are the remains of an old iron gate inside, the remote location allowing for a wealth of beautiful white stalactites to be relatively intact. It is, in this way, at least a pleasant contrast to Katnot, though decidedly shorter – the passage becoming uncomfortably low after about 120m. You've done more than enough crawling for one day.

What remains is a pleasant, if soggy walk back along the gill and eventually to the dry clothes waiting for you in the car. As you've enjoyed being a Ribblehead rabbit, now revel in the unique experience of being a goblin. At least you'll be keeping folk happy when there are no trains about.

Awe-inspiring: Looking up Britain's most famous pothole entrance, the 'Old Woman of Gaping Gill' in profile on the right. *Top right:* A precarious-looking gantry is rigged over the 340-foot shaft, where Fell Beck falls in the nation's highest waterfall.

7. Gaping Gill:
Dangling Down the Plughole

Grid Reference: SD751727 (the pothole) and SD745694 (starting point in Clapham village). A 2.5 mile (4km) walk to the winch at the main shaft with some strenuous underground exploring.

In a Nutshell: A delightful walk through the grounds of the Ingleborough estate, followed by a winch descent into the largest cavern in the country: reputedly big enough to swallow a cathedral. Not only that, but the vertical shaft contains the longest unbroken waterfall in the British Isles – yes, higher than Niagara – and the chamber leads into a breathtaking network of tunnels and caverns which will need several visits to be fully appreciated. All this is experienced in the company of experienced cavers whose enthusiasm helps make this the ultimate underground adventure.

Essentials: Gaping Gill is open to the public twice a year. The Bradford Pothole Club operates a winch during the Spring Bank Holiday week (usually the first week in June), while the Craven Pothole Club do likewise during the last week in

A Three Peaks Up and Under

August. Both clubs have websites giving the exact details. Basically, you turn up and book in your name and address before being given a numbered tag so they can check who's actually in the system. You can then borrow a caving suit and helmet from the cavers before sitting to wait your turn. When your 'number's up' you are locked into a bosun's chair and lowered 340 feet into the Main Chamber, where kind ladies and gentlemen are waiting to calm your nerves and show you round. It's possible to spend a full day down there if you take a reliable map and have had some previous caving experience.

The price varies of course, and there is an old joke that they ask for nothing to drop you down, but charge only for the return journey, while some authors state the cost to be as much as four pints of beer! The price in 2013 was ten pounds. The minimum age is six, and children are secured into the chair by a fixed harness.

You will need warm clothing and a waterproof, even in summer, and wellingtons are a must. Also, the trip is much better with a caving lamp, which can be hired from Ingleton. Food and drink are essential and small rucksacks can generally be clipped onto the winch so you can have an underground picnic. The clubs usually erect a portable toilet near to the pothole, but there is no underground facility! Aim to arrive early as large queues develop, especially on fine days. Keep children supervised at all times as the dangers of Gaping Gill are appallingly obvious. Stay well away from the shaft until your turn arrives.

Access: Clapham is situated off the A65 between Settle and Ingleton. Walk up to Gaping Gill by the same route as the 'Clapham Classic' adventure (*see Ingleborough section*). The pothole is about a mile up the valley from Ingleborough Cave, and the walk involves a slippery scramble through Trow Gill, requiring care. Only very rarely does bad weather affect the winch meets, and rainy days often have smaller queues and the added bonus of an even bigger waterfall, so don't be put off.

Adventure: 'There is feeble light of day, which, filtering through the water, produces the effect of a myriad prisms by its falling drops. The charm of its ethereal delicacy is utterly unlike anything else upon which the human eye has ever gazed. I thought it was one of the most extraordinary spectacles it has ever been my pleasure to behold.'

These words were penned by the modest Edouard Alfred Martel on 1 August 1895, after becoming the first human being ever to set foot in the main chamber of Gaping Gill. Others had tried before him, and one local man, Edward Calvert of the Yorkshire Rambler's Club, had even fixed himself a date to be the first, only to be beaten to it: 'To have a ripe plum taken out of your mouth just when you are going to put your teeth into it is not a bit pleasant.'

Martel, however, was pleasant enough. On hearing of Calvert's disappointment he wrote to him saying that, if he had known of Calvert's ambitions, the two men could have performed the first descent together. As it was, a crowd of over a hundred people gathered to watch the Frenchman disappear down a rope ladder into the 'bottomless pit', defeating a previous attempt by Settle farmer John Birkbeck, who had managed to reach a ledge 50 metres down before his rope frayed and he was persuaded to 'get out – quick!' Martel's modesty has become legendary. After spending over an hour in the main chamber and noting several passages leading out of it, he returned to the surface in 28 minutes to a standing ovation, just as a customary storm was breaking over Ingleborough. He was spending the night at the New Inn in Clapham, where the visitors' book indicates how he appeared to take everything in his stride: 'On Thursday, 1st August, I went down Gaper Gill Hole, etc.'

Over a hundred years and thousands of visitors later, it would still be difficult for even the most experienced caver to react with such nonchalance at Gaping Gill. No matter how many times you experience the thrill of the winch and 'dangle down the plughole', this most famous of potholes still has the power to shoot that adrenalin like no other. The sheer scale, majesty and grandeur of the place put it, in Tony Waltham's words 'in a completely different league than any other British cave.' No visitor will disagree, and the main chamber is one of the few genuine places that have to be seen to be believed. Those pensioners no longer able to reach the high slopes, who descended Gaping Gill maybe forty years before and are looking back over the experiences of a long life, will have nothing more magnificent in their memories.

Fell Beck has a massive drainage area, gathering all the water from the southeast slopes of Ingleborough and the southern flanks of the adjoining Simon Fell. On reaching the Great Scar Limestone it bubbles along merrily – mirroring the nonchalance of Martel himself, before suddenly plunging aggressively into an oval shaft at the bottom of an otherwise ordinary shakehole. The precise point of the sink is governed by faults that wrenched the rock strata below and created a weakness for the mildly acidic water to exploit. The shaft itself is 340 feet (110 metres) deep, with Britain's highest waterfall dropping into Britain's biggest chamber. These facts in themselves have turned Gaping Gill into a cathedral for the caving congregation; and, yes: it is true that the nave of St Paul's will fit snugly inside. Gear and experience are usually essential, but on two marvellous occasions each year the public are afforded the chance to do what would otherwise be the impossible.

Carry on camping: The stream is diverted down nearby Rat Hole to make the descent possible.

Waterbeds and Watering Holes

Arriving at Clapham village, the best way to the pothole is to follow the 'Classic From Clapham' route, described in part one of this book. Pay a small fee to enter the grounds of Ingleborough Hall, formerly the estate of the Farrer family, and enjoy an hour trudging past the joys of Ingleborough Cave and Trow Gill. The anticipation of such a journey, knowing what comes at the end of it, can be overwhelming, especially for the first-timer. A 'village' of coloured tents will instantly give away the big attraction – many club members spending one or two weeks up here in the harsh conditions. Several years ago, when I acted as a guide in the Main Chamber, I spent over a week under canvas with my son. It was August, but I felt like Scott at the Antarctic. Ingleborough was invisible, the rain unrelenting, and so much liquid had gathered daily under the groundsheet that getting into sleeping bags was like manoeuvring on a waterbed. The peat-stained Fell Beck had to be boiled before drinking, and going to the toilet in the middle of the night was virtually impossible in the conditions. Some cavers were actually substituting saucepans for bed-pans, and quickly popping them outside their tents in a pitch dark quagmire. This led to an amusing scene one night when a group returned from the 'beer tent' – the legendary 'Trenchfoot Arms', having had a heavy day in the far reaches of Gaping Gill – and more than a few pints of 'main shaft' ale. Like a set of toppling dominoes, they tumbled one by one over the bed pans in the darkness, with great commotion. One of them, I later heard, went back to the beer tent for his tankard, and, being caught in a rain shower, he actually sprinted back – only to meet the trusty bed pans at double speed! Somersaults and swear words rapidly ensued. We can laugh, but it wasn't pleasant for the man – was it, Darren?

When your Number's Up

It costs, traditionally – the equivalent of four pints of beer – not to descend, we are told with true Yorkshire wit, but to be hauled back up again. The procedure is to part with your money, and then be labelled like an evacuee with a metal tag. Fear builds on delay of course, and you can see many first-timers nervously pacing up and down the banks of Fell Beck until their number pops up on the blackboard. When the moment arrives, it's a 'walk of the plank' across precarious looking scaffolding to the 'chair' and generally a great beaming smile from one of the winch operators, who seem to have the same role as dental nurses: 'Course it's going to be all right. Now you just sit back and relax, my lovely ...'

Gaping Gill: Dangling Down the Plughole

The drop is hard to describe to anyone unless they've done it. This truly is an experience like nothing else in Britain, and from the moment the plank is pulled out and you make that first plunge, you are on your own. Darkness only gradually envelopes the visitor as the descent is made down the narrow shaft, and a glance upwards shows a gradually contracting oval of light where the outside world lay just a few seconds before. The limestone walls are encrusted with lichens, mosses and ferns: the vivid greens diminishing slowly to browns and greys as the light fades. An obvious shelf, at 190 feet down, is the famous Birkbeck's ledge, where the pioneer potholer had to call it a day in 1850. Most limestone lovers would die happily with their own ledge in Gaping Gill. I'm sure John must have done. Beyond this, the chair begins to wander off centre and the walls, which have been accompanying the journey thus far, disappear suddenly. The visitor is now dangling inside a vast chamber, 110 feet above the landing point, often described as being like a spider suspended from the dome of St Paul's Cathedral. The eyes, unaccustomed to the inky black of what lies beneath, decipher nothing, allowing the mind to concentrate on an inevitable soaking from the waterfall spray. For a few seconds a combination of darkness and roaring water is so intense that the visitor can lose all sense of whether he is going up or down. Everything 'normal' has seemingly evaporated.

Suddenly, speed decreases as the winch brakes are applied. The chair is a single-manned aircraft coming in to land, and, for the first time, there is a glimpse of colour in the gloom beneath – spots of yellow where cavers' suits reflect the feeble amount of light reaching them down the shaft. A little nearer, and helmets sporting pin-pricks of light can be recognized. This is the moment the dentist takes out his drill. The worst is over – and the pulse quickens again at what

Ready for exploration: All loaded up and ready to go. A few seconds later the plank is pulled out and the great descent begins...

might lay in store. A boulder floor can be seen, and as the chair grinds to a halt, the smiling face of the 'whistler' unclips the visitor from the chair.

One Small Step For Man ..

Even the experienced pause for breath here: staggered by the scene that confronts them. It can take up to twenty minutes for the eyes to adjust to Martel's 'feeble light of day' but twenty years could never dim the memory. This is an immense space: 140 metres (nearly 500 feet) long, 34 metres (100 feet) high and 27 metres (80 feet) wide; the largest cavern so far discovered in Britain. As the visitor stands with his back to the chair, he is facing south, with the west side of the chamber on his right and the east to his left. This simple bearing will be important for what comes later. It will soon be realized that the south wall of the chamber merges into a roof of limestone inclined at an acute angle: this meeting the almost vertical north wall behind the waterfall. This superficial 'loft' appearance, all be it on a grand scale, is due to a combination of jointing and a network of minor faults both of which have created the ideal conditions for water to exploit. Falling blocks from the faulted ceiling have also enlarged the chamber and added to the cobbled floor. This mass of pebbles and water-washed boulders is actually a 'false landing' – with the solid floor of the chamber lying, it is believed, as much as 30 metres (90 feet) below. Clearly, this is a much bigger monster than even first impressions suggest.

Another curious feature is the 'dado rail' of pale limestone encircling the walls about 6 to 8 metres (20 feet) from the floor and known as the Porcellanous Band. It is believed that this very fine layer was laid down at a time of extremely low sea-levels in a shallow lagoon, as it differs considerably from the surrounding rock. It is also an indicator of the rocky goings-on in the region when all was aggressive and 'faulty.' The Porcellanous Band on the south wall is about 4 metres (15 feet) higher than that of the north, indicating the powerful 'wrenching' caused by the fault before the cavern was formed.

Now that you have your surroundings in order, we'll head off in an anti-clockwise direction around the main chamber, taking great care on the cobbles and moving slowly. Britain's highest waterfall is, of course, the dominating feature, but here, due to the diversion dam, it is crashing down the shaft of Rat Hole instead – a challenging way-in for experienced potholers. Only those who enter the 'winchless' system see the main shaft waterfall in all its glory – but this is still a peerless feature for most.

A Three Peaks Up and Under

Heading right, avoiding the waterfall spray, the light dims as, in a few minutes, we reach a smooth, circular mud bank just before the West Slope. Close to here, most of the Rat Hole water sinks into the floor – the exact position depending on the weather conditions. Its precise journey, after that, is a great mystery, and it has been referred to as 'the lost river of Gaping Gill.' What we do know is that, in normal conditions, it can be under there for four days before finally popping its head out at Clapham Beck Head, as dye tests have proved. Divers meeting the same stream in a section of cave known as 'Far Waters' – actually made the connection with the Ingleborough cave water on 22 January, 1983 – after 146 years of determined exploration! More than a few champagne corks were popped on that occasion. The difficulties of the final connection, Gerald Benn's hand shaking Geoff Crossley's boot for a few chilling seconds, can only be imagined.

Rock Around the Clock

The West slope is for cavers only, leading to intricate connections with the 'Stream Chamber' beyond. Having admired it from a safe distance and examined the disappearing water, continue the anti-clockwise circuit along the right wall, with fine views of the Porcellanous Band as well as the beautifully formed, sloping ceiling. Pause occasionally to admire the waterfall, and to observe each tiny 'spider', dangling in the bosun's chair as the public drop at intervals into the void. When the eastern side of the Main Chamber is reached, two exits are usually illuminated by the caving clubs for those with a head for adventure. The first, at the top of the steep boulder slope ahead, is nearly at roof level and is accessed by a ladder. We'll leave that alone for now. Our route instead lies up a natural rocky staircase just off the right wall, polished by generations of explorers to appear like marble. A mounted caving lamp is essential for this move, but even children can scramble up with care. One of the great things about wandering in Gaping Gill during the winch meet is that, if something does go wrong, you know rescue is never more than a few metres away. That said, great care should always be taken and the slopes and boulders treated with respect – but it still remains, strangely, one of the safest 'wild' caves to explore for the beginner, providing a simple map is taken.

Down the Rabbit Hole … and What You'll Find There

The rocky staircase leads to the exciting 'tunnel' of South Passage. This would have been a great place to film 'Alice in Wonderland' as the impression is of following a smooth-floored rabbit burrow. This passage is an old phreatic tube that was originally formed entirely under water and has now been completely abandoned. The branch off to the left should be ignored. This is Booth Parson's Crawl, which connects with the Old East Passage and the notoriously long Hensler's Crawl – best left to the imagination. When Eric Hensler, a Mendips caver, wormed his way through this passage in 1936 he returned with a suit cut to ribbons – but at least a feature named after him. It was well worth it.

The passage continues as a delightful adventure, sometimes permitting walking but mostly hands and knees crawling without discomfort, as the floor is of hardened clay – deposits left by the melt water of ice age glaciers. Eventually, after ten minutes or so of puffing and panting, the roof lowers to just a couple of feet and the visitor can have great fun squeezing through the 'portcullis'; breathing a sigh of relief as a wide chamber is entered.

Claustrophobics will be horrified at the thought of the squeeze, but there are usually enough people about to shout encouragement, and if I can fit through, anyone can! Looking back, the fangs of rock guarding the obstacle really do resemble the bottom part of a castle gateway. It's a good name.

The rift chamber is a great stopping point to get out the flask or have a bite to eat. The way on is to the left, as the enigmatic Pool Chamber lies to the right, floored by dark water. This can be examined, and even waded into a short distance with wellingtons. One of the mysteries of this chamber is that, despite being 40 feet above the floor of the Main Chamber itself, a sideways current of water has been recognized crossing the canal from left to right and vanishing to 'goodness knows where'. From the Pool, retrace your steps and head left out of the rift, beyond the Portcullis, where a short section of 'rabbit burrow' leads to a well-known T-Junction. Left leads to the South East passages marking the entrance of Bar Pot, where most cavers make their way in when the winch isn't around. Our way on is to the right this time, where, after a short hands and knees crawl on the smooth floor, the passage swings left into the spectacular Sand Cavern. Nothing to worry claustrophobics here: the chamber being over 90 metres (270 feet) long, 15 metres (45 feet) wide and about 10 metres (30 feet) in height.

This is an unworldly place. Little here has changed through world history. There is no sound ... no life ... no movement ... and even twenty caving lamps make a scant job of the darkness. The sandy floor means that footsteps go largely unheard. Sand Cavern is as removed from normal existence as one can be in England. Geoffrey Workman, a single-minded cave enthusiast and something of an eccentric, recognized this in the summer of 1953. Subjecting his body to an extreme test of human endurance, he set up a camp here and spent a full two weeks without the rising and setting of the sun to govern the time; even drawing up his own 12 hour calendar to ensure equal periods of wake and sleep. By the end of the second week the lack of light was too much and normal bodily functions were slowing down. He began to find it increasingly difficult to do anything but sleep.

Walking in the vicinity of Geoff's ordeal today, a wall of stratified sand on the back wall can be climbed, worn-smooth by the boots of cave explorers. A further sand banking can then be descended to the left, to emerge in another wonderful void, 'Stalagmite Chamber' – containing masses of formations which give a clue to water accessing the cave from the surface. The chamber is a great one for the camera, so consider this the furthest reaches of your journey … relax, have a bite to eat and savour this unique natural wonder.

The return to 'base camp' at the Main Chamber can feel like 'coming home' after such an expedition, and it is surprising how soon an affection grows for a cavern which, maybe an hour before, had been a forbidding monster. Just to remind you, keep right out of Stalagmite Chamber, dropping down the mud slope into Sand Cavern: head right again at the exit to the cavern, and, when the T-Junction is reached, turn left towards the Portcullis. If you didn't like it the first time, it will be much easier the second!

Eastern Promise

The roar of the great waterfall and glimpses of daylight from the shaft indicate the end of the passage as you return, and extra care should be taken on the staircase climb – as limbs now are likely to be tired. Some may wish to join the queue for a return to daylight, but others may wish to tackle Old East Passage, the first connection to the Main Chamber ever explored. This is a more difficult prospect than the 'rabbit burrow', with a daunting ascent of the Eastern boulder slope followed by a fixed ladder climb into the roof. Dangerous loose boulders are usually taped off by cavers, and if you are a first-timer it is wise to follow someone who has done it before. The climb up itself is well worth it, if only for the magnificent full length view of the Main Chamber, its dimensions now far more discernible after a good hour underground. Only the world's best camera can capture its vastness from here. I've tried countless times ... with nothing more than a 'blob' as the result.

The trick in Old East is to follow the taped-off sections, where cavers have sensibly discouraged visitors from further disturbing the once gorgeous formations. There are still lots of pretties to admire, but sections can be low, awkward and very muddy. Well-worn areas indicate the route if you are in doubt, but the rocky floor is much more annoying and can play havoc with the knees! Younger children will love the trip to Sand Cavern, but I wouldn't advise taking them here as some of the drops between boulders can be nasty and slippery. Confident teenagers will have no problem. Here, however, the photographer can have a field day, as the masses of stalactites and flowstone formations are, despite the mud, still very impressive.

After a tricky section negotiating a series of boulders, progress is positively halted at the stupendous Mud Hall: Britain's second largest natural chamber, and impossible to fathom, or even to imagine. All that can be described on first – and even on subsequent visits, is quite literally a 'Black Hole' or even, as my friend put it, 'a glimpse into hell.' A natural balcony of limestone provides a view into nothingness on the very edge, and lamp beams penetrate sufficiently to allow a glimpse of the cavers' traverse rope along the right wall; but keep well away. Mud Hall is actually made up of two colossal 'pits' with a steep rib of rock between, down which cavers make their descent before heading into the far reaches of the system. Even the surroundings of Sand Cavern seem ordinary in comparison. Mud Hall is over 250 feet (85 metres) from floor to ceiling, and over 400 feet (130 metres) long: just be grateful to have been near it!

The route back to the Main Chamber should be undertaken with caution, especially when mounting the ladder for the descent to the boulder slope. I always 'bottom walk' down it to avoid a slip. No-one wants an accident after all that hard work. As you join the queue for the return journey, take the time to enjoy all the more this unique experience. You will already be full of mud, so if you require the ultimate photograph up the 'chimney' of the main shaft, lie on your back on the cobbles: why not? – and point your camera upwards. You won't get a second glance, as nothing is of a 'normal world' down here. People expect the unexpected …

Your turn arrives, at last, and a cheery 'whistler' locks you in the chair. A tug of the cable and your feet leave the cobbles for the last time: Martel's rope ladder route into the sky being yours, and yours only, for a few precious seconds. You blink, uneasily, as pitch black becomes vibrant green: mosses and ferns welcoming you to a living world. The walls close in, engulfing you in a beam of spray-washed sunlight. You tuck in your knees as the rock threatens to scrape your skin, but the chair jerks to a sudden halt. Smiling faces reassure you: you've made it! You've been up …. You've been under. You're a Three Peaks connoisseur.

Isn't this a life worth living?

Select Bibliography

CD versions of rare Victorian texts listed may be online – though nothing beats the book itself, if you can find it.

BALDERSTON, R. and M. *Ingleton, Bygone and Present* (Simpkin, Marshall and Co, 1888)

BECK, HOWARD *Gaping Gill, 150 Years of Exploration* (Robert Hale, 1984)

BROOK, A., BROOK, D., GRIFFITHS, J. and LONG, M.H *Northern Caves: Volume 2. The Three Peaks* (Dalesman, 1991)

CARR, JAMES *A Guide to the Caves, Mountains, River Scenery And Other Remarkable Natural Curiosities in the Neighbourhood of Ingleton and Clapham* (Third edition: British Library, 1876)

CRUTCHLEY, DAVID *Geology of the Three Peaks* (Dalesman, 1981)

DUNHAM, K.C., HEMINGWAY, J.E., VERSEY, H.C. and WILCOCKSON, W.H *A Guide to the Geology of the District Around Ingleborough* (Proceedings of the Yorkshire Geological Society: Volume 29, part 2, number 6, 1953)

EYRE, JIM *The Easegill System: Forty Years of Exploration* (BCRA, 1989)

HOUSMAN, JOHN *A Descriptive Tour to the Lakes, Caves, Mountains and Other Natural Curiosities in Cumberland, Westmoreland, Lancashire and Part of the West Riding of Yorkshire* (C. LAW, 1800)

HUTTON, REVEREND J. *A Tour to the Caves in the Environs of Ingleborough and Settle, in the West Riding of Yorkshire* (1780, Revised edition EP Publishing, 1970)

JOHNSON, DAVID *Ingleborough: Landscape and History* (Carnegie Publishing, 2008)

LOWE, DAVID and WALTHAM, TONY *Caves and Karst of the Yorkshire Dales: Volume 1* (BCRA, 2013)

LOWE, DAVID and WALTHAM, TONY *Dictionary of Karst and Caves* (BCRA Cave Studies Series 10, 2002)

MITCHELL, ALBERT *Yorkshire Caves and Potholes Volume 1: North Ribblesdale. Volume 2: Under Ingleborough* (Dalesman, 1949)

MITCHELL, W.R. *Yorkshire's Hollow Mountains* (Castleberg, 1989)

MITCHELL, W.R. and FOX, PETER *The Story of the Ribblehead Viaduct* (Castleberg, 1990)

MITCHELL, W.R. *Ingleborough: The Big Blue Hill* (Castleberg, 1994)

MITCHELL, W.R. *Tot Lord and the Bone Caves* (Castleberg, 1999)

A Three Peaks Up and Under

MURPHY, P. *Exploring the Limestone Landscapes of the Three Peaks and Malham* (BCRA, 2005)

REE, HARRY and FORBES, CAROLINE *The Three Peaks of Yorkshire* (Whittet Books, 1983)

RILEY, FREDERIC *Guide to Settle: A Practical Handbook for the Tourist and Visitor* (Lamberts Printers, Settle, No date)

RODGERS, PETER *Geology of the Yorkshire Dales* (Dalesman, 1978)

SPEIGHT, HARRY *The Craven and North West Yorkshire Highlands* (Eliot Stock: London, 1888)

WAINWRIGHT, ALFRED *Walks in Limestone Country* (Westmorland Gazette, 1970)

WAINWRIGHT, ALFRED *Wainwright in the Limestone Dales* (Michael Joseph, 1991)

WALTHAM, TONY (ed.) *Limestones and Caves of North West England* (David and Charles, 1971)

WALTHAM, TONY *Yorkshire Dales; Limestone Country* (Constable, 1987)

WALTHAM, TONY *Caves and Karst of the Yorkshire* Dales (BCRA, 1987)

WALTHAM, TONY *Yorkshire Dales: Landscape and Geology* (Crowood Press, 2007)

Appendix 1

Suppliers of Caving Gear in the Three Peaks Area:
Bernie's Café and Caving Shop
4 Main Street, Ingleton, via Carnforth LA6 3EB
www.berniescafe.co.uk

Legendary suppliers of big breakfasts: all things caving with cheap and reliable gear hire.
Inglesport, 11 The Square, Ingleton via Carnforth LA6 3EB
Next door to Bernie's and healthily competitive: great café and caving gear for hire.

Appendix 2

Watering Holes/Cafes in the Three Peaks Area to End Your Adventure:

The Game Cock
The Green, Austwick LA2 8BN
Recommended for all adventures around Clapham, as well as for the Crummackdale Stadium walk.

The Marton Arms
Thornton-in-Lonsdale LA6 3PB
A good choice after the Ingleton waterfalls and any routes in Kingsdale.

A Three Peaks Up and Under

Ye Olde Naked Man Café
Market Place, Settle BD24 9ED
Famous old café with home-made cakes a speciality.

The Old Hill Inn
Chapel-le-Dale, North Yorkshire LA6 3AR
Very old indeed, and one of the most famous inns in Yorkshire. Recommended after all visits to Ingleborough's west flank along Chapel-le-Dale. Great food and accommodation.

Penyghent Café
Horton-in-Ribblesdale BD24 0HE
The starting point for the Three Peaks marathon, but a fine café in its own right. Very friendly and lots of good books and maps on offer.

The Station Inn
Ribblehead LA6 3A6
Popular inn with good food and easy access. Recommended after all walks around Ribblehead and Whernside. Popular with cavers.

Appendix 3

Access to the Caves and Potholes Mentioned in the Text

Yordas Cave: Open access – please close the field gates.
Great Douk Cave: No permission required.
Old Ing and Browgill Caves: Ask permission at Birkwith Farm, as for parking.
Weathercote Cave: This cave is on private land. Walkers are

usually permitted on writing to the owner, at Weathercote House, but large groups, cavers and children are discouraged. A disclaimer is usually signed before entry.

Long Churn Caves: These are on private land. A small charge is payable to Selside Farm. They are the most popular caves in Yorkshire.

Bruntscar Cave: Call at Bruntscar Hall, where a church collection box gathers proceeds for St Leonard's Church, Chapel-le-Dale.

Ribblehead Caves: Open access with no permission required.

The Allotment/Long Kin East/Juniper Gulf area: Owned by the Ingleborough estate: no access from March to the beginning of October (grouse breeding). Save the adventure for early spring or autumn.

Victoria Cave: Though not strictly private and still accessible, the signs make it clear that the cave is unstable and the deposits are precious. If you do enter, take great care throughout and cause minimal damage. For most people, the entrance chamber is enough.

Attermire/Jubilee Caves: Open access but as these are important archaeological sites, take great care throughout.

Appendix 4

Cave Rescue: We never expect it to happen to us – just as we don't think of breaking down on a motorway – but a slip can have serious consequences underground. This - combined with the fact that mobile phone reception can be weak in the Dales, can be a little alarming. It is best always to bear the following points in mind.

- Know where the nearest main line phone is before entering any cave.
- Always have enough people on the trip to allow one to go for help while another stays with the casualty. Caving in pairs is risky for beginners.
- Dial 999 and ask for CAVE RESCUE – this is based in Clapham.
- NEVER enter caves in rain – or if imminent downpours are forecast.
- Know your limits – and don't climb where you don't have to!

After hundreds of trips in the Dales' caves, I have yet to have an accident. Follow the guidelines in this book to the letter and it's highly likely you'll be safe as houses, too.

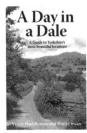

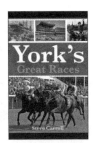

The Barefoot Shepherdess
and Women of the Dales

By Yvette Huddleston & Walter Swan

The Barefoot Shepherdess and Women of the Dales celebrates the variety and versatility of a dozen or more determined women who have made a distinctive life for themselves "far from the madding crowd".

The Yorkshire Dales attracts tourists aplenty to appreciate the beauties of the local landscape but most visitors return to their towns and cities, renewed by the peace and quiet of the countryside, though unable to leave their modern, urban lifestyle for too long.

Women like Alison O'Neill, who owns her own flock of sheep and designs her own brand of tweed clothing, demonstrate that you can live a life of independence and fulfilment even in Britain's remotest regions. There are inevitable hardships to be endured but innumerable compensations when the Dales are on your doorstep.

Each chapter features inspirational women who have made the choice to live and work collaboratively with the people and places of the Yorkshire landscape. What they have in common - farmers, artists, vets, publicans, entrepreneurs, artisans, academics, curators and vicars - is a passion for life where Yorkshire countryside and community coincide.

Featuring personalities from the ITV series **The Dales**

Headingley Ghosts

A collection of Yorkshire Cricket Tragedies

By Mick Pope

Compiled by Yorkshire cricket writer and researcher Mick Pope, *Headingley Ghosts* is a dark collection of over 60 Yorkshire cricket biographies, spanning more than 180 years of the game in the county. It has just been long-listed for the prestigious Cricket Society and MCC Book of the Year Awards, the winner of which will be announced at Lords in 2014.

From the Sheffield pioneers of the 1820s to the modern tragedy of David Bairstow, this haunting book - through original research and a wide selection of rare images - recalls what became of these tragic Yorkshire cricketers beyond the boundary.

They died young, they died old; they died in obscurity; they died in poverty; they died on the road, in the air and on the rail track; they died by their own hand; they died on the battlefields of war and sickness - collectively they are *Headingley Ghosts*.

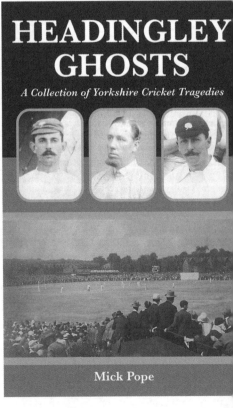

HEADINGLEY GHOSTS

A Collection of Yorkshire Cricket Tragedies

Mick Pope

They shared three common threads - Yorkshire, cricket and tragedy

Just what *is* Yorkshireness...?

Yorkshire ... God's Own County ... The Broad Acres ... the Texas of England ... home to some of the UK's most captivating landscapes, coastlines, food, literature, history, music, tea, film, sport and beer, when Britain's largest county and its residents get you in their grip, you are unlikely to escape soon.

Venue for Le Grand Départ of 2014's Tour de France and voted the Leading Tourist Destination in Europe - beating off the challenges of Paris, Rome, London (ha!) and Vienna - the White Rose county is on the rise. *Slouching Towards Blubberhouses* is a timely and comical look at a region that is by turns friendly, uncompromising, boastful, blunt and maddeningly self-aware, from the viewpoint both of its chosen ones, who wouldn't live anywhere else, and those who look on in envy - or irritation - from outside.

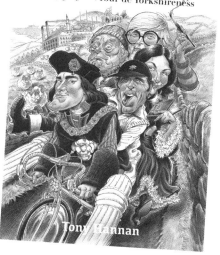

It delves beneath the eeh bah gum clichés of whippets, clogs, flat caps and moth-eaten wallets to explore what really makes Tykes tick. And it wonders if coming from Yorkshire still means owt in a changing and diverse 21st century.

Slouching Towards Blubberhouses

- A (right grand) Tour de Yorkshireness

By Tony Hannan

Investigate all our other titles and
stay up to date with our latest releases at
www.scratchingshedpublishing.co.uk